ARM Microcontrollers

ARM Microcontrollers

Theory and Practical Applications

First Edition

Hung Q. Le, PhD
University of Houston

Bassim Hamadeh, CEO and Publisher
John Remington, Executive Editor
Gem Rabanera, Senior Project Editor
David Rajec, Associate Editor
Alia Bales, Production Editor
Jess Estrella, Senior Graphic Designer
Stephanie Kohl, Licensing Coordinator
Natalie Piccotti, Director of Marketing
Kassie Graves, Senior Vice President of Editorial
Jamie Giganti, Director of Academic Publishing

Printed in the United States of America.

Brief Contents

Detailed Contents

Acknowledgments

To get a book published is hard work and you need a lot of help to accomplish it. On that note, I would like to thank Cognella for publishing this book, and John Remington for getting this project started in the first place. I want to thank my editor, Gem Rabanera, and her assistants for putting up with my delay, correcting my writing, accommodating my schedule, and fixing many other issues to get the book to production. I also want to thank my production editor at Cognella, Alia Bales, together with Larry Baker and Alia's assistants for getting the book to press.

I want to thank Dr. Jonathan Valvano at the University of Texas at Austin, and Dr. Yuhua Chen, Dr. Badri Roysam, Dr. Len Trombetta, and Dr. John Glover at the University of Houston for inspiring me.

Last but not least, I want to thank my wife, Kim-Chi, and my children, Drs. Andrew, Valerie, and Andrea, for having supported and believed in me. This book could not have been completed without their love, patience, and encouragement. I also want to express my deep appreciation and love to my late mother for having raised me and instilled in me hopes for the future when the world was collapsing around us.

Summer 2021

Hung "Harry" Le, PhD

Introduction

This book is intended as an introductory textbook on ARM microcontrollers for college students at the sophomore level or higher. It can also be used as a reference source for working engineers or hobbyists who want to refresh their memory or look up example code for a project.

How the Book Is Organized

The book has ten chapters, each of which deals with a different topic. Chapter 6 is the longest chapter of all, and it also provides example code and programming details of important and popular peripheral modules of the Tiva C LaunchPad. You can use chapter 6 as a source of instruction or reference materials. Here is a breakdown of all the chapters and appendices:

- Chapter 1 is a review of or an introduction to electronics and digital logic. We summarize some important theorems on electrical circuits such as Ohm's Law, Kirchhoff's Laws, and Thevenin's Theorem. We also discuss the construction of CMOS digital gates, and different number bases such as binary, octal, decimal, and hexadecimal and how to convert from one base to another.
- Chapter 2 is an introduction to embedded systems, many of which are used in our everyday lives. Several examples of real embedded systems are described and explained.
- Chapter 3: The most important component of an embedded system is the microcontroller. An overview of the ARM Cortex-M4 microcontroller's architecture is presented in this chapter.
- Chapter 4 provides an overview of the ARM Cortex-M4 Assembly language. The chapter explains its syntax, addressing modes, and instructions and provides examples of how to use Assembly instructions. Finally, the chapter covers details of different types of instructions such as arithmetic, branching, memory access, etc.
- Chapter 5: Besides using Assembly language, one can also use C language, which is very popular in embedded system software designs. Chapter 5 provides a summary of the C

language's features and its usages in embedded systems, and discusses how to use Keil IDE to support software development using the C language.

- Chapter 6: As mentioned above, this is the longest chapter of the book, and it covers popular peripheral modules such as general purpose input/output (GPIO), the clocks and phase-locked loop, general purpose timers, the analog-to-digital converter, universal asynchronous receiver/transmitters (UARTs), pulse-width modulation (PWM), and the SysTick timer. The chapter provides detailed instruction on how to program registers used in these modules and provides example code on how to use these registers.
- Chapter 7: This chapter describes how interrupts and exceptions are handled in ARM Cortex-M4 microcontrollers. Using the Keil IDE, the chapter explains how an interrupt sequence happens and how and where registers are saved in memory locations. Lastly, the chapter goes over ways to program interrupts and write interrupt service routines (ISRs), and provides examples of interrupt initialization and interrupt service routines.
- Chapter 8: This chapter reviews the Bluetooth Low Energy (BLE) protocol, which is being widely adopted in embedded systems. We provide BLE examples of using TI CC2650 BLE modules and ESP32 microcontrollers.
- Chapter 9: Wi-Fi is one of the most popular technologies discussed in this chapter. The chapter explains how wireless devices operate, as well as different modes of operation such as the infrastructure mode, the ad hoc mode, and the monitor mode. The chapter introduces readers to a popular and free tool called Wireshark, used to analyze Wi-Fi frames, and it provides examples of using low-cost microcontrollers like the ESP-32 to connect to a Wi-Fi network or scan for Wi-Fi networks.
- Chapter 10 suggests several projects for readers to try because one of the best ways to learn is to apply your knowledge to a project or a lab. Some projects can be complex, like building and programming an autonomous robot, while others can be fun and practical, like designing a smart plant-watering system for your garden.
- Appendix A provides a list of parts needed to construct the autonomous robot described in Chapter 10.
- Appendix B describes a state machine that can be used to handle the navigation of the autonomous robot discussed in Chapter 10 and Appendix A.
- Appendix C details bit description of registers running clock configuration (RCC) and RCC2, macros for bit fields of pulse-width modulation (PWM) registers.
- Appendix D provides a full list of the programs discussed in Chapter 6.

My hope is that this book will encourage students, hobbyists, and engineers to study, research, or work in the field of embedded systems. Almost every electronic device around us, from our smartphones to our TV controllers, is an embedded system, and with the explosion of the Internet of Things (IoT), the future of embedded systems is very bright indeed. The ARM microcontroller is the most essential component inside an embedded system, so understanding it is the first big step toward understanding embedded systems.

Chapter 1

Introduction to Digital Logic

1. Introduction

Nowadays, an increasing number of systems that used to run with analog circuits are being replaced by digital logic. Hardly anyone knows that there used to be analog computers, which have become obsolete with the advent of digital logic. An analog signal can have a value ranging continuously from V_{ss} to V_{DD}, while a digital signal can only take on discrete values. For example, a TTL (transistor-transistor logic) digital logic input is considered a logic "1" if its voltage is greater or equal to 2V, and it's a "0" if its voltage is less than or equal to 0.8V.

In the following sections, we will go over some basic electronics laws and theorems, and then we'll discuss how to implement digital logic circuits, how to represent numbers in digital logic, and how characters are defined.

2. Basic Electronics Review

It's assumed that readers are familiar with electronics and the following is just a review.

2.1. Ohm's Law

Ohm's law (Figure 1.1) describes the relationship between current (A), voltage (V), and resistance (Ω) in a circuit in the following equation:

$$V = R * I \text{ (Voltage = Resistance * Current)}$$

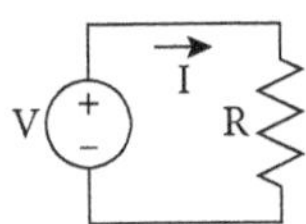

FIGURE 1.1 Ohm's Law.

2.2. Kirchhoff's Voltage Law

The sum of the voltages around a circuit loop is zero.

In Figure 1.2, U1 + U2 + U3 + U4 + U5 = 0

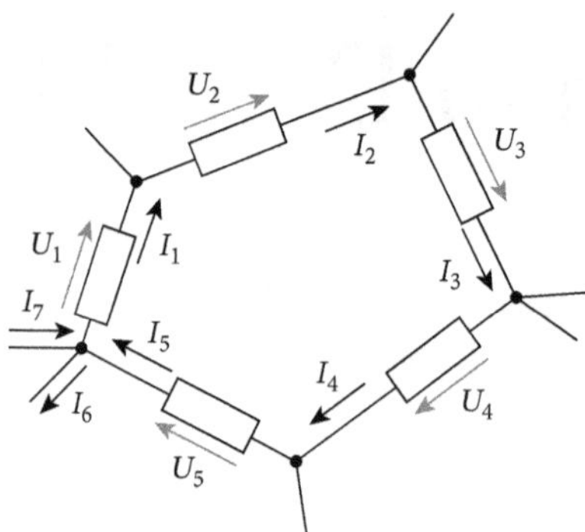

FIGURE 1.2 Kirchhoff's Law.

2.3. Kirchhoff's Current Law

At a node in a circuit, the sum of all incoming currents is equal to the sum of all outgoing currents. For example, at one node of Figure 1.2, $I_5 + I_7 = I_1 + I_6$.

2.4. Thevenin's Theorem

"Thevenin's theorem states that a linear and bilateral network can be replaced by an equivalent circuit consisting of a voltage source Vth in series with a resistance Rth."[1]

For example, to find the current going through resistor RL in Figure 1.3, we can use Thevenin's theorem to find Thevenin's equivalent circuit of the circuit between NodeA and NodeB without resistor RL in Figure 1.3, as shown in Figure 1.4. It's much simpler now to calculate the current going through RL by using Ohm's law. To find Vth, we need to remove resistor RL and then find the voltage between NodeA and NodeB by simplifying the resistor network of R1, R2, R5, and R4. The calculated value of Vth is 1.25V (between NodeA and NodeB). Rth can be found by calculating the equivalent resistance between NodeA and NodeB after we short-circuit the battery (i.e., connecting terminal 1 and 2 of the battery). We obtain an Rth of 2K, so the final circuit after reattaching resistor RL to NodeA and NodeB is shown in Figure 1.4. Finally, the current going through RL is equal to

$$I_{RL} = Vth / (RTH + RL) = 1.25V / (2K + 2K) = 312.5 \text{ uA}.$$

1 "Thevenin's Theorem," Thevenin-Theorem.c, accessed May 8, 2021, https://www.thevenin-theorem.com/2020/01/thevenins-theorem.html.

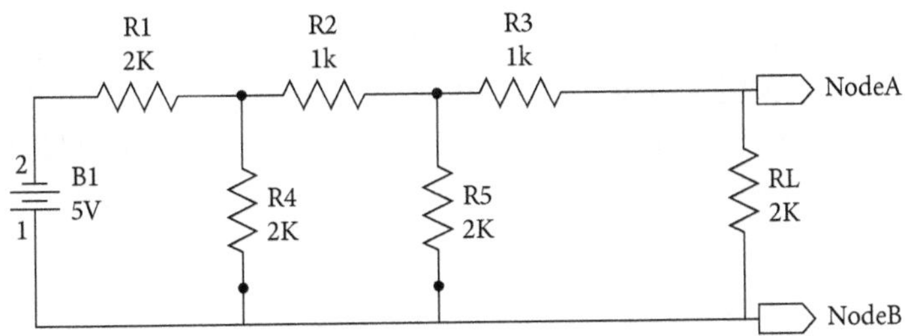

FIGURE 1.3 Finding the Current through Resistor RL.

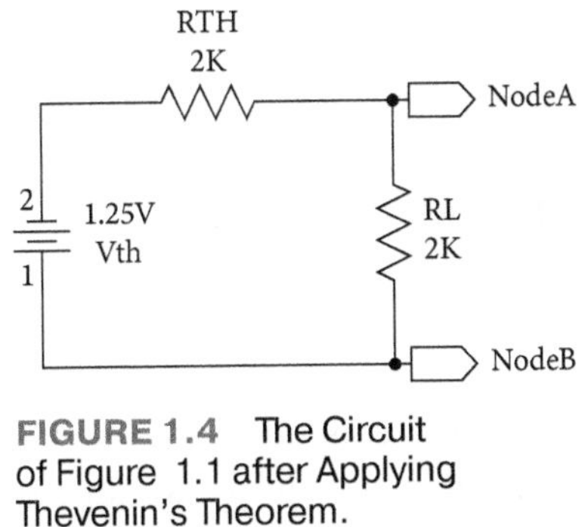

FIGURE 1.4 The Circuit of Figure 1.1 after Applying Thevenin's Theorem.

3. CMOS Logic

The complementary metal oxide semiconductor (CMOS) logic gate is composed of two types of metal oxide semiconductor field effect transistors (MOSFET): N-channel and P-channel devices. A MOSFET (Figure 1.5) typically has a gate made of aluminum or polysilicon put on top of a silicon dioxide layer. For an N-channel field effect transistor (NFET) device, its drain and source are N-doped material inside a P substrate, and for a P-channel field effect transistor (PFET), its drain and source are P-doped material inside an N substrate. The transistor can be thought of as a switch that can be turned on or off depending on the voltage at the gate. The drain and source of the transistor is connected, and the drain-source current flows when the transistor is turned on. Otherwise, no current flows when the transistor is turned off. Typically, in CMOS gates, the sources of the PFETs are connected to V_{DD} and the NFETs' sources are connected to the ground.

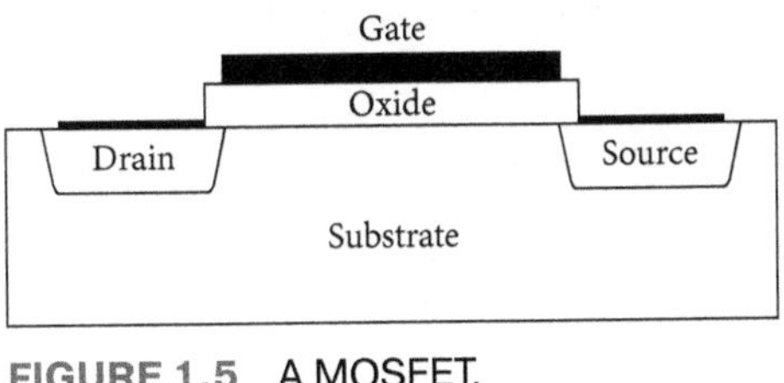

FIGURE 1.5 A MOSFET.

An example of a simple CMOS inverter is shown in Figure 1.6. The voltage at OUT will be pulled to V_{DD} (PFET is on and NFET is off) when the voltage at IN is low (below the threshold voltage of the NFET or zero volts). On the other hand, if the voltage at IN is high (above the threshold voltage of the NFET or V_{DD}), the PFET is turned off and the NFET is turned on, pulling the voltage at OUT toward the ground level. In summary, if IN is at logic 0 (0V), OUT is at logic 1 (V_{DD}), and if IN is at logic 1 (V_{DD}), OUT is at logic 0 (0V).

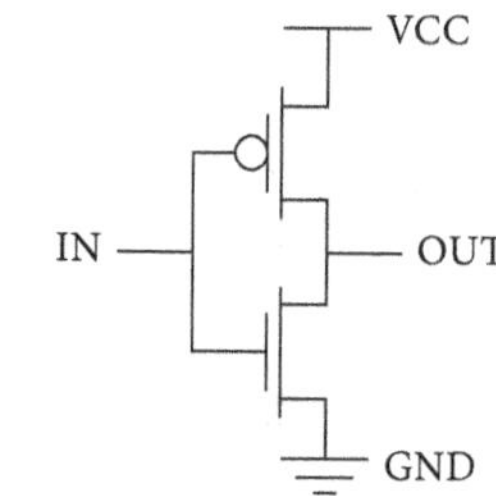

FIGURE 1.6 CMOS Inverter.

4. Digital Logic

Nowadays, most of the digital logic systems, such as computers and microcontrollers, are made of CMOS logic circuits since they are simple to implement, and they consume very little power when not switching. In the following, we will show some basic CMOS logic gates that are widely populated inside digital systems.

Figure 1.7 shows the implementation of a CMOS NOR gate, which has two PFETs connected in a series with a pair of parallelly connected NFETs. When either input signal a or b is at logic 1, one or both the NFETs are turned on, pulling the output signal to ground, and one or both the PFETs are turned off, preventing the path from the output to V_{DD} from turning on. On the other hand, when both signals at a and b are at logic 0, both the PFETs are on, pulling the output toward U_{DD} and at the same time turning off both NFETs, thus preventing the output from being pulled to the ground. In short, if either a or b is "1," then the output is "0." When both a and b are "0," then the output becomes "1."

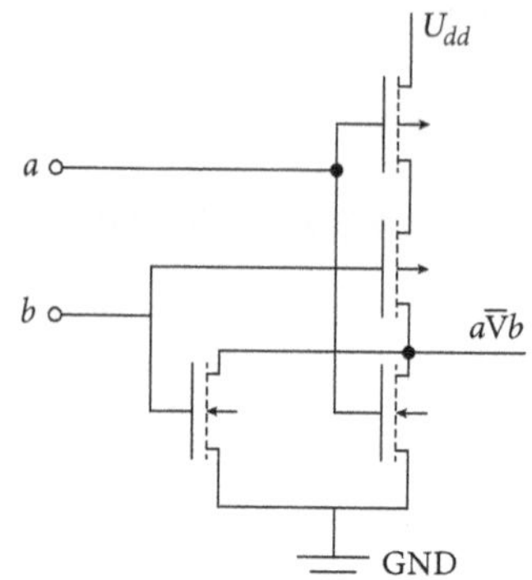

FIGURE 1.7 CMOS NOR Gates.

Figure 1.8 shows the implementation of a CMOS NAND gate. When the signal at A or B is at logic 0, one or both PFETs are turned on, making a connection path between the output OUT and V_{DD} and turning off one or both the NFETs, preventing OUT from connecting to the ground. When both the input signals are at logic 1, both the NFETs are turned on, pulling the output to ground. At the same time, both PFETs are turned off, not allowing a path between V_{DD} and OUT.

From the AOI gate in Figure 1.9, we can find the output signal Out = ~(A || (B & C)).

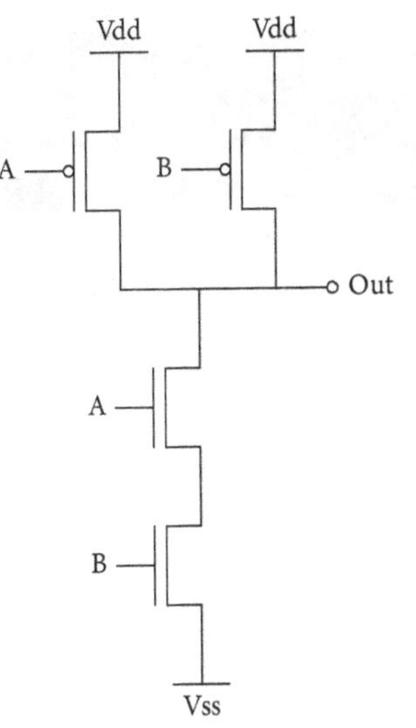

FIGURE 1.8 CMOS NAND Gate.

5. Number Systems

A decimal number can be represented by a sum of products where each product is a digit (of the number) multiplied by some power of 10, depending on the position of the digit in the number. For example,

$$1357.29 = 1 \text{ x } 10^3 + 3 \text{ x } 10^2 + 5 \text{ x } 10^1 + 7 \text{ x } 10^0 + 2 \text{ x } 10^{-1} + 9 \text{ x } 10^{-2}.$$

In general, a number N in any radix base R can be expressed as a sum of products as follows:

$$N = (X_7X_6X_5X_4X_3X_2X_1X_0.X_{-1}X_{-2}X_{-3})_{R=} X_7 \times R^7 + X_6 \times R^6 + X_5 \times R^5 + X_4 \times R^4 + X_3 \times R^3 + X_2 \times R^2 + X_1 \times R^1 + X_0 \times R^0 + X_{-1} \times R^{-1} + X_{-2} \times R^{-2+} + X_{-3} \times R^{-3}. \quad (1)$$

Using the previous equation, a sum of products can represent a binary number of base 2. For instance,

$$101101.11_2 = 1 \times 2^5 + 0 \times 2^4 + 1 \times 2^3 + 1 \times 2^2 + 0 \times 2^1 + 1 \times 2^0 + 1 \times 2^{-1} + 1 \times 2^{-2}$$
$$= 32 + 0 + 8 + 4 + 0 + 1 + ½ + ¼ = 45.75_{10}.$$

Similarly, a hexadecimal number (Table 1.1) or base 16 number can also be represented by a sum of products. For instance,

$$2DA_{16} = 2 \times 16^2 + 13 \times 16^1 + 10*16^0 = 730_{10}.$$

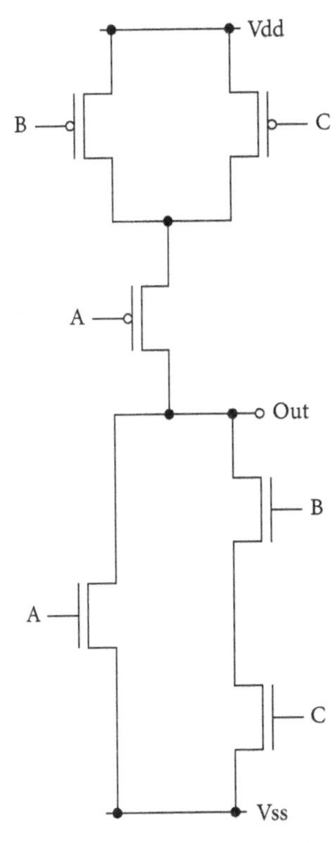

FIGURE 1.9 CMOS AOI Gate.

TABLE 1.1 CONVERSION BETWEEN DECIMAL, BINARY, AND HEXADECIMAL NUMBERS

Decimal	Binary	Hexadecimal
0	0000	0
1	0001	1
2	0010	2
3	0011	3
4	0100	4
5	0101	5
6	0110	6
7	0111	7
8	1000	8
9	1001	9
10	1010	A
11	1011	B
12	1100	C
13	1101	D
14	1110	E
15	1111	F

5.1. Conversion of an Integer Decimal Number to a Binary Number

Similar to equation (1), a decimal number d can be expressed as a sum of products, as follows:[2]

$$d = a_n \times 2^n + a_{n-1}.2^{n-1} + \ldots + a_1.2^1 + a_0.2^0. \qquad (2)$$

If we divide d by 2, we get the quotient q, and the remainder is a_0 (the least coefficient):

$$q = d / 2 = a_n.2^{n-1} + a_{n-1}.2^{n-2} + \ldots + a^1.2^0.$$

Continue dividing q by 2, we get another remainder, which is a_1. By dividing the new quotient by 2 again, we'll get a_2, etc. We can continue dividing until the quotient becomes 0, and we'll get all the coefficients.

Example: Convert 25_{10} to a binary number.
Divide 25 by 2; the remainder is 1 (a_0), and the quotient is 12.
Divide 12 by 2; the remainder is 0 (a_1), and the quotient is 6.
Divide 6 by 2; the remainder is 0 (a_2), and the quotient is 3.
Divide 3 by 2; the remainder is 1 (a_3), and the quotient is 1.
Divide 1 by 2; the remainder is 1 (a_4), and the quotient is 0.
Therefore, the equivalent binary number is 11001_2.

5.2. Conversion of an Integer Decimal Number to a Hexadecimal Number

Using a similar approach as the previous example, but instead of dividing by 2, we divide by 16, we'll get an equivalent hexadecimal number.

Example: Convert 197_{10} to a hexadecimal number.
Divide 197 by 16; the remainder is 5, and the quotient is 12.

2 D. K. Kaushik, *Digital Electronics* (New Delhi: Dhanpat Rai Publishing Company, 2005), 15–18.

Divide 12 by 16; the remainder is 12 (C), and the quotient is 0.

The hexadecimal number is $5C_{16}$.

5.3. Conversion of a Decimal Fraction to a Binary Number[3]

A fractional decimal number can be expressed as an equivalent sum of binary numbers, as follows:

$$f = a_{-1}.2^{-1} + a_{-2}.2^{-2} + \ldots + a_{-n}.2^{-n}. \quad (3)$$

If we multiply f by 2, we get an integer part a_{-1} and the fractional part f1 ($a_{-2}.2^{-1} + \ldots + a_{-n}.2^{-n+}$).

$$2.f = a_{-1} + a_{-2}.2^{-1} + \ldots + a_{-n}.2^{-n+1}$$

If we multiply the fractional part f1 by 2 again, we'll get the coefficient a_{-2} and the fractional part f2 ($a_{-3}.2^{-1} + \ldots + a_{-n}.2^{-n+2}$).

$$2.f1 = a_{-2} + a_{-3}.2^{-1} + \ldots + a_{-n}.2^{-n+2}$$

Continue multiplying the fractional parts to obtain other coefficients until the fractional parts become zero or a recurring pattern or after you get four or five coefficients.

Example: Convert 0.75 to a binary number.

Multiply 0.75 by 2; the integer of the result is 1, and the fractional part is 0.5.

Multiply 0.5 by 2; the integer of the result is 1, and the fractional part is 0.

So, the binary number is 0.11_2.

5.4. Conversion of a Decimal Fraction to an Octal or Hexadecimal Number

Using the same approach, we can convert a fractional decimal number to an octal or hexadecimal number by repeatedly multiplying its fractional result by 8 or 16, respectively.

Example: Convert 2627.62890_{10} to a hexadecimal number.

First, we convert the integer part, 2,627, by dividing it by 16. The quotient is 164, and the remainder is 3 (a_0).

Divide 164 by 16. The quotient is 10, and the remainder is 4 (a_1).

Divide 10 by 16. The quotient is 0, and the remainder is 10 ($A = a_2$).

The equivalent hexadecimal number of $2{,}627_{10}$ is $A43_{16}$.

Second, we convert the fractional part, 0.62890, by multiplying it by 16. The result is 10.0624, so a_{-1} is 10 or A.

Multiply 0.0624 by 16. The result is 0.9984, so a_{-2} is 0, and the fractional part is 0.9984.

---

3 Kaushik, 18–20.

Multiply 0.9984 by 16. The result is 15.9744, so a_{-3} is 15 or F, and the fractional part is 0.9744.

Multiply 0.9744 by 16. The result is 15.5904 so a_{-4} is 15 or F and the fractional part is 0.5904.

Multiply 0.5904 by 16. The result is 9.4464 so a_{-5} is 9 and the fractional part is 0.4464.

Multiply 0.4 by 16. The result is 7.1424 so a_{-6} is 7 and the fractional part is 0.1424.

Stopping at five fractional coefficients, the almost equivalent hexadecimal number is A43. $A0FF97_{16}$.

5.5. Conversion of a Hexadecimal or an Octal Number to a Binary Number and Vice Versa

Since a hexadecimal number's base is 16, which is equal to 2^4, it can be represented by a group of four binary digits. Similarly, an octal number can be expressed as groups of three binary digits.

Example: Convert hexadecimal number $4BA59F.4D3_{16}$ to binary.

4 B A 5 9 F 4 D 3
0100 1011 1010 0101 1001 1111. 0100 1101 0011

So $4BA59F.4D3_{16} = (10010111010010110011111.010011010011)_2$

Example: Convert binary number $(101101011001110110000111.101011)_2$ to hexadecimal.

1011 0101 1001 1101 1000 0111 .1010 1100
B 5 9 D 8 7 A C

So $(101101011001110110000111.101011)_2$ = B59D87.AC.

6. Signed Number[4]

So far, we have assumed that all the numbers we discussed earlier are positive, but computers also have to handle negative numbers. To represent a negative binary number, a sign bit is needed. The sign bit can be assigned to be the extreme left bit of a binary number. By convention, if the sign bit is 0, the number is positive. Otherwise, it's a negative number. For instance, 01000_2 is $+8_{10}$ and 11000_2 is -8_{10}. Even though this sign convention is simple and easy to understand, it's not being used in computers or digital systems since it's much more complex to implement this method in real logic circuits. The most common method is to use the two's complement method because when a negative number is represented by its two's complement number, the arithmetic operation of addition or subtraction between numbers is simply an addition regardless of the signs of the numbers, as we will see later. Before discussing the two's complement method, we need to mention the one's complement number.

4 Kaushik, *Digital Electronics*, 25–28.

6.1. One's Complement Numbers

To get the one's complement of a binary number, we need to invert every digit of the binary number from 0 to 1 or from 1 to 0.

Example: The one's complement number of the binary 1101010 is 0010101.

6.2. Two's Complement Numbers

- To obtain the two's complement of a binary number, we need to take its one's complement number and add "1" to the least significant bit of the number.

  For instance, the two's complement number of the previous number, 1101010, is 0010101 + 1 or 0010110

```
1101010 -> 0010101
       +        1
        ---------
          0010110
```

- For an N-bit microcontroller (e.g., ARM Cortex M4 is a 32-bit microcontroller), the values of an unsigned number can range from 0 to 2^N-1. For example, the ARM Cortex M4 microcontroller can handle unsigned numbers from 0 to $2^{32}-1$ (4,294,967,294). For signed numbers, the most negative number the ARM Cortex M4 can handle is -2^{N-1} or -2^{31} or −2,147,483,648, and the most positive number is $2^{31}-1$ (2,147,483,647). Similarly, for an 8-bit device, such as the PIC microcontroller, it can handle a number from -2^7 or −128 to $+(2^7-1)$ or +127.
- Table 1.2 shows all the unsigned numbers for a 4-bit microcontroller. The signed numbers range from $-2^3(-8)$ to $2^3-1(7)$. Observations from the table include the following:
  - The binary representation of a negative number is the two's complement of the binary representation of a positive number except the most negative number. For example, −7 (1001) is the two's complement of 7 (0111) but −8(1000) is not the two's complement

TABLE 1.2 **4-BIT SIGNED NUMBERS**

Decimal Number	Signed Binary Number
-8	1000
-7	1001
-6	1010
-5	1011
-4	1100
-3	1101
-2	1110
-1	1111
0	0000
1	0001
2	0010
3	0011
4	0100
5	0101
6	0110
7	0111

number of 8 since there is no positive number with a value of 8 in this 4-bit signed number system.

- All the negative numbers have digit "1" at the most significant bit position.
- All the positive binary numbers have digit "0" at the most significant bit position.
- The most significant bit is a sign bit; "1" means it's a negative number and "0" means it's a positive number.

6.3. Arithmetic Addition of Signed Numbers

The addition of two signed numbers is simply an addition of the two numbers, including their sign bits if the negative signed number(s) is/are represented by the two's complement(s). A carryout of the sign-bit position is discarded.[5] Here are some examples:

- For an 8-bit machine addition: 4 + 7 = 0000_0100 + 0000_0111 = 0000_1011 = 11_{10}
- For an 8-bit machine addition: 4 + (−7) = 0000_0100 + 1111_1001 = 1111_1101 = -3_{10}
- For an 8-bit machine addition: (−4) + (−7) = 1111_1100 + 1111_1001 = 11111_0101 = -11_{10} (carryout of the sign bit is discarded)
- For a 4-bit machine addition: (−5) + (−8) = 1011 + 1000 = 10011 (this addition causes an overflow since −13 is outside the range of a 4-bit signed number (range from −8 to +7)). The overflow bit is set in this case to alert users to an addition error (we will discuss more about it in chapter 4).
- The result of an arithmetic operation on signed or unsigned numbers will set or reset the condition codes N (negative), Z (zero), C (carry), V (overflow) in the PSR (Program Status Register) and these bits will determine whether the result is valid or not. More details will follow in chapter 4.

7. ASCII Characters

Characters can be represented using the American Standard Code for Information Interchange (ASCII). The standard ASCII code uses only seven bits to represent 128 different characters, as shown in Figure 1.10. However, seven bits are not enough, so people have extended the standard ASCII codes to eight bits to create the extended ASCII code (Figure 1.11).

5 M. Morris Mano and Michael D. Ciletti, *Digital Design*, 5th ed. (London: Pearson, 2011), 34.

The ASCII code
American Standard Code for Information Interchange

ASCII control characters			
DEC	**HEX**	**Simbolo ASCII**	
00	00h	**NULL**	(caracter nulo)
01	01h	**SOH**	(inicio encabezado)
02	02h	**STX**	(inicio texto)
03	03h	**ETX**	(fin de texto)
04	04h	**EOT**	(fin transmision)
05	05h	**ENQ**	(enquiry)
06	06h	**ACK**	(acknowledgement)
07	07h	**BEL**	(timbre)
08	08h	**BS**	(retroceso)
09	09h	**HT**	(tab horizontal)
10	0Ah	**LF**	(salto de linea)
11	0Bh	**VT**	(tab vertical)
12	0Ch	**FF**	(form feed)
13	0Dh	**CR**	(retorno de carro)
14	0Eh	**SO**	(shift Out)
15	0Fh	**SI**	(shift In)
16	10h	**DLE**	(data link escape)
17	11h	**DC1**	(device control 1)
18	12h	**DC2**	(device control 2)
19	13h	**DC3**	(device control 3)
20	14h	**DC4**	(device control 4)
21	15h	**NAK**	(negative acknowle.)
22	16h	**SYN**	(synchronous idle)
23	17h	**ETB**	(end of trans. block)
24	18h	**CAN**	(cancel)
25	19h	**EM**	(end of medium)
26	1Ah	**SUB**	(substitute)
27	1Bh	**ESC**	(escape)
28	1Ch	**FS**	(file separator)
29	1Dh	**GS**	(group separator)
30	1Eh	**RS**	(record separator)
31	1Fh	**US**	(unit separator)
127	20h	**DEL**	(delete)

ASCII printable characters								
DEC	**HEX**	**Simbolo**	**DEC**	**HEX**	**Simbolo**	**DEC**	**HEX**	**Simbolo**
32	20h	**espacio**	64	40h	@	**96**	60h	.
33	21h	**1**	65	41h	A	**97**	61h	**a**
34	22h	"	66	42h	B	**98**	62h	**b**
35	23h	#	67	43h	C	**99**	63h	**c**
36	24h	$	68	44h	D	**100**	64h	**d**
37	25h	%	69	45h	E	**101**	65h	**e**
38	26h	&	70	46h	F	**102**	66h	**f**
39	27h	‘	71	47h	G	**103**	67h	**g**
40	28h	(	72	48h	H	**104**	68h	**h**
41	29h	)	73	49h	I	**105**	69h	**i**
42	2Ah	*	74	4Ah	J	**106**	6Ah	**j**
43	2Bh	+	75	4Bh	K	**107**	6Bh	**k**
44	2Ch	,	76	4Ch	L	**108**	6Ch	**l**
45	2Dh	-	77	4Dh	M	**109**	6Dh	**m**
46	2Eh	.	78	4Eh	N	**110**	6Eh	**n**
47	2Fh	/	79	4Fh	O	**111**	6Fh	**o**
48	30h	**0**	80	50h	P	**112**	70h	**p**
49	31h	**1**	81	51h	Q	**113**	71h	**q**
50	32h	**2**	82	52h	R	**114**	72h	**r**
51	33h	**3**	83	53h	S	**115**	73h	**s**
52	34h	**4**	84	54h	T	**116**	74h	**t**
53	35h	**5**	85	55h	U	**117**	75h	**u**
54	36h	**6**	86	56h	V	**118**	76h	**v**
55	37h	**7**	87	57h	W	**119**	77h	**w**
56	38h	**8**	88	58h	X	**120**	78h	**x**
57	39h	**9**	89	59h	Y	**121**	79h	**y**
58	3Ah	:	90	5Ah	Z	**122**	7Ah	**z**
59	3Bh	;	91	5Bh	[	**123**	7Bh	{
60	3Ch	<	92	5Ch	\	**124**	7Ch	|
61	3Dh	=	93	5Dh	]	**125**	7Dh	}
62	3Eh	>	94	5Eh	^	**126**	7Eh	~
63	3Fh	?	95	5Fh	-			

FIGURE 1.10 The Standard ASCII Table.

Extended ASCII characters											
DEC	**HEX**	**Simbolo**	**DEC**	**HEX**	**Simbolo**	**DEC**	**HEX**	**Simbolo**	**DEC**	**HEX**	**Simbolo**
128	80h	Ç	160	A0h	á	192	C0h	└	224	E0h	Ó
129	81h	ü	161	A1h	í	193	C1h	┴	225	E1h	β
130	82h	é	162	A2h	ó	194	C2h	┬	226	E2h	Ô
131	83h	â	163	A3h	ú	195	C3h	├	227	E3h	Ò
132	84h	ä	164	A4h	ñ	196	C4h	─	228	E4h	õ
133	85h	à	165	A5h	Ñ	197	C5h	┼	229	E5h	Õ
134	86h	á	166	A6h	o	198	C6h	ã	230	E6h	µ
135	87h	ç	167	A7h	0	199	C7h	Ã	231	E7h	Þ
136	88h	ê	168	A8h	¿	200	C8h	╚	232	E8h	þ
137	89h	ë	169	A9h	®	201	C9h	╔	233	E9h	Ú
138	8Ah	è	170	AAh	¬	202	CAh	╩	234	EAh	Û
139	8Bh	ï	171	ABh	½	203	CBh	╦	235	EBh	Ù
140	8Ch	î	172	ACh	¼	204	CCh	╠	236	ECh	Ý
141	8Dh	ì	173	ADh	¡	205	CDh	═	237	EDh	Y
142	8Eh	Ä	174	AEh	«	206	CEh	╬	238	EEh	‾
143	8Fh	Å	175	AFh	»	207	CFh	¤	239	EFh	´
144	90h	É	176	B0h	░	208	D0h	Ŏ	240	F0h	
145	90h	æ	177	B1h	▒	209	D1h	Đ	241	F1h	±
146	91h	Æ	178	B2h	▓	210	D2h	Ê	242	F2h	_
147	93h	ô	179	B3h	│	211	D3h	Ë	243	F3h	¾
148	94h	ò	180	B4h	┐	212	D4h	È	244	F4h	¶
149	95h	ò	181	B5h	A	213	D5h	ı	245	F5h	§
150	96h	û	182	B6h	Â	214	D6h	Í	246	F6h	÷
151	97h	ù	183	B7h	À	215	D7h	Î	247	F7h	¸
152	98h	ÿ	184	B8h	©	216	D8h	Ï	248	F8h	°
153	99h	Ö	185	B9h	╣║	217	D9h	┘	249	F9h	¨
154	9Ah	Ü	186	BAh		218	DAh	┌	250	FAh	·
155	9Bh	Θ	187	BBh	╗	219	DBh	█	251	FBh	1
156	9Ch	£	188	BCh	╝	220	DCh	▄	252	FCh	3
157	9Dh	Θ	189	BDh	¢	221	DDh	¦	253	FDh	2
158	9Eh	x	190	BEh	¥	222	DEh	ı	254	FEh	■
159	9Fh	*f*	191	BFh	┐	223	DFh	▀	255	FFh	

FIGURE 1.11 Extended ASCII Characters.

EXERCISES

1. Find the Thevenin's equivalent circuit between NodeA and NodeB of the following circuit:

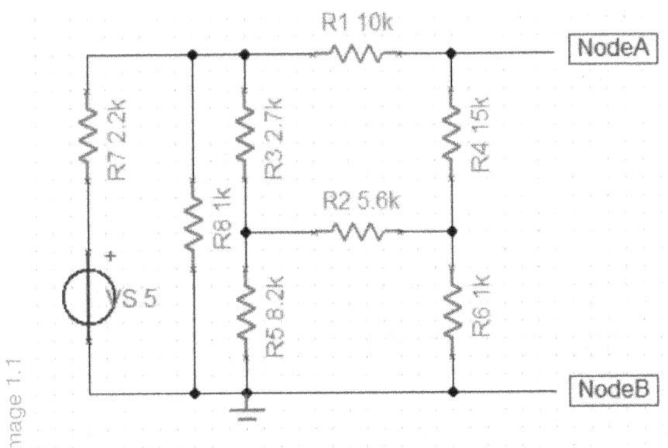

2. Use NFET and PFET to design the CMOS exclusive (XOR) gate.

3. Use NFET and PFET to design the following gates:

   a. Z = A + B + C + D
   b. Z = A. B. C
   c. Z = A.B + C.D

4. Using only NAND gates, design the AND gate, OR gate, XOR gate.

5. Using only NOR gates, design the AND gate, OR gate, XOR gate.

6. Write numbers from 0 to 20 in the following number systems: (a) binary, (b) hexadecimal, (c) octal, (d) radix number of 7.

7. Convert the following numbers to decimal numbers: 11010101.01_2, 10111011.11_2, $0x34FA_{16}$, $0x78EAC2_{16}$, 7356_8, 45017_8.

8. Covert the following numbers to binary numbers: 28_{10}, 192_{10}, 57_{10}, 69_{10}, $0x52FE_{16}$, $0x7AFE_{16}$.

9. Convert the following numbers to binary numbers: 37.75_{10}, 451.165_{10}, 2789.135_{10}, 683.125_{10}.

10. Convert the following numbers to binary numbers: $3A479F.3DF5_{16}$, $4BC78E207.3D_{16}$.

11. Convert the following 4-bit signed numbers to two's complement numbers: −6, −4, −5, −7, 3, −3.

12. Use two's complement numbers to perform arithmetic operations of the following 4-bit signed numbers. Are the results correct? If not, why?

    a. (−4) + (−3)
    b. 5 − 8
    c. (−7) + (−4)
    d. (−4) + (−2)
    e. (−1) − (−4)
    f. (−5) + (−7)

13. Decode the following ASCII codes: 1000100_1101001_1100111_1101001_1110100_1100001_1101100_0100000_1001100_1101111_1101001_1100011.

14. Each byte of the following string is an ASCII character and a leftmost parity bit: C4_E9_67_E9_F4_61_EC_20_4C_7F_E9_E3.

    a. Decode the ASCII string.
    b. Is the parity odd or even?

Credits

Fig. 1.1: Copyright © by Omegatron (CC BY-SA 3.0) at https://commons.wikimedia.org/wiki/File:Ohms_law_voltage_source.svg.

Fig. 1.2: Source: https://commons.wikimedia.org/wiki/File:Masche_und_Knoten.svg.

Fig. 1.3: Adapted from: Finding the current through resistor RL," https://www.thevenin-theorem.com/2019/10/thevenin-theorem.html. Copyright © by thevenin-theorem.com.

Fig. 1.4: Adapted from: After applying the Thevenin's Theorem," https://www.thevenin-theorem.com/2019/10/thevenin-theorem.html. Copyright © by thevenin-theorem.com.

Fig. 1.5: Source: https://commons.wikimedia.org/wiki/File:Cmos2.PNG.

Fig. 1.6: Copyright © by Magnus Persson (CC BY-SA 3.0) at https://commons.wikimedia.org/wiki/File:Static_CMOS_Inverter.png.

Fig. 1.7: Copyright © by MartinThoma (CC BY-SA 3.0) at https://commons.wikimedia.org/wiki/File:Cmos-nor.svg.

Fig. 1.8: Copyright © by JustinForce (CC BY-SA 3.0) at https://commons.wikimedia.org/wiki/File:CMOS_NAND.svg.

Fig. 1.9: Copyright © by JustinForce (CC BY-SA 3.0) at https://commons.wikimedia.org/wiki/File:CMOS_2-1AOI.svg.

Fig. 1.10: The Standard ASCII Table," https://uvalibraryfeb.wordpress.com/2019/03/14/e-a-e-a-u-etc-on-a-laptop-without-numeric-pad/#jp-carousel-2031. Copyright © by uvalibraryfeb.wordpress.com.

Fig. 1.11: Extended ASCII Characters," https://uvalibraryfeb.wordpress.com/2019/03/14/e-a-e-a-u-etc-on-a-laptop-without-numeric-pad/#jp-carousel-2031. Copyright © by uvalibraryfeb.wordpress.com.

Chapter 2

Introduction to Embedded Systems

1. Introduction

There are many definitions of embedded systems. One definition defines an embedded system as a computing system that is not a general-purpose computer. Another says an embedded system is a special-purpose computer that is used to perform some special function. We can find embedded systems everywhere around us, from the washing machine, the refrigerator, or the microwave oven in our homes, to the cameras we use or the airplanes we fly in. There are many more embedded systems than existing computers. Embedded systems are not only found in common systems but also in very special applications, as the following example illustrates:

> Heart surgery often requires stopping the heart, performing the surgery, and then restarting the heart. Such surgery is extremely risky and carries many detrimental side effects. A number of research teams have been working on an alternative where a surgeon can operate on a beating heart rather than stopping the heart. There are two key ideas that make this possible. First, surgical tools can be robotically controlled so that they move with the motion of the heart (Kremen, 2008). A surgeon can therefore use a tool to apply constant pressure to a point on the heart while the heart continues to beat. Second, a stereoscopic video system can present to the surgeon a video illusion of a still heart (Rice, 2008). To the surgeon, it looks as if the heart has been stopped, while in reality, the heart continues to beat. To realize such a surgical system requires extensive modeling of the heart, the tools, the computational hardware, and the software. It requires careful design of the software that ensures precise timing and safe fallback behaviors to handle malfunctions. And it requires detailed analysis of the models and the designs to provide high confidence.[1]

---

1 Edward Ashford Lee and Sanjit Arunkumar Seshia, *Introduction to Embedded Systems: A Cyber-Physical System Approach*, 2nd ed. (Cambridge, MA: MIT Press, 2017), 2.

A typical embedded system is mainly composed of three main components: (1) hardware, (2) application software, and (3) a real-time operating system (RTOS).[2]

- Hardware that includes a microcontroller, which has a microprocessor integrated with several peripheral modules, such as timers, serial ports, general-purpose input/output (I/O) ports, interrupt controller, pulse width modulation (PWM), and analog-to-digital converter (ADC).
- Application software that performs many tasks defined by users in a series or concurrently.
- An RTOS that is the mastermind of the embedded system. It supervises the application software, schedules processes to run, and controls the context switches between them to meet the system performance criteria—namely, deadlines and correctness.

Besides microcontrollers, an embedded system might also include application-specific integrated circuits (ASICs), field-programmable arrays (FPGAs), or digital signal processors (DSP) to offload heavy calculation or complex processing from the microprocessors. Most of the time, an embedded system is a system with one or more microcontrollers, which are microcomputers with microprocessors integrated with random access memory (RAM), read-only memory (ROM), and I/O peripherals.[3] Texas Instruments manufactures many microcontroller products based on the ARM microprocessor, such as the Tiva C (TM4C family) and the MSP432. The Tiva C microcontroller, which will be used in many labs and exercises in this book, has an ARM Cortex M4, RAM, ROM, and many peripherals, such as timers, universal asynchronous receivers/transmitters (UARTs), pulse width modulator (PWM), analog-to-digital converter (ADC), digital-to-analog converter (DAC), general-purpose I/O ports, controller area network (CAN), inter-integrated circuit (I2C), synchronous serial interface (SSI), and serial peripheral interface (SPI). This low-cost microcontroller can be used to interface with many other electronic or mechanical devices to create useful applications. For example, it can be used as part of a robot where it can control the speed and direction of the robot's motor, and it can take direction from users via Bluetooth communication (it needs a BLE module like TI BLE 2650 to interface with BLE devices or a Bluetooth controller like BlueSMIRF RN42 to interface with regular Bluetooth devices). An embedded system needs software to operate. If there is not an RTOS available, then the software's entire system will need to be written, and this can cause the delay of the project and/or miss the desired performance. This approach is called the bare-metal approach. For bigger or more complex systems, we need to use an RTOS to speed up the software development and improve the system performance. C or Assembly, or a combination of both, is usually the language of choice for developing software for embedded systems. However, Python, a very popular and modern computer language, is now supported by Raspberry Pi, another ARM-based microcontroller kit. There are two other

---

2 Dietmar P. F. Möller, *Guide to Computing Fundamentals in Cyber-Physical Systems: Concepts, Design Methods, and Applications* (New York: Springer, 2016), 38.

3 Jonathan W. Valvano, *Embedded Systems: Introduction to ARM Cortex-M Microcontrollers*, Vol. 1, 5th ed. (Scotts Valley, CA: CreateSpace, 2017), 48.

versions of Python—MicroPython and CircuitPython—being developed specifically to support embedded systems.[4] CircuitPython is a derivative of MicroPython, and it's designed to mainly run on Adafruit hardware. MicroPython is developed for microcontrollers whose hardware resources are very limited compared to a desktop environment where standard Python runs. Therefore, MicroPython is not shipped with a whole set of standard libraries like Python. Only the essential modules needed for a certain hardware are included in the interpreter.

2. Embedded Systems

An embedded system, which is also known as a cyber-physical system, is a system of multiple connected components integrated with a small computer containing RAM and ROM memory. ROM is used for storing software and constants, while RAM is used for temporary storage of variables, buffers, and the like. Instead of regular ROM, many microcomputers employ Flash EEPROM (electrically erasable programmable read-only memory) to allow users to reprogram their software since they can be electrically erasable and programmable.[5] We can find embedded systems everywhere. Almost every electronic device that is different from a laptop or desktop computer is an embedded system. Actually, an embedded system is just a special computer wrapped in a special-purpose environment. For example, a cell phone is a special computer used for voice, text, and graphic applications. It is estimated that billions of embedded systems are manufactured every year, and every household is expected to have hundreds of embedded systems.[6] In general, there are several types of embedded systems[7]:

- *Control systems:* In applications in chemical plants, nuclear power plants, flight control, and the like, embedded systems are real-time control systems with closed-loop feedback. They keep processes in plants stable or ensure that process limits are never violated.
- *Sequence logic:* An embedded system is also used in sequential logic, such as finite state machines, to switch modes between control systems.
- *Signal processing:* Embedded systems handle computations with large data streams in applications, such as radar, sonar, and video compression.
- *Application-specific interfacing:* An embedded system helps to interface with I/O, such as buttons, bells, and light, in high-speed I/O applications
- *Fault response:* An embedded system is commonly used for fault detection and diagnosis.

4 "CircuitPython vs MicroPython: Key Differences," Core Electronics, updated July 16, 2018, https://core-electronics.com.au/tutorials/circuitpython-vs-micropython-differences.html.

5 Core Electronics, "CircuitPython vs MicroPython."

6 Frank Vahid and Tony Givargis, "Embedded System Design, A Unified Hardware/Software Approach," Draft Version, Fall 1999, 1-1. I don't have access to the published book.

7 Philip Koopman, "Embedded Systems," accessed August 30, 2019, https://users.ece.cmu.edu/~jzhu/class/18200/F05/Lecture10_f05_koopman_embedded.pdf, 11.

A typical embedded system includes a microcontroller, which has one or more processors integrated with many peripherals, such as timers, general-purpose inputs outputs (GPIO), ADCs, and PWM, and other surrounding parts, such as an electromechanical system, sensors, and actuators, like those in Figure 2.1.

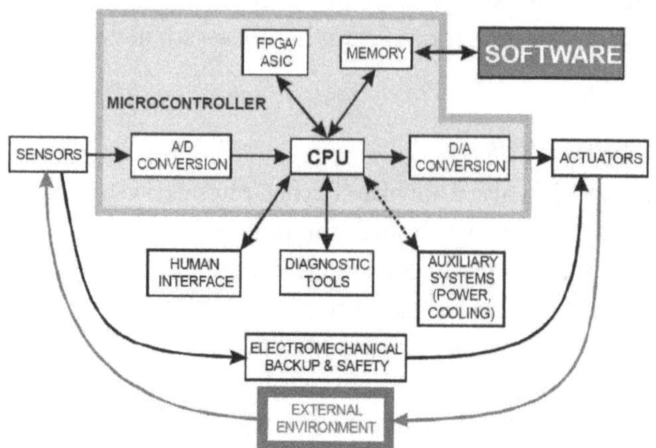

FIGURE 2.1 A Typical Architecture of an Embedded System.

People usually try to design embedded systems without FPGA or ASIC since an embedded system with those parts usually costs much more than a system with off-the-shelves parts. These custom logic chips are expensive to manufacture, and their development time is often very long.

The actuators are used for control and stabilize the environment to a certain desired criteria based on the feedback signals provided by the sensors. The sensors' outputs are usually of the analog type, which has to be converted to digital signals before going to the central processing unit (CPU). Depending on the application software running on the CPU, the sensors' inputs are manipulated and massaged before being sent out to the actuator to control the external environment. Because the actuators mostly operate on analog signals, the outputs from the CPU need to go through a DAC before reaching the actuators.

The heart of an embedded system is a microcontroller, which contains a microprocessor core (or several cores for a multicore system) integrated with memory and several peripheral modules. The microprocessor technology has been improved substantially from 8-bit to 64-bit processors. However, the current processor used inside microcontrollers tends to be a 32-bit ARM processor.

To develop software for an embedded system, one can either use the bare-metal approach or an RTOS. In the bare-metal approach, you access the processor's registers directly to set up, control, or monitor the microcontroller. This approach is time-consuming and subject to error or poor performance. To speed up the development cycle and help improve the system performance, one can use an RTOS, such as Keil MDK, TI Code Composer, or FreeRTOS, which runs on the hardware platform and provides application program interface (API) layers to user software to make calls to the RTOS. As the complexity of embedded systems increases, the use of an RTOS becomes more and more important. We will not discuss much more about RTOS in this book because the text deals primarily with beginners to ARM processors, so we will concentrate on the ins and outs of the ARM Cortex M4.

2.1. Characteristics of Embedded Systems

Embedded systems can be found everywhere around us: from consumer products, such as smartphones, TVs, microwave ovens, washers, dryers, and security systems, to embedded systems in automobiles, airplanes, heavy construction equipment, and the like. There are several common characteristics in an embedded system:[8]

- *Single function:* While a desktop computer executes many different programs, such as PowerPoints, spreadsheets, and simulation software, an embedded system normally runs one program repeatedly. For example, a microwave oven is always a microwave oven.
- *Tightly constrained:* Embedded systems tend to have very tight constraints on design metrics, such as cost, size, performance, and power. Since embedded systems are mainly used in consumer applications, their costs must be very inexpensive and their size must be small to fit consumers' requirements. For example, a pager must be palm size. They must also be fast enough to handle real-time data and consume little power to extend battery life.
- *Reactive and real time:* Embedded systems must be able to handle changes in I/O signals. For instance, an airplane's flight control system must react to changes in the environment, such as wind speed or air pressure, in real time. Any delayed response can cause catastrophic results. On the other hand, a desktop computer usually focuses on computation rather than input ports so that any delayed reaction to I/O ports will cause inconvenience, not system failures.

2.2. Embedded System Design Metrics

There are many design metrics to measure the effectiveness of an embedded system's implementation. Several of the common metrics are described next:[9]

- *Unit cost:* This is the cost for making each product unit, not including the nonrecurring engineering (NRE) cost.
- *NRE cost:* It is a one-time expense used to design the product. After the system is complete, the product can be manufactured without this expense.
- *Size:* The physical size of the product. It is often measured in volume or number of gates for a chip's size or bytes for software.

8 Vahid and Givargis, "Embedded System Design," 5.

9 Vahid and Givargis, 7.

- *Performance:* The execution time or throughput of the system.
- *Power:* The average and maximum consumption power of the system, which are used to calculate the battery's lifetime or to determine whether heat sinks or cooling are required for the system.
- *Flexibility:* Can the system's features be modified without having to pay the NRE cost again? Software can be considered flexible, but hardware, especially ASIC, is considered very inflexible.
- *Time to market or time to production:* The amount of time required before products are available to be sold to customers.
- *Time to prototype:* The amount of time needed to build a system with all specified functionality. It is used to test and verify all the specifications of the product. It can also be used to fine-tune the system's specs.
- *Correctness:* The system is functioning correctly according to its specifications.
- *Safety:* The system will not cause any safety issues.
- There are many other metrics.

Sometimes, these metrics are in conflict with one another. If one tries to improve one metric, it will cause another to fail or to degrade. For example, if you decrease the system's power, its performance might also decrease. Therefore, the designer has to balance between different requirements or technologies. Most of the time, the designer needs to consider the implications of both the software and hardware implementation of a solution. The designer needs to be an expert in both areas. The time to market has increasingly become the dominant metric for embedded systems. A product that is late to market compared to its rivals may lose most of the sales or profits. The profit or sale loss can be millions of dollars for each day that the product is delayed. Adding complications to meet the time to market is the fact that technology has become more and more complex. The famous Moore's law is the observation that the number of transistors in a densely integrated circuit doubles every two years.[10] As the chips become smaller and denser, it's harder and harder to manage the heat dissipated by the circuits. This makes people rethink packaging and cooling.[11] Microfluidic channels may be needed to increase the surface area for heat transfer, and later on, we might even need more exotic technology, such as electronic blood,[12] to solve the thermal problems.

---

10 "Moore's Law," Wikipedia, accessed September 13, 2019, https://en.wikipedia.org/wiki/Moore%27s_law.

11 Sebastian Anthony, "Transistors Will Stop Shrinking in 2021, but Moore's Law Will Live On, ARS Technica, July 25, 2016, https://arstechnica.com/gadgets/2016/07/itrs-roadmap-2021-moores-law/.

12 Sebastian Anthony, "IBM Is Trying to Solve All of Computing's Scaling Issues with 5D Electronic Blood," ARS Technica, November 7, 2015, https://arstechnica.com/gadgets/2015/11/5d-electronic-blood-ibms-secret-sauce-for-computers-with-biological-brain-like-efficiency/.

2.3. Embedded System Examples

The following are several embedded system examples.[13]

Digital Watch

A regular digital watch does not require a lot of processing power or memory. A simple 4-bit processor with no RAM and some ROM is probably good enough for a digital watch. All the electronics needed can be put on a single chip and the only other hardware parts necessary for the watch are the input buttons or the output speaker or display. The watch's software allows customization or flexibility in changing markets.

Video Game Player

Video game players, such as the Sony PlayStation 2, are inexpensive embedded systems whose processing power can be better than a desktop computer. This is a very low-margin market, so the designers must watch their products' costs, but at the same time, they also need to make sure their products can provide a lot of computing power. To keep the unit cost low and to boost the system performance, the processors used in the video game players are usually custom designed. The designers also try to move as much of the memory and other electronics in the main circuit boards to the game cartridges to reduce the cost of the player, but that causes the price of the games to increase.

Mars Rover

There have been seven Mars Rover missions in the past decade. The latest one, Curiosity (Figure 2.2), is a car-sized rover. It's the largest and most advanced robot used for space exploration that has ever been designed or made.[14] Each of the rovers is an embedded system with a lot of redundancy to provide backup systems in case of failure since nobody can anticipate what kind of problems could happen 34 million miles away. Obviously, reliability is the major metric for the design of the rovers.

FIGURE 2.2 The Curiosity Mars Rover.

These examples are just a few instances of embedded systems. There are many more types of embedded systems that we encounter in our everyday lives.

---

13 Michael Barr and Anthony Mason, *Programming Embedded Systems: With C and GNU Development Tools*, 2nd ed. (Sebastopol, CA: O'Reilly Media, Inc.), 16–18.

14 Evan Yares, "How Was the Mars Rover Curiosity Designed? With Siemens PLM Software," 3D CAD World, August 7, 2012, https://www.3dcadworld.com/how-was-the-mars-rover-curiosity-designed/.

3. Embedded System Design

To design an embedded system, the first thing you need to do is select the microcontroller platform that your software will run on. There are a variety of ARM-based microcontrollers, such as Arduino, Raspberry Pi, TI Tiva C Launchpad, TI MSP432 Launchpad, STMicro STM32 Nucleo development boards, and STMicro STM32 discovery kits. The selection of the hardware and software depends on the requirements for speed, power, I/O interfaces, and so on. The following is a ten-step procedure to help you select a proper microcontroller for your embedded system:[15]

- *Step 1:* Make a list of the required hardware interfaces. Usually, there are two types of interfaces that you need to consider. The first one is the communication interface, such as UART, SPI, I2C, universal serial bus (USB), SSI, CAN, Ethernet, Bluetooth, and Wi-Fi. The second type of interface is digital I/O, PWMs (pulse width modulation), DMA (direct memory access), and so on. These interfaces will determine which microcontroller has built-in peripheral modules, as well as the microcontroller packages that have the pinouts to support them. The chosen interfaces also affect the program space of the microcontroller.
- *Step 2:* Examine the software architecture. You need to know in advance how heavy or light the processing power needs to be for your system. It will determine whether you select an 80 MHz microcontroller or an 8 MHz one. You also need to know if there are any special requirements, such as floating-point calculation or encryption/decryption.
- *Step 3:* Select the architecture. Based on your answers to Step 1 and Step 2, you can determine whether an 8-bit, 16-bit, or 32-bit processor is needed. You also need to consider future enhancement or feature creep of the system.
- *Step 4:* Identify memory needs. You need to make sure you have enough space (RAM and ROM) for programs and variables. It is better to have more space than to find out that you need to cut features so that your programs can fit. Again, like in Step 3, you need to make sure you have enough room for your next versions or future enhancements.
- *Step 5:* Start searching for microcontrollers. With information from the previous steps, you can now start searching for microcontrollers that meet the requirements of the previous steps by visiting websites of microcontroller suppliers, such as Arrow, Mouser, Avanet, TI store, or STMicro store. It's also a good time to discuss your needs with a field application engineer (FAE) to make sure you have an optimal solution.
- *Step 6:* Examine costs and power constraints. Now that you have a list of potential microcontrollers that may meet your needs, you can start looking into the power spec and the cost of the part. If your system is portable or mobile, you might need to choose parts with low consumption power, or you may have to add support for low power or

15 Jacob Beningo, "10 Steps to Selecting a Microcontroller," Arm Community, January 12, 2014, https://community.arm.com/developer/ip-products/system/b/embedded-blog/posts/10-steps-to-selecting-a-microcontroller.

hibernation modes. After power, unit cost is another key element in your consideration since it greatly affects your profit margin and the future of your projects.

- *Step 7:* Check parts availability. If the parts you choose meet all the requirements, but they are not available, or the lead time is too long, or they are sole sourced, you need to think twice about choosing these parts. The lifetime of the part is also another issue that needs consideration.
- *Step 8:* Select a development kit. After picking out a part for your embedded system, the next step is to find a development kit to help with the software development and debugging of your system.
- *Step 9:* Investigate compilers and tools. Before finalizing the selection of the microcontroller, you need to investigate the tools and compilers available for that microcontroller. Without the right tools, the development process may be bogged down or become more time-consuming than necessary.
- *Step 10:* Start experimenting. The development kits are usually available before the first prototype of your system, so you should take advantage of that time by experimenting with the kits by building up test circuits and checking out the interfacing with the microcontroller. You may find surprises or unforeseen issues that may lead you to reconsider your microcontroller selection. The sooner you work out these issues, the less of an impact they will have on your system.

In addition to the ten-step procedure, there may be other issues that you need to consider, such as what language to use to develop the software for your embedded system. C is the most common and popular language used for embedded systems. Modern languages, such as Python, supported in Raspberry Pi, and new Python derivatives, MicroPython and CircuitPython, are beginning to be supported to run on microcontrollers such as ESP8266 or STM32 discovery kits.

Another issue is whether you need an RTOS to run between the user software and the hardware platform. If you do, which RTOS should you choose, since there are numerous RTOS to select from? Some are freely available, and some require licenses. Some like SAFERTOS is used for special applications, such as medical devices whose requirements are very stringent. Some publicly available RTOS, such as the TI RTOS, Mbed, or FreeRTOS (owned by Amazon), are free and popular with embedded system designers.

EXERCISES

1. Get familiar with the Tiva C microcontroller kit (model TM4C123GH6PM) from TI by downloading the document at https://processors.wiki.ti.com/index.php/Getting_Started_with_the_TIVA%E2%84%A2_C_Series_TM4C123G_LaunchPad.

2. Get familiar with the TI MSP432P401R, a later version of the Tiva C, by following this link https://www.ti.com/tool/MSP-EXP432P401R. What are the differences between this microcontroller and the Tiva C? What are their advantages and disadvantages?

3. Get familiar with Keil version 4, a software developing tool, by downloading it at https://www.keil.com/demo/eval/armv4.htm. There's a new version, version 5, that can be downloaded at http://www2.keil.com/mdk5/install, but you need to download a Stellaris ICDI add-on at http://www.keil.com/support/docs/4196.htm before you can use it for the Tiva C microcontroller kit. Please note that before you are allowed to download the Keil software, you have to register for it by following a few simple steps on the website.

4. Investigate a popular microcontroller kit, Raspberry Pi, at https://www.raspberrypi.org/. Explore the differences between Raspberry Pi and TI TivaC or TI MSP432.

5. Learn about Arduino, another popular microcontroller kit for hobbyists, by accessing the link https://www.arduino.cc/en/Guide/HomePage. What are the advantages and disadvantages of using Arduino compared to the other microcontrollers mentioned earlier?

6. ESP32 is a low-cost microcontroller with built-in Wi-Fi and dual-mode Bluetooth support. Explain all the features and the software support for this microcontroller. You can get more information at http://esp32.net/.

Credit

Fig. 2.1: A Typical Architecture of an Embedded System," https://users.ece.cmu.edu/~koopman/lectures/ece348/02_embedded_hw_handouts.pdf. Copyright © by Philip Koopman.

Fig. 2.2: Copyright © by xiquinhosilva (CC BY 2.0) at https://commons.wikimedia.org/wiki/File:02820-National-Air-and-Space-Museum_(27304414135).jpg.

Chapter 3

Introduction to ARM Processors

1. Introduction

ARM provided a wide range of processors to be used in various applications ranging from low power, low performance, to high performance or machine learning.[1] For example, the Cortex-A family is tailored to applications that need high performance at optimal power. The Cortex-R family is for applications that need reliable mission-critical performance. The Cortex-M family is mainly used in energy-efficient embedded systems. We will concentrate on the ARM Cortex-M4 since it's one of the most popular microcontrollers used for embedded system applications.[2] The low gate count ARM Cortex-M4 processor consumes very low power, and it also offers low interrupt latency. The Cortex-M4F is similar to the Cortex-M4, except that it supports floating-point arithmetic. Because of its low interrupt latency, the ARM Cortex-M4 architecture is designed to be used in embedded systems.

Before ARM became famous for a variety of processors, it began as a humble manufacturer named Acorn Computers.[3] Its ARM-based products were used as coprocessor modules in BBC microcomputers. After Acorn cooperated with Apple Computer and VLSI Technology to create their first ARM processors—the ARM610 for Apple Newton PDA—the ARM processors' popularity began to rise exponentially because of their low cost, low power, and high performance. In 2005, roughly 98 percent of all mobile phones sold had at least one ARM processor, and in 2010, about 6.1 billion ARM-based processors were shipped worldwide.

2. Cortex-M4 Architecture

The ARM Cortex-M4 has a processor core, a bus matrix, and a nested vectored interrupt controller (NVIC) block, which provides support for low latency interrupts. It also includes several optional blocks, such as a memory protection unit (MPU), a data watchpoint and

1 Leo Kelion, "What Is ARM and Why Is It Worth £24bn?" BBC News, July 18, 2016, https://www.bbc.com/news/technology-36826095.

2 Joseph Yiu, *System-on-Chip Design with Arm Cortex-M Processors* (Cambridge, UK: Arm Education Media, 2019), 22.

3 "ARM Architecture," Wikipedia, accessed October 1, 2019, https://en.wikipedia.org/wiki/ARM_architecture.

trace (DWT), flash patch breakpoint (FPB), advanced high-performance bus (AHB) access port, and instrumentation trace macrocell (ITM).[4]

The following are features of the Cortex-M4 processor:

- A low gate-count processor with low latency interrupts and the following supports:
  - Thumb-2 instruction set
  - Stack pointers
  - Integer divide instructions
  - Handler and thread modes
  - Automatic registers saving and retrieving when entering or exiting interrupt service routines (ISR)
  - Big-endian byte-invariant or little-endian accesses
  - Unaligned accesses
- NVIC works with the processor core to support low latency interrupts. More details on how to program the NVIC registers can be found in Chapter 7 ("Interrupts and Exceptions"). The NVIC has the following features:
  - External interrupts, configurable from 1 to 240
  - Priority, configurable from 8 to 256 priority levels depending on implementation[5]
  - Interrupt priority can be dynamically changed
  - Tail-chaining support (i.e., back-to-back interrupt processing can skip the restoration and state savings between interrupts)
  - Processor states are automatically saved and restored upon the entry and exit of interrupts
- Optional memory protection unit provides memory protection and enhances the security of the processor against malicious coding
- Bus interfaces provide support for three AHB busses: (1) the instruction, (2) the data, and (3) the system bus
- Debug provides access to all the memory locations and internal registers of the processor core or the memory-mapped devices. It also supports the Serial Wire Debug Port, the Serial Wire JTAG Debug Port, or the optional embedded trace macrocell (ETM) for instruction trace and several other optional debug modules
- Harvard bus architecture (separate data and instruction busses) and the memory space is shared between data and codes
- 4 GB memory space with 32-bit addressing
- Low-power and sleep-modes support
- Single instruction, multiple data support

4 ARM Limited, *Cortex-M4 Revision r0p1: Technical Reference Manual* (Cambridge, UK: ARM, 2020), 2.2–2-3.

5 Joseph Yiu, *The Definitive Guide to the ARM Cortex-M3 and Cortex-M4 Processors*, 3rd ed. (Waltham, MA: Newnes, 2014), 2.

- Support for optional floating-point operations
- The processor has two operating modes:[6] (1) thread and (2) handler modes
  - *Thread mode:* The processor enters thread mode when it returns from an exception or a reset. Privileged or unprivileged code can run in thread mode. Unprivileged code cannot access some resources, while privileged code has no limitation. The process stack pointer (PSP) works in this mode.
  - *Handler mode:* The processor enters handler mode when an exception happens. Only privileged code can run in handler mode. The main stack pointer (MSP) works in the handler mode.
- ARM Cortex M4 core is a 32-bit RISC processor, and it has twenty-one 32-bit registers. Its internal data path and its bus interface are 32 bits wide
- Since the processor core has a three-stage pipeline, it can handle three instructions simultaneously[7]
- Cortex-M4 processor is based on a load-store architecture. So, to process data, one needs to load it from memory into registers and process it before writing it back to the memory
- There are twenty-one 32-bit registers in the processor core
  - Thirteen registers, R0–R12, are general-purpose registers.
  - Register R13 is the stack pointer (SP), which can be either an MSP or a PSP, depending on the operating mode of the processor.
  - Register R14 is the link register, which contains the returning address for a subroutine or a function to return after its execution is complete. When an interrupt or exception happens, the upper 24 bits of this register will be set to 0xFFFFFF to signal that the processor is executing an ISR, and the lowest 8 bits will be set to one of the following values:[8]
    - *0xF1:* Return to handler mode using MSP to retrieve registers
    - *0xF9:* Return to thread mode using MSP to retrieve registers
    - *0xFD:* Return to thread mode using PSP to retrieve registers
  - Register R15 is the program counter (PC).
  - There are several special registers (Table 3.1) that are not memory mapped. In other words, you cannot access them using memory addresses. Instead, you have to use special register access assembly instructions, such as instruction "MRS" (move from a special register to a general-purpose register), or instruction "MSR" (move from a general-purpose register to a special register), or some C function provided by the Cortex Microcontroller Software Interface Standard (CMSIS) library. For example,

---

6 ARM Limited, *Cortex-M4 Revision r0p1*, 2.2–3-3.

7 Ying Bai, *Practical Microcontroller Engineering with ARM Technology* (Hoboken, NJ: John Wiley & Sons, 2016), 20.

8 Jonathan W. Valvano, *Embedded Systems: Introduction to ARM Cortex-M Microcontrollers*, Vol. 1, 5th ed. (Scotts Valley, CA: CreateSpace, 2017).

TABLE 3.1 SPECIAL REGISTERS

Bits	31 30 29 38 27	26–18	19–16	15–9	8 7 6 5 4 3 2 1 0
APSR	N Z C V Q	Reserved	Reserved	GE (greater or equal)	Reserved
IPSR	Reserved	Reserved	Reserved	Reserved	Exception/interrupt number

Bits	31 30 29 28 27	26–25	24	23–20	19–16	15–10	9	876543210
EPSR	Reserved	ICI/IT (ICI=interrupt continuable interrupt) IT=IF-Then-Else Instruction Status	T	Reserved		ICI/IT	Reserved	
PSR	N Z C V Q	ICI/IT	T		GE	ICI/IT		Exception/interrupt number
PRIMASK								Bit 0 = disable/ enable interrupts
FAULT-MASK								Bit 0 = disable/ enable faults
BASEPRI								3 or 4 bits to denote interrupt priority

to read register PRIMASK, use the CMSIS function `uint32_t__get_PRIMASK (void)` or this Assembly instruction `MRS R0, APSR` (move the content of register APSR to register R0).

- Program status register (PSR) is a combination of three registers: (1) application program status register (APSR), (2) interrupt program status register (IPSR), and (3) execution program status register (EPSR). Each of these three registers can be individually accessed or accessed as a combined register—PSR.

Bits N Z C V Q are set or reset after an arithmetic logical unit (ALU) operation (for more information, read chapter 4), and the Q bit is set if a sticky saturation happens after an SSAT or USAT command. The GE bits are set if a greater or equal comparison happens.

2.1 System Memory Map

The following Figure 3.1 shows a memory map of all the areas of ROM, RAM, SRAM, EEROM, Peripheral registers and the Private Peripheral Bus (PPB) in the TM4C123 microcontroller.

- The flash ROM (from address 0x0000_0000 to 0x0003_FFFF) area contains the exception and interrupt tables, the system controls, and the user code.
- The internal ROM can be used to store the TivaWare Driver Libraries, the TivaWare Boot Loader, the Advanced Encryption Standard tables, and the cyclic redundancy check function.
- The SRAM area is used to keep user data and bit-band alias of bit-banded, on-chip SRAM.
- The addresses of all the on-chip devices and interfaces to external I/O devices are mapped to the I/O peripheral area. The devices include timers, ADCs, analog comparators, general-purpose I/O ports, synchronous serial interfaces, universal asynchronous receiver/transmitter (UART), controller area network (CAN), and universal serial bus (USB).
- The PPB area contains addresses of the ITM, the DWT, the FPB, Cortex-M4F system peripherals (SysTick, NVIC, MPU, FPU [floating point unit], SCCB [serial camera control bus]), trace port interface unit, and ETM.
- Right after power is applied to the processor or when a reset button is pressed, a reset cycle happens. It causes the 32-bit content of the flash ROM at address 0 to be loaded to the MSP since the processor runs in thread mode at the privileged level[9] and the 32-bit value at address 4 (reset vector) to be loaded into the PC. This is the starting address of the reset ISR.

Address range	Area
0x000000000 – 0x0003FFFFF	Flash ROM (256KB)
0x010000000 – 0x000000000	Internal ROM
0x200000000 – 0x20007FFF0	SRAM (32KB)
0x400000000 – 0x400FFFFFF	EEPROM & Peripheral
0xE00000000 – 0xE0041FFFF	Private Peripheral Bus (PPB)

FIGURE 3.1 System Memory Map of TM4C123GH6PM Microcontroller.

2.2 The Stack Memory

- The stack memory is a first-in, last-out memory, and data involved in every stack operation is always 32 bits wide.
- For a PUSH instruction, the SP is decremented by 4 before the 32-bit data is stored into the memory location pointed to by the SP.
- For a POP instruction, the 32-bit data from the memory location pointed to the SP is read out before the SP is incremented by 4.
- Initially, right after reset, the SP is set to the RAM memory address 0x20007FFF, the bottom of the stack memory.

9 Valvano, 84.

2.3 The Program Models and States[10]

- The Cortex-R-M4 processor supports several privilege levels, operation modes, and operation states to provide flexibility, efficiency, and reliability to both system and user programs.
  - *Privileged levels:* For privileged levels, software has no access limits to resources, while unprivileged-level software has limited access to the priority mask register and restricted access to memory or peripherals, such as the FPU or MPU. Neither has access to the NVIC, timer registers, or the system control block.
  - Modes:
    - The processor can be in either the thread mode (has privileged access) or the handler mode (has either privileged or unprivileged access). When a program is in the thread mode, it can switch from the privileged level to the unprivileged level by setting bit 0, thread mode privilege level, of the control register. However, it cannot switch itself back from the unprivileged level. You may have to use an ISR to handle this switch.
    - The processor automatically facilitates the switching between the thread mode and the handler mode.
- *Operation states:* The processor can be either in the Thumb state (normal state) or the debug state, which halts or stops the processor for debugging purposes.

EXERCISES

1. How many registers are there in the ARM Cortex-M4? How many are general-purpose registers, and how many are not general-purpose registers? What are the uses of the non-general-purpose registers?

2. What is the value of register R14 (the link register) when there is an interrupt?

3. What register is used for a subroutine to return after its execution is complete?

4. Can you read register PRIMASK directly? If not, how do you read from or write to this register?

5. What is the difference between the ARM Cortex-M4 and the ARM Cortex-M4F?

6. Are the registers saved by the processor when entering and exiting an ISR?

7. What is the tail-chaining feature of the ARM Cortex-M4 core?

---

10 Bai, *Practical Microcontroller Engineering*, 70.

8. What is the computer architecture of the ARM processor, Harvard or von Neumann? What are the differences between these two architectures?

9. Are the registers of the ARM Cortex-M4 I/O mapped or memory mapped? What are the differences? Are there any registers of the ARM Cortex-M4 that are not memory mapped? How do you access them if they are not memory mapped?

10. Does the stack memory of the ARM Cortex-M4 behave like a first-in, first-out or a last-in, first-out? Does the stack memory increase or decrease after a push? What about a pop?

11. After a power-on reset, how does the reset ISR get executed?

12. After a power-on reset, how does the SP get initialized?

Chapter 4

ARM Cortex-M Assembly Language

1. Introduction

In this chapter, we will discuss the assembly language that runs on the ARM Cortex-M processor, which implements the Thumb instruction set extended with Thumb-2 technology. The difference between ARM and Thumb instructions is ARM instruction has a 4-byte encoding, while Thumb instruction has a variable encoding (2 bytes or 4 bytes). Thumb-2 technology added more instructions to the Thumb instruction set and allows conditional execution to most instructions.

2. ARM Cortex-M4 Assembly Language

In general, an instruction has four fields: (1) label, (2) opcode, (3) operand, and (4) comment fields, which are separated from one another by space(s) or tab(s).

- The label field always starts at Column 1, and it is optional. It is used as a symbolic memory address for a branch instruction or as a constant or as a variable. The other three fields never start at Column 1. The label has to start with an alphanumeric character, and its length is limited to fifteen characters.
- The opcode field tells the CPU what operation to do. An opcode or a pseudoinstruction can be put here. An opcode, such as ADD or MOV, is the encoding of an ARM Cortex-M4 instruction, whereas a pseudoinstruction is an assembler instruction, such as EQU or DCD.
- The operand field follows the opcode field, and it contains an address or data for the instruction in the opcode field to work on. Depending on the type of instructions, some can have zero, one, two, three, or four operands. For example, while instructions such as NOP have no operands, instructions such as ADD can have four operands.
- The comment field that must begin with a semicolon allows the programmer to add comments to show the purpose of the related instruction. This field is also optional, like the label field.

Since ARM Cortex-M4 only supports Thumb instruction, the least significant bit, bit 0, of any address written to the PC with a BX, BLX, LDM, LDR, or POP instruction should have the value of 1.[1]

2.1. ARM Cortex-M4 Pseudoinstruction

To help the compiler to convert users' programs successfully, pseudoinstructions are used to provide more information to the compiler, such as defining memory spaces for programs, variables, or data. Since they are pseudoinstructions, they are not converted to object codes like the real instructions. The following are some popular ARM Cortex-M4 pseudoinstructions:

- *AREA directive:* A group of data or codes that is linked by the assembler. There can be many AREAs, and there must at least be one defined AREA for code.
- *ENTRY directive:* Identifies the entry point of the first instruction in the program to be executed. There can be only one ENTRY directive within a program. If the program contains C code, the entry point is located inside the C library. The line that is right below ENTRY should be the first Label like Start. Start needs to be exported (EXPORT Start) so a Startup.s program can recognize it. Startup.s is a program provided by the microcontroller vendors like TI that contains a vector table of all the interrupts and the Reset_Handler, which is to branch to the first line of Users code (Start).
- *THUMB:* Indicates that the codes used in the program are Thumb codes.
- *END directive:* Specifies the end of the program. Hence, the assembler will stop processing the program when encountering the END directive. Every program must end with the END directive.
- *ALIGN:* Align the current location to a boundary by adding NOP or zeros. For example, we should use "ALIGN = 2" means to align the current location to a 16-bit boundary since Thumb instruction opcodes can be a multiple of 2 bytes.
- *DCB:* Reserves space for 1 byte of data.
- *DCW*: Reserves space for 1 halfword or 2 bytes of data.
- *DCD*: Reserves space for 1 word or 4 bytes of data.
- *Export:* Declares a local symbol that can be used by modules in different files.
- *Import:* Declares a symbol that is defined in another module in a different file to be used locally.
- Here is a sample of a simple assembly program, which needs file Startup_TM4C123.s to run:

```
        AREA Data, READWRITE, ALIGN=2
Number DCD 0x0
        AREA Hello, CODE, READONLY, ALIGN=2
```

1 Bai, *Practical Microcontroller Engineering*, 37.

```
        Export Start

        ENTRY

Start LDR R0, =Number

        MOV R1, #0xAB

        STR R1, [R0]

Loop B Loop

        END
```

Program 4.1. Hello

- Startup_TM4C123.s is a file provided by TI that contains the ARM vector table and the Reset_Handler. We need to modify the Reset_Handler to make it look like the following (to allow the system to branch to the label Start after reset):

```
      .....

; Reset_Handler

             EXPORT  Reset_Handler

Reset_Handler

      IMPORT Start

      B Start
```

2.2. ARM Cortex-M4 Addressing Modes[2]

There are several addressing modes in assembler language for ARM Cortex-M4. In all of the addressing modes, the instruction can have a suffix of B (unsigned byte), SB (signed byte), H (unsigned halfword), SH (signed halfword, sign extends to 32 bits [LDR only]), or none (for 32-bit word), which is used to denote the size of the data involved.

Register

In this mode, the data flow from right to left.

MOV R1, R0; copy R0 to R1
AND R0, R1; R0 = R1 & R0

2 Valvano, *Embedded Systems,* 92–96.

Register List

The instructions for the stack operate on one register or a list of registers.

> PUSH {R1}; push register R1 onto the stack
> PUSH {R2-R4, LR}; push registers LR, R4, R3, R2 onto the stack in that order (i.e. PUSH LR first then R4, then R3, then R2).

Note that the stack push or pop instructions map the lower-numbered registers with the lower memory addresses. For instance, PUSH {R7, R0, R4, R2} will push registers R7, R4, R2, R0 in that order. Register R0 is pushed last (to map to the lowest stack address) since it's the lowest-numbered register in that example.

When a register is pushed, the stack pointer is decremented by 4 before the value of the register is put into the memory location pointed to by the stack pointer. On the other hand, when we pop the stack to a register, the content of the memory location currently pointed to by the stack pointer is transferred to the register before the stack pointer is incremented by 4. All the stack operations are done on a 4-byte boundary.

Immediate Addressing Mode

In this mode, the data is contained within the instruction. For example, after the instruction MOV R1, #0x40, R1 will contain number 0x40.

Indexed Addressing Mode

In this mode, a register containing a pointer to the memory address of the data is used to access the data. The following are examples of instruction using the indexed addressing mode:

- LDR R1, [R2]; load R1 with the content of the memory location that register R2 points to.
- LDR R1, [R2, #8]; load R1 with the content of the memory location whose address is equal to R2 + 8. Register R2 is not changed.
- LDR R1, [R2, #8]!; change the value of register R2 to R2 + 8, then load R1 with the content of the memory location pointed to by R2.
- LDR R1, [R2], #0x10; load R1 with the content of the memory location pointed to by R2 and then change the value of R2 to R2 + 0x10.
- LDR R1, [R2, R3]; load R1 with the content of the memory location pointed to by R2 + R3. Register R2, and R3 remain unchanged.
- LDR R1, [R2, R3, LSL #2]; load R1 with the content of the memory location pointed to by R2 + R3*4. Only LSL can be used in this mode.

PC-Relative Addressing

This mode is similar to the indexed addressing mode, except that the PC is used as the address pointer. The PC's value used in the calculation is the actual address of the next instruction line, not the current one.

LDR R1, [PC, #0x40]; load R1 with the content of the memory location pointed to by the next line PC + 0x40. The following example is a piece of code in the Disassembly windows of Keil:

0x0000028E F8DF2002 ;LDR R2, [PC, #2]

0x00000292 F04F0110 ;MOV R1, #10

The current PC is 0x0000028E. When executing the current instruction, the system adds the value of the PC (of the next instruction line, which is 0x00000292) with 2 resulting in memory address 0x00000294 whose content is transferred to register R2.

Flexible Second Operand

Some instruction has a flexible form for the second operand.

ADD R3, R2, #0x50; R3 = R2 + 0x50

ADD R3, R2, R1, LSL #2; R3 = R2 + R1*4

2.3. The ARM Cortex-M4 Instruction Set[3]

There are many ways to classify the instruction set. The following is just one way to describe the instruction categories[4]. An instruction can have zero, one, or many operands, and an operand can be a register, a constant, or another specific parameter. Since the data flows from right to left in an instruction, if there is a destination register, it appears before the operands. Some instructions do not allow operands to be the SP or the PC.

Memory Access Instruction

Table 4.1 is a list of all the memory access instructions.

ADR

Syntax: ADR {cond} Rd, label where cond is an optional condition code, such as EQ, NE, or LT. Rd is the destination register (cannot be PC or SP), and label is an address of an instruction or a literal data. Be careful when using this instruction since the address of the label must be within ±4K for 32-bit Thumb encoding or within 0 and 1K for 16-bit Thumb encoding.

ADR R0, cnt; write the address of variable cnt to register R0.

3 *Cortex M4 Instruction Set: Technical User's Manual* (Austin, TX: Texas Instruments, 2010–2011), 32–41.

4 *Cortex M4 Instruction Set, Technical User's Manual.*

TABLE 4.1

Mnemonic	Brief Description
ADR	Load PC-relative address
CLREX	Clear exclusive
LDM{mode}	Load multiple registers
LDR{type}	Load register using immediate offset
LDR{type}	Load register using register offset
LDR{type}T	Load register with unprivileged access
LDR{type}	Load register using PC-relative address
LDRD	Load register using PC-relative address (two words)
LDREX{type}	Load register exclusive
POP	Pop registers from stack
PUSH	Push registers onto stack
STM{mode}	Store multiple registers
STR{type}	Store register using immediate offset
STR{type}	Store register using register offset
STR{type}T	Store register with unprivileged access
STREX{type}	Store register exclusive

LDR and STR

LDR and STR can be used with several addressing modes, such as immediate offset, preindexed or postindexed immediate offset, register offset, register with PC-relative label.

Syntax:

`Op{type} {cond} Rt, [Rn {,#offset}]` ;immediate offset, the memory address used to retrieve a value is equal to Rn + offset. Rn is not impacted.

`Op{type} {cond} Rt, [Rn, #offset]!` ; preindexed immediate offset, Rn is changed to Rn + offset and then the new value of Rn is used as the memory address to retrieve a value for Rt.

`Op{type} {cond} Rt, [Rn, #offset]` ; postindexed immediate offset, Rn is used as the memory address to retrieve a value for Rt and then the value of register Rn is changed to Rn + offset.

`Op{type} {cond} Rt, [Rn, Rm {, LSL #offset}]` ; register offset, load Rt with a value from the memory location whose address is equal to Rn plus Rm or Rn + (Rm << offset). Rn and Rm can be any register, except register SP and/or register PC in some cases. Rn and Rm are not changed in this mode.

`LDR{type} {cond} Rt,` *label*; register with PC-relative label, load Rt with the content of a memory location whose address is equal to *label*. Label must be within a limited range of the current instruction location (−4095 to +4095 from the PC).

Op can be either LDR or STR.

Type can be B (unsigned byte), SB (signed byte, sign extend to 32 bits, only used for LDR), H (halfword or 2 bytes), SH (signed halfword, sign extends to 32 bits, only used for LDR), or none (4 bytes).

Cond is a condition code, such as EQ, NE, PL, MI, NE.

Examples

`LDR R1, [R0, #0x100]` ; load register R1 with a number from the memory at address (R0 + 0x100) and register R0 retains its original value.

`LDR R2, [R1], #0x100` ; load register R2 with the content of the memory address equal to R1 and then register R1 is changed to R1 + 0x100.

`LDRB R1, [R2, R3, LSL #2]`; load R1 with the content of the memory address equal to R2 + (R3*4).

`LDRH R1, DataTable`; load R1 with two bytes from a memory location whose address is named DataTable.

LDR Pseudoinstruction

This is a pseudoinstruction and not the LDR instruction as described previously. The address loaded is done at link time, so it is not limited by address position as the real LDR instruction.

LDR {cond} {.W} Rt,=expr (or label_expr) where expr is a numeric value and lable_expr is an address expression of a label added or subtracted by a numeric value. You should use this instruction to load a 32-bit-long number instead of using the MOV instruction since the MOV instruction can only load a 16-bit-long number.

Examples

LDR R0, =0xF1F2F3F4 ; loads 32-bit number 0xF1F2F3F4 into R0

LDR R1, =Cnt ; load the address of variable Cnt into R0

LDM and STM

LDM and STM allow multiple registers to be loaded or stored into memory.

Syntax:

`Op{addr_mode} {cond} Rn{!}, reglist ;`

Op can be LDM or STM.

Addr_mode can be either IA (default, increment address after each access) or DB (decrement address before each access).

Cond is an optional condition code.

Rn contains the starting memory address that the registers in reglist will be loaded from or stored into. Regardless of the order of the registers in the reglist, the lower-numbered register is mapped to the lower memory address, and the higher-numbered register is mapped to the higher memory address. Rn must not be PC.

! is the write-back suffix. The address after the last memory access is written back to register Rn.

The reglist is a list of registers. It contains resister range, or a list of multiple registers separated by commas. The reglist cannot contain SP and cannot contain Rn if the ! option is used.

`LDM R0, {R10, R8, R7, R9}; R7 = [R0], R8 = [R0+4], R9 = [R0 + 8], R10 = [R0 + 12]`

`LDM R0!, {R10, R8, R7, R9}; R7 = [R0], R8 = [R0+4], R9 = [R0 + 8], R10 = [R0 + 12], R0 = R0 + 16`

PUSH and POP

Push and Pop are used to push register onto or off a stack, respectively.

```
Op{cond} reglist
```

Cond is an optional condition code, such as NE, MI, or PL.

The reglist is a list of registers. It contains a resister range, or a list of multiple registers separated by commas. Regardless of the order of the registers in the reglist, the lower-numbered register is mapped to the lower memory address, and the higher numbered register is mapped to the higher memory address. When the PC is in the reglist in a pop instruction, two things have to happen:

1. Bit 0 of the value loaded into the PC must be 1. A branch will happen to this 16-bit aligned address.
2. If the pop instruction is part of an "IT" (If-Then) block, it must be its last instruction.

The address of the stack is descending when being pushed and ascending when being popped. The stack always operates on a 4-byte boundary. To push a register onto the stack, the system puts the register onto address (SP – 4) and then decrements the SP by 4. To pop from a stack to a register, the system pulls the content of the memory location pointed to by the SP onto the register and then increments the SP by 4.

`PUSH {R0, R5, R4, R6}`; push registers R0, R4, R5, R6 onto the stack, with R0 being the last register pushed and R6 being the first register pushed.

`POP {R0-R3}`; pop register R0, R1, R2, R3, with R0 being the first register popped and register R3 being the last register popped.

Example: The following is a stack with the SP having a value of 0x20000400; we will execute the following instructions:

```
PUSH {R0, R1, R2, R3}
POP {R8, R4-R7}
```

Value	Address
0x00	0x200003F0
0x00	0x200003F4
0x00	0x200003F8
0x00	0x200003FC
0x00	0x20000400

The above table is before the PUSH instruction is executed. If R0 = 0x0102, R1 = 0x0304, R2 = 0x0506, R3 = 0x0708, R4 = 0x090A, R5 = 0x0B0C, R6 = 0x0D0E, then after the instruction PUSH {R0, R1, R2, R3}, the stack memory becomes:

0x0102	0x200003F0
0x0304	0x200003F4
0x0506	0x200003F8
0x0708	0x200003FC
0x00	0x20000400

When a PUSH instruction is executed, the Stack Pointer SP is moved to a lower address (4-byte lower) before data starts to be put into memory beginning with that memory location. Notice that in the pushing of data into the stack of the above example, the order of the registers in the instruction is not followed to fill data into the memory. Instead, the higher numbered register is mapped to the higher memory address. Register R3 is the highest-numbered register in the above example so it's mapped to the highest stack address, 0x200003FC. The same as register R2, R1 are mapped to address 0x200003F8 and 0x200003F4, respectively. Lastly, register R0 is put into address 0x200003F0 and the new Stack Pointer's value is now 0x200003F0.

When a POP instruction happens, the stack pointer is incremented by 4 after data from the memory location pointed to by the stack pointer is put into the lowest numbered register in the register list of the POP instruction. In this example, it's the register R4. So R4 = 0x0102 and then R5 = 0x0304, R6 = 0x0506 and R8 = 0x0708. The stack pointer is now at address 0x20000400.

In a program or subroutine, the number of pops and pushes should always be equal. Otherwise, the program may crash.

Data Processing Instructions

Table 4.2 provides a list of all the data processing instructions for ARM Cortex-M4.

TABLE 4.2

Mnemonic	Description	Comments
ADC	Add with carry	Use format 1 or 2
ADD	Add	Use format 1 or 2
AND	Logical AND	Bitwise AND. Use format 1
ASR	Arithmetic shift right	Use formats 3, 4, or 5
BIC	Bit clear	Bitwise clear. Use format 1

(continued)

TABLE 4.2 **(CONTINUED)**

Mnemonic	Description	Comments
CLZ	Count leading zeros	Use format 5
CMN	Compare negative	Use format 11
CMP	Compare	Use format 11
EOR	Exclusive OR	Bitwise exclusive OR. Use format 1
LSL	Logical shift left	Use formats 3, 4, or 5
LSR	Logical shift right	Use formats 3, 4, or 5
MOV	Move	Use formats 6, 7
MOVT	Move top	Use format 7
MOVW	Move 16-bit constant	
MVN	Move NOT	Use format 6
ORN	Logical OR NOT	Use format 1
ORR	Logical OR	Use format 1
RBIT	Reverse bit	Use format 8
REV	Reverse byte order in a word	Use format 8
REV16	Reverse byte order in each halfword	Use format 8
REVSH	Reverse byte order in bottom halfword and sign extend 68	Use format 8
ROR	Rotate right 60	Use formats 3, 4, or 5
RRX	Rotate right with extend	Use formats 3, 4, or 5
RSB	Reverse subtract	Use format 1 or 2

(*continued*)

TABLE 4.2 **(CONTINUED)**

Mnemonic	Description	Comments
SADD8	Signed add 8	Use format 9
SADD16	Signed add 16	Use format 9
SASX	Signed add and subtract with exchange	Use format 10
SSAX	Signed subtract and add with exchange	Use format 10
SEL	Select bytes	Use format 12
SHADD8	Signed halving add 8	Use format 9
SHADD16	Signed halving add 16	Use format 9
SHASX	Signed halving add and subtract with exchange	Use format 9
SHSAX	Signed halving subtract and add with exchange	Use format 9
SHSUB8	Signed halving subtract 8	Use format 9
SHSUB16	Signed halving subtract 16	Use format 9
SSUB8	Signed subtract 8	Use format 9
SSUB16	Signed subtract 16	Use format 9
SUB	Subtract	Use format 1 or 2
SUBW	Subtract	
TEQ	Test equivalence	Use format 11
TST	Test	Use format 11
UADD8	Unsigned add 8	Use format 9
UADD16	Unsigned add 16	Use format 9

(*continued*)

TABLE 4.2 **(CONTINUED)**

Mnemonic	Description	Comments
UASX	Unsigned add and subtract with exchange	Use format 9
USAX	Unsigned subtract and add with exchange	Use format 9
UHADD8	Unsigned halving add 8	Use format 9
UHADD16	Unsigned halving add 16	Use format 9
UHASX	Unsigned halving add and subtract with exchange	Use format 9
UHSAX	Unsigned halving subtract and add with exchange	Use format 9
UHSUB8	Unsigned halving subtract 8	Use format 9
UHSUB16	Unsigned halving subtract 16	Use format 9
USAD8	Unsigned sum of absolute differences	Use format 9
USADA8	Unsigned sum of absolute differences and accumulate	Use format 9
USUB8	Unsigned subtract 8	Use format 9
USUB16	Unsigned subtract 16	Use format 9

The instructions in Table 4.2 have one or more of the following formats:

1. `Op{S} {cond} {Rd,} Rn, Operand2`
2. `Op{S} {cond} {Rd,} Rn, #imm12`
3. `Op{S} {cond} Rd, Rm, Rs`
4. `Op{S} {cond} Rd, Rm, #n`
5. `Op{S} {cond} Rd, Rm`
6. `Op{S} {cond} Rd, Operand2`
7. `Op{S} {cond} Rd,  #imm16`
8. `Op{S} {cond} Rd, Rn`
9. `Op{S} {cond} {Rd,} Rn, Rm`

10. Op{S} {cond} {Rd,} Rm, Rn
11. Op{S} {cond} Rn, Operand2
12. Op{<c>}{<q>} {<Rd>,} Rn, Rm
13. Op{S} {cond} Rdlo, RdHi, , Rm, Rn

Op is one of the instructions in Table 4.2.

S is an optional suffix that when specified is used to set the condition codes after the instruction operation.

Cond is the condition codes, such as NE, LT, EQ.

Rd is the destination register.

Rn is the register holding the first operand.

Rm is the register holding a value that "Op" operates on.

Rs is the register holding the shift length for "Op" to use on register Rm.

RdHi, RdLo are the destination registers, where RdLo is the lower 32-bit value, and RdHi is the upper 32-bit value of a 64-bit integer.

For example,

LSL R0, R1, R2; logical shift left register R1 by the value of the LSB byte in register R2 and put the result in register R0.

Operand2 is a flexible second operand. Operand2 can be a constant, such as #constant, or a register with an optional shift, such as Rn, LSL #2.

The following are some examples of data processing instructions:

ADD R0, R1, R2; R0 = R1 + R2

SUBS R1, R2, #0x100; R1 = R2 - 0x100, condition codes (N,Z,V,C) will be set after the operation of the instruction.

RSB R1, R2, #0x100; R1 = 0x100 - R2

BIC R0, R1, #0x0F; R0 = R1 & ~0x0F

ORR R2, R1, R0, LSL #2; R2 = R1 | (R0 << 2)

CLZ R1, R2; count the number of leading zeros in R2 and put that in R1, so if R2 = 0xFF, R1 = 24.

RBIT R1, R0; reverse bit order of R0 and write it to R1. For example, R0=0xA5A5 -> R1= 0xA5A50000.

REV R1, R0; reverse byte order in R0, and write it to R1. For example, R0 = 0x3A7B -> R1=0x7B3A0000.

The following Table 4.3 lists all the multiplication and division instructions and also uses one of the formats listed above.

Multiply and Divide Instructions

TABLE 4.3

Mnemonic	Description	Comments
MLA	Multiply with accumulate, 32-bit result	Use format 1, 2
MLS	Multiply and subtract, 32-bit result	Use format 1, 2
MUL	Multiply, 32-bit result	Use format 1, 2
SDV	Signed Divide	Use format 1
SMLA[B,T]	Signed multiply accumulate (halfwords)	Use format 1, 2
SMLAD, SMLADX	Signed multiply accumulate dual	Use format 2
SMLAL	Signed multiply with accumulate (32 × 32 + 64), 64-bit result	Use format 3, 4
SMLAL[B,T]	Signed multiply accumulate long (halfwords)	Use format 3, 4
SMLALD, SMLALDX	Signed multiply accumulate long dual	Use format 3, 4
SMLAW[B|T]	Signed multiply accumulate (word by halfword)	SMLAW<y>{cond} Rd, Rn, Rm, Ra
SMLSD	Signed multiply subtract dual	Use format 2
SMLSLD	Signed multiply subtract long dual	Use format 2
SMMLA	Signed most significant word multiply accumulate	Use format 2
SMMLS, SMMLSR	Signed most significant word multiply subtract	Use format 2
SMUAD, SMUADX	Signed dual multiply add	Use format 2
SMUL[B,T]	Signed multiply (word by halfword)	Use format 2
SMUL, SMULR	Signed most significant word multiply	Use format 2
SMULL	Signed multiply (32 × 32), 64-bit result	Use format 13

(*continued*)

TABLE 4.3 **(CONTINUED)**

Mnemonic	Description	Comments
SMULWB, SMULWT	Signed multiply (word by halfword)	Use format 2
SMUSD, SMUSDX	Signed dual multiply subtract	Use format 12
UDIV	Unsigned divide	Use format 1
UMAAL	Unsigned multiply accumulate long (32 × 32 + 32 + 32), 64-bit result	Use format 2
UMLAL	Unsigned multiply with accumulate (32 × 32 + 64), 64-bit result 128	Use format 2
UMULL	Unsigned multiply (32 × 32), 64-bit result 128	Use format 2

Examples

`MUL R0, R1, R2 ; R0 = R1 x R2`

`MLA R0, R1, R2, R3; R0 = (R1 x R2) + R3`

`MLS R0, R1, R2, R3; R0 = R3 - (R1 x R2)`

`SMLAD R0, R1, R2, R3;` multiply the two halfwords of R1 with the corresponding halfwords in R2, then add the multiplication results to R3, and write the final result to R0.

`SMLADX R0, R1, R2, R3;` multiply the top halfword of R1 with the bottom halfword of R2, multiply the bottom halfword of R1 with the top halfword of R2, then add the multiplication results to R3, and write the final result to R0.

`SMLAL R0, R1, R2, R3;` multiply R3 and R2 then add the 64-bit result to the combined 64-bit {R1, R0}. Write the final 64-bit result to {R1, R0}.

Before discussing about branch and jump instructions, we need to mention how arithmetic and compare instructions affect the condition codes. The branch instructions are usually placed after arithmetic or compare instructions to branch to different places depending on the outcome of the previous arithmetic or compare instructions. There are four condition codes: N, Z, C, and V. N (Negative) is set high if the result of an operation is a negative number. Z (Zero) is set high if the result is zero. C (carry) is set high after a subtraction of unsigned numbers if the result is good—for example, it's not out of range. After an addition of unsigned numbers, C is cleared to zero if the result is good. V (overflow) is set if an operation on signed numbers causes an overflow.

Here are some examples of additions and subtractions of unsigned numbers and how C (carry) is set or clear.

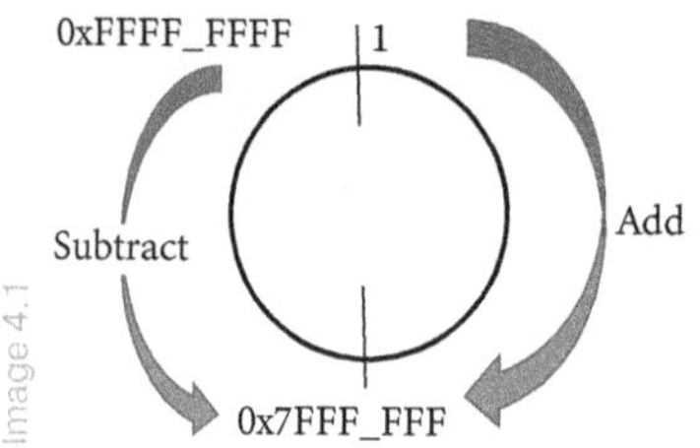

Unsigned Number Addition

When adding two unsigned numbers and the result is incorrect due to the crossing of the zero boundary between the numbers 0xFFFF_FFFF and 0x1, C bit will be set. For example, adding numbers 0xFFFF_FFFE and 0x04 results in 0x2, which is incorrect so C will be set.

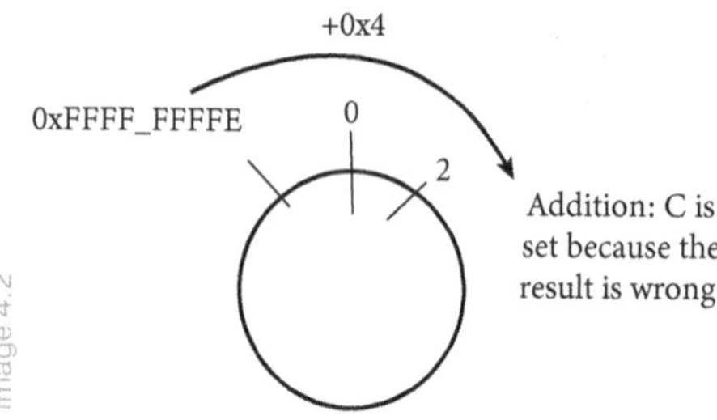

If an addition of unsigned numbers produces a correct result—that is, not crossing the 0 boundary—C will be clear. For example, adding numbers 0x100 and 0x200 yields 0x300, which is a correct result. Thus, C is clear.

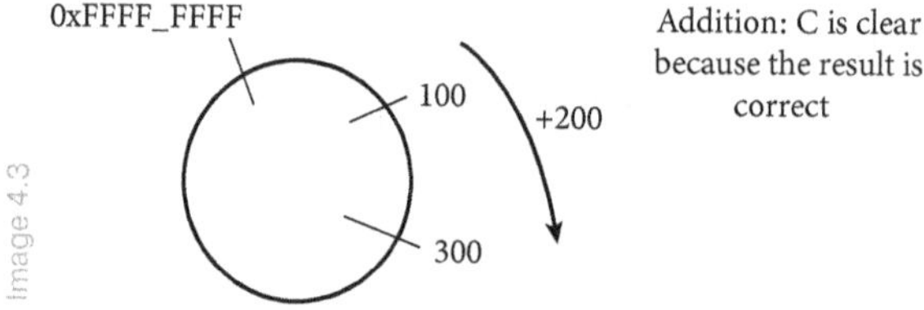

Unsigned Number Subtraction

If the result of a subtraction of unsigned numbers is correct (not crossing the 0 boundary), the carry bit C is set. Otherwise, it's clear (crossing the 0 boundary) as shown in Table 4.4.

For example, the following figure shows the result of number 100 subtracted by 200 (crossing the 0 boundary) is 0xFFFF_FF9C, which is incorrect.

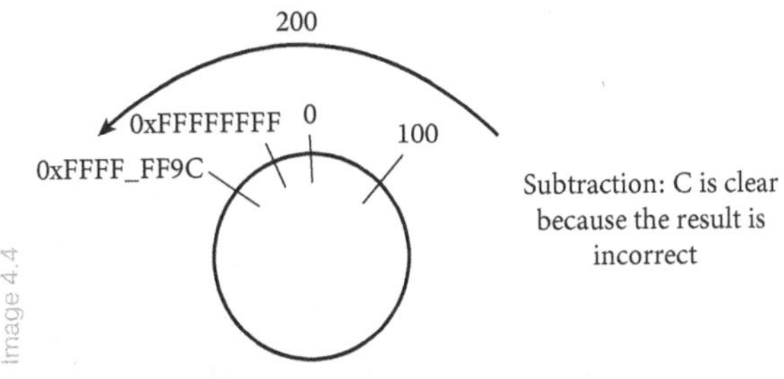

TABLE 4.4 **UNSIGNED NUMBER ARITHMETICS**

Carry (C)	Addition	Subtraction
1	Bad Result (crossing the 0 boundary)	Good Result
0	Good Result	Bad Result (crossing the 0 boundary)

32-bit Signed Number Arithmetic

For signed numbers, the Overflow V bit is set whenever the results of additions or subtractions of 32-bit signed numbers are not correct. In other words, if the operations subtraction or addition cross the boundary between the most negative number 0x8000_0000 and the most positive number 0x7FFF_FFFF, the V bit is set.

Example: the subtraction of number -0x7FFF_FFFE with 0x100 causes it to cross the boundary between 0x8000_0000 and 0x7FFF_FFFF. The result is 0x7FFF_FF02, and it's wrong, so V is set.

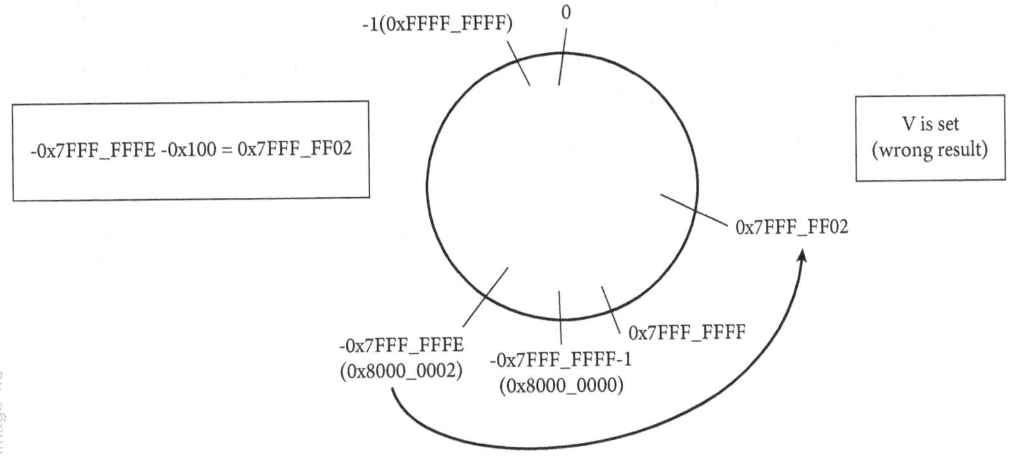

Example: Adding number -0x100 with 0x200 results in 0x100 (correct) and it does not cross the boundary between 0x8000_0000 and 0x7FFF_FFFF. Since the result is correct and the boundary between 0x8000_0000 and 0x7FFF_FFFF is not crossed, V is not set.

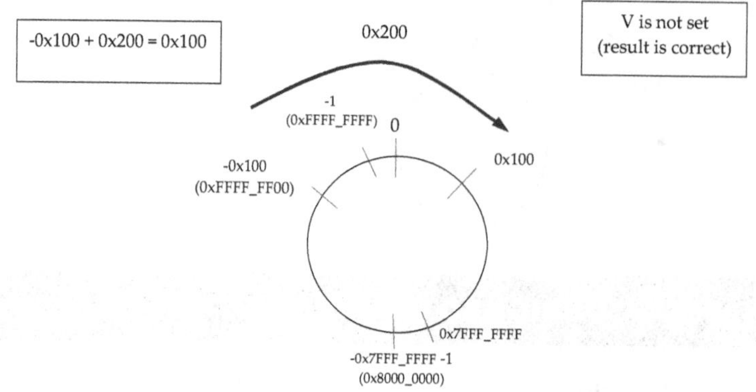

Image 4.6

Overflow (V)	Crossing the -1/0 boundary	Crossing the 0x8000_0000/ 0x7FFF_FFFF boundary
0	Yes/No	No
1	N/A	Yes

The condition codes (N, Z, C, V) are used in conditional branch instructions as described below.

All the branch and control instructions listed in Table 4.4 use one of the formats discussed below.

Branch and Control Instructions

TABLE 4.5

Mnemonic	Description	Comments
B	Branch	Use format 1 or 2, −16 MB to +16 MB
BL	Branch with link	Use format 1 or 2, −16 MB to +16 MB
BLX	Branch indirect with link	Use format 1 or 2
BX	Branch indirect	Use format 1 or 2
CBNZ	Compare and branch if nonzero	Use format 1
CBZ	Compare and branch if zero	Use format 1
IT	If-Then	Use format 3

1. `Op {cond} label`
2. `Op {cond} Rm`
3. `Op cond`

Label is a PC-relative expression.

Rm is the address that the system branches to. Bit 0 of Rm must be one to indicate that this is a Thumb instruction. However, the address that the system branches to is a 16-bit aligned address (i.e., Bit 0 is 0).

BL or BLX instruction writes the address of the next instruction into register LR (R14).

Examples:

`B Loop1`

`BEQ Loop2`

`BX LR`; Return from a subroutine call

`BL function1`; go to function1

Examples:

`ITEE EQ`; the next three instructions are conditional

`MOVEQ R0, #1`; If EQ Then

`MOVNE R3, #100000`; Else if NE then

`MOVNE R4, #0x0F1`; Else if NE then

Unsigned Conditional Branch Instructions

The following branch instructions are based on an unsigned arithmetic operation such as CMP, SUBS, or CMN[5]

Branch Instruction	
BLO target	Branch if unsigned less than (C=0). Same as BCC
BLS target	Branch if unsigned less than or the same (C=0 or Z=1)
BHI target	Branch if unsigned greater than (C=1 and Z=0). Same as BCS
BHS target	Branch if unsigned greater than or equal (C=1 or Z=1). Same as BCS

5 Valvano, *Embedded Systems*, 204.

Example:

```
CMP A, B
BLS LessThan    ; Branch to LessThan if A < B (unsigned compare)
BHI MoreThan    ;Branch to MoreThan if A > B (unsigned compare)
.....
    LessThan
.....
    MoreThan
....
```

Signed Conditional Branch Instructions[6]

The following branch instructions are based on condition set from a signed arithmetic operation such as CMP, CMN, SUB, and the like.

Branch Instruction	
BLT target	Branch if signed less than. If (~N&V | N&~V) = 1 if N!=V
BLE target	Branch if unsigned less than or equal. If (Z | ~N&V | N&~V) = 1 if Z=1 or N!=V)
BGE target	Branch if signed greater than or equal. If (~N&V | N&~V) = 0 if N=V
BGT target	Branch if signed greater than. If (Z | ~N&V | N&~V) = 0 if Z=0 or N=V

Example:

```
SUBS A, B
BLT LessThan      ; Branch to LessThan if A < B (signed compare)
BGT MoreThan      ;Branch to MoreThan if A > B (signed compare)
.....
    LessThan
.....
    MoreThan
```

6 Valvano, 206.

Subroutine Conditional Branch: BL{cond} Label

We can call a subroutine if a certain condition is met. For example, BLGT is an instruction that is executed if the condition GT is true. Table 4.6 lists all the conditions that BL can use to branch to a Label.

TABLE 4.6 **CONDITION CODES**

Suffix	Branch Condition	Flags
EQ	Equal	Z=1
NE	Not Equal	Z=0
HS/CS	Unsigned Higher or Same/Carry Set	C=1 or Z=1 *(continued)*
HI	Unsigned Higher	C=1 and Z=0
LO/CC	Unsigned Lower/Carry Clear	C=0
LS	Unsigned Lower or Same	C=0 or Z=1
MI	Negative/Minus	N=1
PL	Positive or Zero/Plus	N=0
VS	Overflow	V=1
VC	No Overflow	V=0
GE	Signed Greater Than or Equal	N=0 and V=0
GT	Signed Greater Than	Z=0 and N=V
LT	Signed Less Than	N=1 and V=0
LE	Signed Less Than or Equal	Z=1 or N!=V

Example: BLMI subroutine1 ; jump to subroutine1 if condition code N is set.

BLVL subroutine2 ; jump to subroutine2 if the overflow bit V is set

If Then (IT Block Instruction)

IT<X>:<Y><Z>cond: depending on the "cond" (listed in Table 4.5 above), the IT block allows up to four subsequent instructions to be executed.

Example: CMP R4, #100; compare R4 with 100. If it's equal, set Z = 1

ITTTT EQ; allowing four subsequent instructions to be executed if condition EQ is true (Z = 1).

MOVEQ R0, #1; if R4 is equal to 100, load R0 with 1. Otherwise, this instruction is skipped.

MOVEQ R1, #2; if R4 is equal to 100, load R1 with 2. Otherwise, this instruction is skipped.

MOVEQ R2, #3. if R4 is equal to 100, load R2 with 3. Otherwise, this instruction is skipped.

BEQ next; if R4 is equal to 100, branch to Label next. Otherwise, this instruction is skipped. This branch instruction is allowed if it's the only branch instruction and it's the last instruction in the IT block.

Example: CMP R4, #20; if R4 less than 20 (unsigned number comparison), the condition LO is true. Otherwise, the condition HS is true.

ITTE LO; allowing two subsequent instructions to be executed if the condition LO is true (Unsigned Lower, C = 0) and the last subsequent instruction to be executed if the opposite condition of LO, which is HS (Unsigned Higher or Same, C=1 or Z=1), is true.

MOVLO R0, #1; if R4 > 20, load R0 with 1. Otherwise, this instruction is skipped.

BICLO R1, #0xFF; if R4 > 20, clear the first 8 bits of register R1. Otherwise, this instruction is skipped.

LDRHS R2, =0xFFFF_FFFF; Else case. If R4 <= 20, load R2 with number 0xFFFF_FFFF. Otherwise, this instruction is skipped.

Miscellaneous Instructions

The following are some popular miscellaneous instructions:

CPSID: disable interrupts

CPSIE: enable interrupts

NOP: no operation

WFE: wait for event

WFI: wait for interrupt

There are registers that are not memory mapped. In other words, they cannot be directly accessed. In that case, you need to use ARM instructions MSR and MRS to access them.

MRS: read the Control registers. For example: MSR R0, PRIMASK; move register PRIMASK's content into register R0.

MSR: Set the Control registers. For example: MSR PRIMASK, R1; move register R1's content into register PRIMASK.

EXERCISES

1. Assume there is a 32-bit signed number K. Write an assembly program that implements the following C code: if ((K < 100) and (K > 10)) function1();

2. Assume there is a 32-bit signed number G. Write an assembly program that implements the following C code: if (G > 100) function1() else if (G < 50) function2() else function3();

3. Assume there is a 16-bit signed number G. Write an assembly program that implements the following C code: while (G > 0) funcA();

4. The following is a short memory map.

Address	Contents
0x2000001C	0x0708
0x20000020	0x090A
0x20000024	0x0B0C
0x20000028	0x0D0E
0x2000002C	0x0304
0x20000030	0x0506
0x20000034	0x0102
0x20000038	0x00FF

If R0 = 0x20000020, R2 = 0x02, use the original value of R0 to answer the following questions.

a. `LDR R1, [R0], #0x04;` R1 = ? R0 = ?
b. `LDR R1, [R0, #0x04]! ;` R1 = ? R0 = ?
c. `LDR R1, [R0, #0x04];` R1 = ? R0 = ?
d. `LDR R1, [R0, R2, LSL #2];` R1 = ? R0 = ? R2 = ?

5. The following is a stack with the SP having a value of 0x20000038.

0x00		
0x00		
0x00		
0x00		
0x00		0x20000038

SP = 0x20000038

R0 = 0x0102, R1 = 0x0304, R2 = 0x0506, R3 = 0x0708, R4 = 0x090A, R5 = 0x0B0C, R6 = 0x0D0E

```
PUSH {R0}               <---- a
PUSH {R1-R2}            <----b
PUSH {R3-R6}            <----c
POP {R5-R7}             <----d
POP {R2, R6, R5, R1}    <----e
```

a. After executing point a, what is the content of the stack (SP and every location in the following picture)?

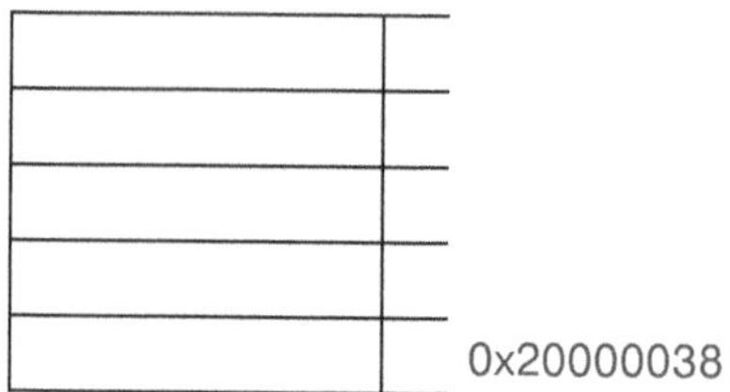

b. After executing point b, what is the content of the stack (SP and every location in the following picture)?

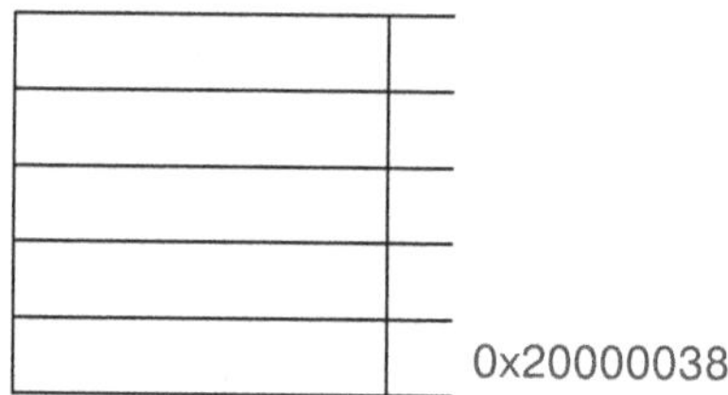

c. After executing point c, what is the content of the stack (SP and every location in the previous picture)?

d. After executing point e, what are the values of the SP and register R1–R6?

6. Write an assembly language subroutine to copy a string array, string1, to a 2nd string array string2. Simulate it using Keil in simulation mode.

7. Write an assembly language program to find the maximum, the mean, the minimum, and the average of the following numbers: 10, 11, 12, 13, 14, 15, 16, 18, 19.

8. Write a subroutine that counts the number of characters in a string. The string is null-terminated. Register R0 is a call by reference pointer to the string. The number of characters in the string is returned in register R0. For example, consider this string:

   Name1 DCB "ECE3436",0
   The calling sequence is:
   ```
   LDR R0, =Name1
   BL Count_char
   ```

9. Assume n is an unsigned 16-bit global variable. Write an assembly code version of the following C code (10pts):

   ```
   n = 80; while (n!=0) {n--; body();}
   ```

10. Given a string of lower characters, "Happy World", write an assembly program to convert this string to all uppercase. The string is supposed to be stored in RAM. Note that the original string has a mix of upper and lowercase characters.

11. Write an assembly program to display number 0–9 on a 7-segment display.

12. 2-digit packed BCD numbers are decimal numbers encoded into a byte contains 2 BCD digits. One is the upper nibble and the other is the lower nibble. For example, number 56 is represented in binary by 0101_0110. Write an assembly program to add 2 BCD numbers—for example, 25 and 49—to produce another BCD number.

13. An unpacked BCD number is a decimal digit encoded into a byte with 4 binary bits representing the numbers and the rest are ignored. For example, number 74 is represented in binary by 00000111 00000100. Write an assembly program to add 2 unpacked BCD numbers—for example, 36 and 57—to produce another unpacked BCD number.

14. Use assembly language to implement a state machine that controls the lock of a subway turnstile. Initially, the turnstile is locked. Depositing a token will unlock the turnstile to allow a single access [4].

    A turnstile is normally used to allow entry to subways, and it typically has two states: locked and unlocked. Initially, the turnstile is in the locked state, and it's unlocked when a coin or token is deposited in a slot on the turnstile. The turnstile will become locked again after one customer passes through by pushing it. If a coin was not deposited after the turnstile is locked, no pushing can cause it to open. When the turnstile is in the unlocked state, more coin deposits

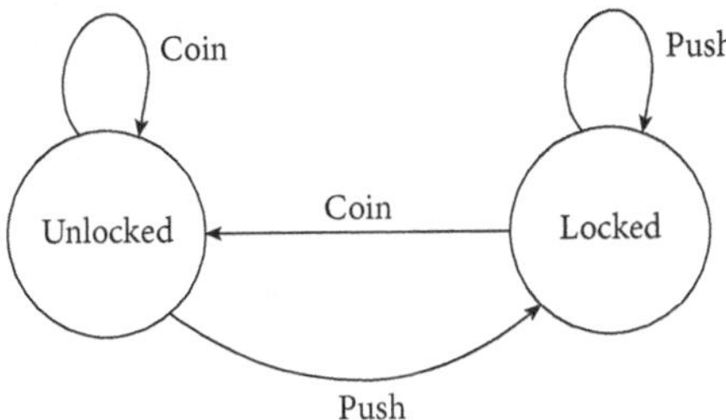

FIGURE 4.1 State Diagram.

will not change its state and only a single push is allowed to open it. The diagram of this state machine is shown in Figure 4.1.

15. Use assembly language to implement a state machine for an elevator, which runs between the ground floor and the first floor. There is one button—up and down—to control the elevator and two lead lights—red and green—to indicate the ground or the first floor, respectively.[7]

7 https://www.cs.princeton.edu/courses/archive/spring06/cos116/FSM_Tutorial.pdf. Accessed 5/28/2020.

C Programming in Embedded Systems

1. Introduction

C is one of the oldest and most mature languages still being used. It is supported by most microcontroller systems, and it is also the language of choice for critical systems.[1] There are a million lines of code that use the C language in machines or computers operating around the world. Almost all of the problems facing a computer language have been discovered and resolved with the C language. C also allows you to interface seamlessly with the assembly language of your microcontroller of choice. C is fast and takes a small memory footprint. C is used to implement most real-time operating systems (RTOSs). However, to use C effectively in embedded systems, we need to support the modular programming concept.[2]

1.1. Modular Programming

An RTOS must usually deal with many peripherals, such as UART, GPIO, and timers, so it will be hard to visualize or design the software without using the modular concept. The design will become more manageable if it can be broken down into submodules, each of which serves a particular function. For example, a GPIO module can be used to initialize all the GPIO pins used in the system, as well as support other requirements of the GPIO pins, such as GPIO interrupts, or the UART module can set up and initialize the UART port.

1.2. In-Line Assembly

To embed assembly language code in a C language program, one can use the symbol `__asm` to mark the beginning of the assembly code. Please note that the in-line assembly code cannot directly access the physical ARM registers. The assembly code located within the preprocessors is processed by a macroassembler included in the C compiler, but it will not optimize the assembly code.

---

1 "A Brief History of MISRA C," MISRA C Online, accessed July 29, 2019, https://www.misra.org.uk/Activities/MISRAC/tabid/160/Default.aspx.

2 Valvano, *Embedded Systems*, 194–204.

In the following example, the variables *r*0, *r*1, *r*2, and so on, will not necessarily be mapped to the exact physical ARM registers.

```
int add(int x)
{

  int r0 = 5;
    int r1 = 1;
    int r2 = 2;
    int r3 = 3;
    int r4 = 4;
    int a = 5;
      __asm
      {
      ADD r1, a, r2;
      ADD r0, r3, r4;
    }

    return r1;
  }
```

Program 5.1: In-line Assembly

2. Variables

2.1. Some Special Keywords

The following are some special keywords that are often used in microcontroller applications.

- `Volatile`: This keyword is placed in front of a declaration for a variable, and it forces the compiler to fetch a new value for the variable every time it is used. It's often used for variables related to I/O ports since the variable can change value outside of a software routine. It's also used with global variables that share the main program and interrupt service routines
- `int8_t`: Signed 8-bit integer
- `int16_t`: Signed 16-bit integer
- `int32_t`: Signed 32-bit integer
- `uint8_t`: Unsigned 8-bit integer
- `uint16_t`: Unsigned 16-bit integer
- `uint32_t`: Unsigned 32-bit integer
- `CPSIE I`: This is a CMSIS core intrinsic function used to enable the interrupt globally
- `CPSID I`: This is a CMSIS core intrinsic function used to disable the interrupt globally
- `__asm`: Specifies an in-line assembler. With this special keyword, you can insert assembly code to be executed in a C program

2.2. Variables

A variable is an object defined by using one of the previously noted keywords (e.g., uint32_t x). It can be read from or written to, and it resides in RAM. On the other hand, a constant variable cannot be modified, but it can be read from, and it resides in ROM.

A variable can be defined as static or automatic. A static variable exists for the entire lifetime of a program, and it is allocated a permanent location in memory. Meanwhile, an automatic variable is dynamically allocated a place in memory, and its location only exists during the time its program is executed. The following examples will illustrate the differences between a static variable and an automatic variable.

```
uint8_t function_ex (void) {

    static uint8_t count;

    count = count + 1;

    return count;

}
```

Program 5.2: Function with Static Variable

Every time function_ex is called, count will be incremented from its old value so that the returned value is always the newly updated value of count. The value of count is maintained throughout the life of the program.

```
uint8_t function_ex1 (void) {

    uint8_t count;

    count = count + 1;

    return count

  }
```

Program 5.3: Function with Automatic Variable

Here, in Program 5.3, count is defined as an automatic variable. Every time function_ex1 is called, count will be incremented from zero. In other words, after function_ex1 is called, its returned value is always one. The value of count is not maintained, and it is reset at the beginning of function function_ex1.

A static global variable can only be accessed from codes inside the same file that the static variable is defined. A static local variable can be accessible only in the function where it is defined.

An "extern" declaration can enable a global variable that is defined in other modules to be visible in the current module. However, if a variable is declared by an extern but not defined anywhere in the program space, the program will not compile since that variable is not allocated any memory.[3] For example, the following program will not compile.

```
extern int x; //Assume x is not defined anywhere else

void main(void)

{

    x = 1;

}
```

Program 5.4: Bad Extern Variable

3 "Understanding 'Extern' Keyword in C," GeeksforGeeks, accessed July 29, 2019, https://www.geeksforgeeks.org/understanding-extern-keyword-in-c/.

But the following program will compile because variable *x* is already defined somewhere else.

```
#include "Anyfile.h" //Assume x is defined in this file

extern int x;

void main(void)

{

    x = 1;

}
```

Program 5.5: Good Extern Variable

2.3 I/O Ports

Some of the addresses of ARM I/O Port registers are, for example, 0x4000_43FC (GPIO_PORTA_DATA_R register) or 0x4000_53FC (GPIO_PORTB_DATA_R register). How do you read from or write to these registers? One way is to create macros for these registers as a following example shows:

```
#define GPIO_PORTA_DATA_R (*((volatile uint32_t *)0x400043FC))
```

Notice that there is no semicolon at the end of the above define line since this is a macro, not C code. This define is a typecast to convert number 0x400043FC to a pointer that points to a 32-bit address ((volatile uint32_t *)0x400043FC) and then get its content by dereferencing it: (*((volatile uint32_t *)0x400043FC)). The word *volatile* is a C keyword that when applied to a variable forces the compiler to get a new value of the variable and not depend on a previous value since the value of the variable can change any time.

In C language, to access a specific bit or bits of the data register of a port, we can add the following constant in Table 5.1 to the base address of a port's data register:

TABLE 5.1 **ADDRESS OFFSET FOR DATA REGISTER**

Accessing bit	Constant
0	0x004
1	0x008

(continued)

TABLE 5.1 **ADDRESS OFFSET FOR DATA REGISTER (*CONTINUED*)**

Accessing bit	Constant
2	0x010
3	0x020
4	0x040
5	0x080
6	0x100
7	0x200

For example, if we want to write to bit 0 of data register of port A, we can add the base address of PORTA base register, 0x40004000, with 0x0004 (corresponding to bit 0 from Table 5.1) and define the following macro:

```
#define PORTA_D0 (*((volatile uint32_t *)0x40004004))
```

In another example, the following macro allows us to access bit 3-0 of Port A's data register:

```
#define PORTA_D30 (*((volatile uint32_t *)0x4000403C))
```

If we add all the numbers of the above table, we can access bit 7-0 of port A's data register:

```
#define GPIO_PORTA_DATA_R (*((volatile uint32_t *)
0x400043FC))
```

Table 5.2 lists all the base data registers of all the ports.

TABLE 5.2 **BASE GPIO DATA REGISTER**

Port	Base Data Register
Port A	0x40004000
Port B	0x40005000
Port C	0x40006000
Port D	0x40007000
Port E	0x40024000
Port F	0x40025000

3. Pointers

"A pointer is a type of variable that can store the address of another object or a function."[4] It can be declared a regular

4 "CNotes For Professionals," GoalKicker.com, accessed July 29, 2019, http://goalkicker.com/CBook.

variable, except an asterisk is placed between the data type declaration and the pointer name. The following is an example of a pointer declaration.

`char *cpointer;` //this is the declaration of a pointer variable named cpointer, which is the address of a character object.

To initialize a pointer address, we can assign it to the given address of a variable of the same data type. The pointer must point to the same data type as the variable that is assigned to the pointer.

```
char *cptr;        //declare cptr as a pointer to a character variable

char char1 = 'a';  //define a character variable char1 and ini-
tialize it to 'a'

cptr = &char1;      // assign the address of char1 variable to
pointer variable cptr
```

Program 5.6: Pointer Declaration

To get the value of the object pointed to by a pointer (dereference a pointer), we can use the symbol * (dereference operator), as in the following example.

```
//Continue from program 5.6

char char2;          //declare a new char variable

char2 = *cptr;    //assign  'a' to char variable chr2
```

Program 5.7: Pointer Dereference

In embedded system application, a lot of times, you can use a pointer to point to an address of a register as follows.

```
uint32_t *gpio_porta_data_ptr = (volatile unint32_t *)0x40058000;
// Port A data register of the Tiva C

// launchpad
```

As mentioned earlier, we add the keyword "volatile" to force the compiler to fetch an updated value of the register anytime it is used.

If a pointer is used to point to a structure or union type of data, the dereference operator -> can be used to dereference a member of the structure.

```
AnyStruct *sptr = &AnyStruct;

sptr->AnyMember = 0x10;
```

Pointers are often used together with arrays of the same data type. A pointer can point to any element of an array and an array name can be thought of as a pointer pointing to the first element of the array.

```
int array1[4]  = {1, 2, 3, 4};

int *aptr;

aptr = &array1;   //or aptr = array1;
```

Pointer to a const int: The value of the int variable cannot be changed, but the pointer's value can change.

```
const int *p;

int a;

p = &a;  //ok. the pointer can point to any address

*p = 20; //compiler error because the value of the integer cannot
be changed
```

const pointer to an int: The pointer can only be initialized to a value one time, but the int variable's value can change.

```
int x, y;

int *const p = &x;

*p = 10;  // ok. Int variable's value can be changed

P = &y;    // compiler error since pointer p cannot be changed
```

Const pointer to a const int: The pointer points to an int, and both the values of the pointer and the int cannot be changed.

```
int x, y;

const int *const p = &x; // initialization is ok but not modi-
fiable afterward

p = &y; // compiler error since p is a const pointer

*p = y; // compiler error since *p is a const int
```

Pointer to a pointer to an int:

```
int x, y;

int *p;

int **dp;

p = &x;

*dp = &y;

**dp = 20;
```

Pointer to a pointer to a const int: The value of the const int variable cannot be modified.

```
int x;

const int *ptr;

const int **dptr;

dptr = &ptr;

*dptr = &x;

**dptr = 20; //compiler error, **dptr is not modifiable
```

Pointer to a const pointer to an int: The pointer to the const pointer cannot be modified.

```
int x;

int *ptr;

int *const * dptr;

dptr = &ptr;  //ok

*dptr = &x;    // compiler error since *dptr points to a const
pointer

**dptr = 20;  //ok since **dptr points to an int
```

Const pointer to pointer to an int:

```
int x;

int *p;

int ** const dp = &p;

dp = &p;
```

3.1. Function Pointer

As a pointer can be used to point to an int variable, it can also be used to point to a function like in the following example.

```
int Sub(int i, int j) {

   return (i -j);

}



int (*Sub_fp) (int, int) = Sub; //or = &Sub
```

Program 5.8: Function Pointer Declaration

Like a regular pointer, to dereference the function pointer:

```
Sum = *Sub_fp(4, 2); //Sum = 2.
```

To avoid typing when a function pointer is used many times, for Program 5.8, we can use typedef as follows.

```
typedef int (*fp)(int, int);

int Sub(int i, int j) {

   return (i - j);

}

int Add(int i, int j) {

   Return (i + j);

}


void main (void) {

int Sum, Diff;

fp Sub_fp = Sub;

fp Add_fp = Add;

Sum = (*Add_fp)(4, 2);

Diff = (Sub_fp)(5, 1);

}
```

Program 5.9: Function Pointer Dereference

Function pointer is often used as a callback in embedded system applications. "A callback is any executable code that is passed as an argument to other code, which is expected to call back (execute) the argument at a given time."[5]

```
#include <stdio.h>

void A() {

  printf("I am function A\n");

}

void B(void (*ptr)()) {

   (*ptr)();

}

void main(void) {

    void (*ptr)() = A;

    B(ptr);

}
```

Program 5.10 A simple C program to demonstrate callback.

3.2. Pointer Arithmetic[6]

When doing pointer arithmetic, such as addition or subtraction, we need to take into account the size of the pointer's objects. For example, if we add one to a pointer pointing to an int, the address corresponding to the new pointer's value should be incremented by two compared to the previous address since an int occupies 2 bytes. Similarly, a long integer occupies 4 bytes, so by incrementing by one, a pointer pointing to a long integer corresponds to a new address being equal to the old address plus four. The same thing is applied to subtraction.

5 Geeksforgeeks. "Callbacks in C," https://www.geeksforgeeks.org/callbacks-in-c/. Accessed 9/5/2020.

6 Valvano, *Embedded Systems*, 238–41.

3.3. Pointer Comparison

Pointers are always considered to be unsigned since pointers contain memory addresses, which are always unsigned. Therefore, all pointer comparison operations are considered unsigned ones.

4. Arrays[7]

An array is a data structure that is a collection of fixed size data with the same data type. The collection is ordered and is stored contiguously in memory without gaps. C allows arrays of pointers, as well as multidimensional arrays in which each element of the array is another array.

In general, the size of the array can be statically allocated or dynamically allocated at run time.

4.1. Array Syntax

```
Data type array_name[size];
```

Data type can be any built-in or user-defined data form, such as int or structures; array_name is a user-defined name, and size is an integer constant.

```
int array1[10]; //declare an array of ten int elements of unde-
termined values since the array is not initialized yet
```

```
char array1[10][5]; //define array of 50 char elements
```

The following examples show that there are several ways to initialize an array.

```
int array1[10] = {0}; //all ten elements are initialized to 0
```

```
int array1[10] = {0, 1, 2, 3}; //the first four elements of array1
are 0, 1, 2, 3, respectively. All the rest are zero.
```

```
Int array1[10] = {[1] = 1, [0] = 0, [2] = 2}; //array1[0] = 0,
array1[1] = 1, array1[2] = 2 and the rest are zero.
```

We can also let the compiler determine the size of the array by leaving the square bracket empty.

```
int array1[] = {0, 1, 2, 3}; //an array of four elements with
values of 0, 1, 2, 3, respectively
```

7 "CNotes For Professionals," GoalKicker.com/CBook, page 60–69.

```
int array1[] = {[2] = 2, [5] = 4}; // an array of length six with
array1[2] = 2, array1[5] = 4, and the rest are zero.
```

An array can also be initialized to all zeros using the memset command from string.h.

```
int array2[10];
memset(array1, 0, sizeof array1);
```

Program 5.11

Note that memset initializes each byte of an array so that it can only be used to initialize an array to all zeros. To initialize an array to values different from zeros, refer to other methods mentioned earlier.

4.2. Array Subscripts

Since the elements of an array are stored contiguously in memory in the "row major order,"[8] we need to access a multidimensional array in an efficient way. Otherwise, the system performance can be degraded because of cache misses [4]. For example, an array with a dimension 1,000 × 1,000 will store element [0][0] then [0][1], etc., until [0]999] before element [1][0] so that if we try to access element [1][0] immediately after element [0][0], that will cause a cache miss. A computer system's performance will be severely degraded if there are many cache misses since each one will cause the system to go to the memory to bring in a new cache line, and that will take time, hence, slowing the computer.

4.3. Arrays and Pointers

We can refer to elements of an array by their subscripts or by using pointers, as in the following examples:

```
int x, *pt, data[10];

x = data[2];        // set x equal to the third element of array
data

x = *data;         // set x equal to the first element of array dat

pt = data;           //set pt equal to the address of the first
element of the array data

pt = &data[0]; //set pt equal to the address of the first element
of the array data
```

8 "CNotes For Professionals," GoalKicker.com/CBook, 64–66.

```
pt = data + 2;    // set pt equal to the address of the third
element of the array data

pt = &data[3];   // set pt equal to the address of the fourth
element of the array data
```

Note that even the array name points to the address of the array, and it looks like a pointer; it cannot be used as a pointer on the left-hand side of an equation (i.e., it is not modifiable).

```
data = &buffer; // Compiler error.
```

4.4. Address Arithmetic

Addresses, like pointers, array names, or values created by the address operator, can be used in expressions, and they are treated as unsigned numbers. Address arithmetic needs to take into account the size of the data the address points to. For instance, if an address points to a long integer (size of 4 bytes), adding one to the pointer indicating that address should point to the next long integer whose address is incremented by four.

5. Structure

Structure is a collection of variables of different data types that share a single name. Compared to the array whose elements must have the same data type, the structure can have members with different subnames and different/same data types. A structure can be referenced by its name or pointer, and structure members can be accessed by the structure name with the member subnames.[9]

5.1. Structure Syntax

A structure must be declared before it can be used. Declaration of a structure does not allocate any memory space; we need to define a variable of this structure type before the system will assign memory space to it. There are various ways to declare and define a structure, as shown in the following examples.

```
struct a_int {    //declare a structure a_int

    int x;

    int *ptr;

};
```

9 "CNotes For Professionals," page 83–92.

```
struct a_int a_int_ex;  //define a_int_ex as a variable of struct
type a_int

struct a_int a_int_ex1;  //define a_int_ex1 as a variable of
struct type a_int
```

We can combine the declaration and definition of a struct variable.

```
struct a_int {    //declare a structure a_int

   int x;

   int *ptr;

} a_int_ex, a_int_ex1; //define two structures a_int_ex, a_int_ex1
```

Program 5.12

We can define a struct type and use it to define a struct variable. For instance, we can define a struct type called a_int_s and then use it to define variable a_int_ex and a_int_ex1.

```
typedef struct a_int a_int_s;

a_int_s a_int_ex;

a_int_s a_int_ex1;
```

We can also combine the declaration and typedef.

```
typedef struct {    // declare a structure type a_int_s

   int x;

   int *ptr;

} a_int_s;

a_int_s a_int_ex, a_int_ex1;
```

Program 5.13

Like defining and initializing a variable at the same time, we can initialize a structure at the time it is defined.

```
int x, y;

typedef struct {    // declare a structure type a_int_s

   int x;

   int *ptr;

} a_int_s;



a_int_s a_int_ex = {10, (int *)(0x20000010));     // define and
initialize a new struct variable, a_int_ex.

A_int_s a_int_ex1 = {20, };                               //
the value of pointer ptr of struct a_int_ex1 is NULL



//since it's blank in the initialization
```

Program 5.14

Be careful when blanking a field or fields in a struct initialization since some compilers will work and some won't.

5.2. Accessing Fields of a Structure

We can access members of a structure using the dot operator (.) between the structure name and the member name if the structure is a variable. However, *if we use a pointer to a structure, we need to use the arrow operator (->) instead.*

```
Int y;

typedef struct {    // declare a structure type a_int_s

   int x;

   int *ptr;

} a_int_s;
```

```
a_int_s a_int_ex, a_int_ex1;

a_int_ex.x = 10;

(a_int_ex.ptr) = &y;
```

Program 5.15

```
int y;

typedef struct {    // declare a structure type a_int_s

   int x;

   int *ptr;

} a_int_s;

a_int_s a_int_ex, a_int_ex1;

a_int_s *sptr;

sptr = a_int_ex;

sptr.x = 10;   //compile error

sptr->x = 10; //ok. This is the right syntax for using struct
pointer to access members of a struct.

(sptr->ptr) = & (sptr->x);
```

Program 5.16

5.3. Passing Structures to Functions

We can pass structures to functions using the call "by value" approach (not recommended if the structure contains a lot of data) or the "call by reference" method (the preferred way). The "call by value" method will copy all the parameters of a structure to the stack, and that might cause the stack to overflow if there is too much data to copy or if the stack does not have a lot of spaces left. On the other hand, for the "call by reference" approach, we pass only a structure pointer to the function. However, in this method, the original structure's data will be changed if the function modifies them, while the "call by value" method keeps the original data intact.

```
void mod_struct(ex1_struct *ex1) ;

typedef struct ex1 {

   int i1;

   int i2;

   int i3;

   int i4;

   char *cpt;

   int *iptr;

   //int flex[];

} ex1_struct;

void main(void) {

   ex1_struct ex1_2 = {1, 2, 3, 4, "Hello", (int *)(0x20001000)};

   ex1_struct *sptr2 = &ex1_2;

   mod_struct(sptr2);

}

void mod_struct(ex1_struct *ex1) {

   (ex1->i1) = (ex1->i1) + (ex1->i2);

   (ex1->i2) = ex1->i2 + ex1->i3;

   (ex1->i3) = ex1->i3 + ex1->i4;

   (ex1->i1) *= 2;

   (ex1->i4) *= 2;

   *(ex1->iptr) = 0x100;

}
```

Program 5.17

6. Development Systems

There are several software development systems that are available for writing application programs for the ARM Cortex microcontrollers. Two of the free and widely used integrated development environments (IDE) are Keil from ARM and Code Composer Studio (CCS) from Texas Instruments (TI).

6.1. Keil uVision IDE 5

Keil development tools provide support for various microcontroller architectures, including 8051, ARM microcontrollers like ARM4 Cortex M-4, and ARM Cortex-M7. Keil MDK-ARM supports most ARM microcontroller versions, and there are two Keil versions that are freely available to download. Keil version 4 is an older version, but it works for almost all the examples in this book and it's free. Keil version 5 is an updated version of version 4, and with an optional legacy support pack, it can also run all Keil version 4 programs. You do not need a license to use MDK-Lite v5 to develop your programs, but the size of your programs is limited to 32 Kbytes, which are enough for most educational purposes. Other Keil editions require a license for activation, and they allow you to access Keil middleware, which provides support for ARM peripherals.

You can download Keil MDK-ARM from the following link: https://www.keil.com/demo/eval/arm.htm. You need to register before you can download it.

The Keil IDE includes C/C++ compilers, RTX RTOS Kernel library, uVision IDE and device database, uVision debugger and analysis tools, and device simulation. The MDK-Lite version does not provide support for the RTX RTOS and middleware components. Without these components, you can still develop software for embedded systems, but it may take longer than with programs that have the help of the RTX RTOS and the middleware library.

One of the best features of the Keil IDE is that it allows the user to simulate the program without using the underlined microcontroller since Keil includes simulation models for many popular microcontrollers, such as the TivaC and STM32. However, even if a simulation model is available, not all of its features may be implemented.

Here's a typical sequence of steps taken to open a Keil project.[10] You will run an example project called uart_echo. The TivaC is communicating with the art and echo characters on the screen as you type.

1. Double-click on the icon Keil 5.
2. Click on "Open Project" from the Project menu.
3. Browse to C:\TITivaware_C_Series-2.1.4.178\examples\boards\dk-tm4c123g\uartecho and select file uart_echo.uvproj.
4. Figure 5.1 shows the opened project.

10 Bai, *Practical Microcontroller Engineering*, page 127–151.

5. You can look at any files in the Project Explore pane (residing on the left) by double-clicking that file.
6. You can (re)build the project by double-clicking on the Project menu, Project Rebuild, or click the hammer symbol. The result is displayed in the Build/Rebuild window at the bottom of the Kiel IDE.

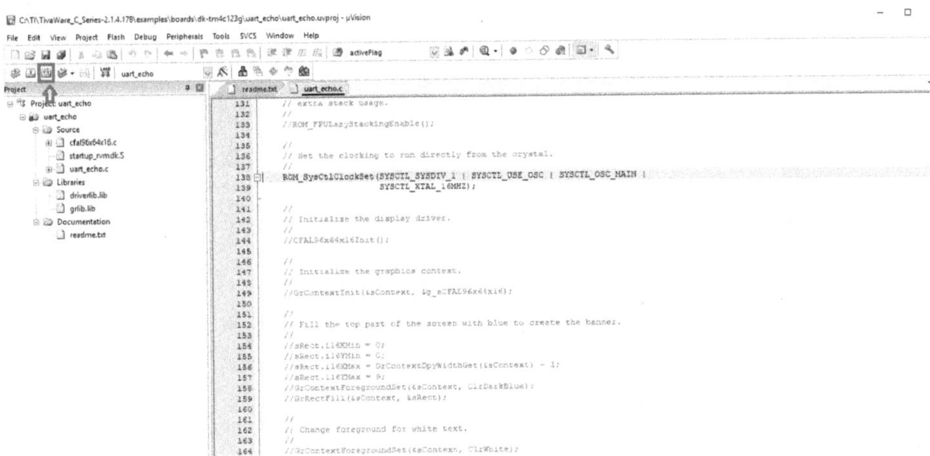

FIGURE 5.1 Rebuild the Project.

7. After the files were compiled and linked, and assuming there is no compilation error, you can download the executable output file uartecho.axf to the flash of the TivaC launchpad with the onboard ICDI (in-circuit debug interface) by clicking on the Debug button (Figure 5.2).

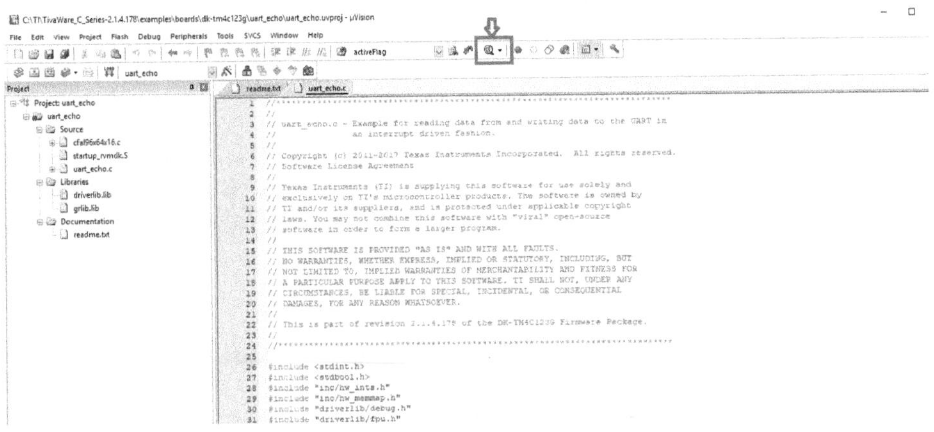

FIGURE 5.2 Download the Program and Enter the Debug Mode.

8. When you are in the debug mode, you can run the program (first arrow on the left) or step through the program (several options, second arrow; Figure 5.3).

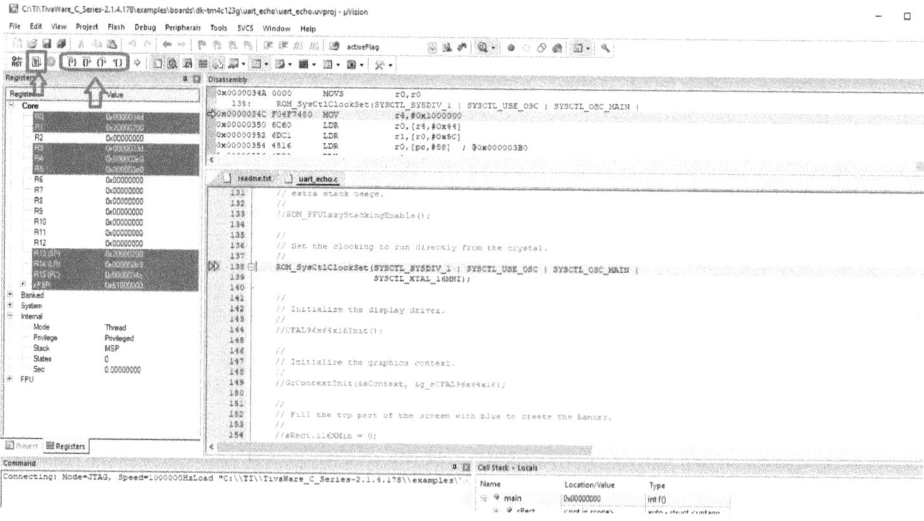

FIGURE 5.3 Run the Program.

9. You can set a break point on any line of code for debugging. You can also monitor the value of variables by adding them to a watch window (Figure 5.4).

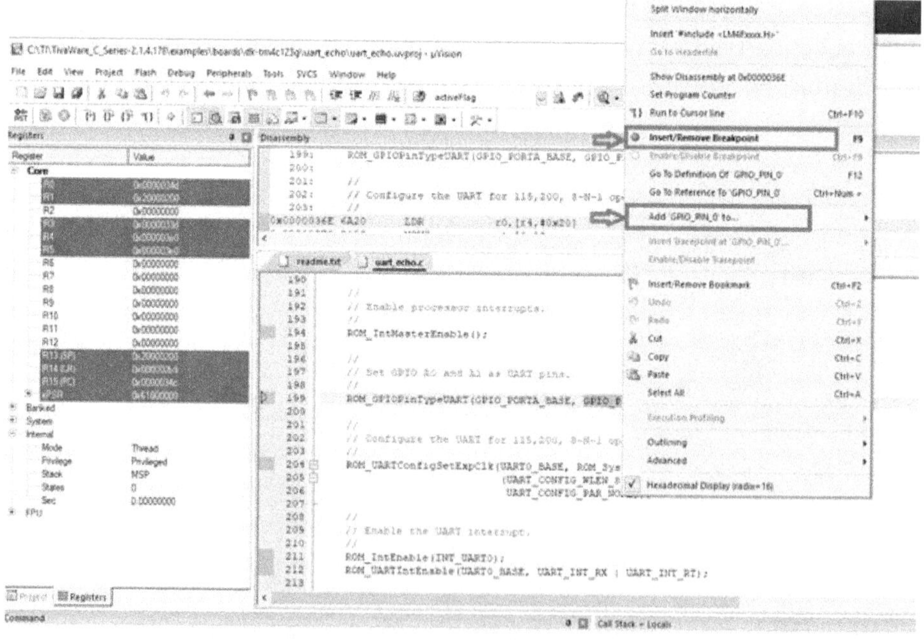

FIGURE 5.4 Insert Break Point or Add Variable to be Monitored.

6.2. CCS

CCS is a popular IDE that was developed by TI. The latest CCS version is version 10, which does not support the TivaC but version 7 and version 6.2, the last stable version, still support the TivaC. It's better to import a working example from the resource library and then modify it to suit your requirement than to create a brand-new project. The following are steps taken to open an example project inside the Resource Explorer Classic (Figure 5.5).

1. View -> Resource Explorer Classic

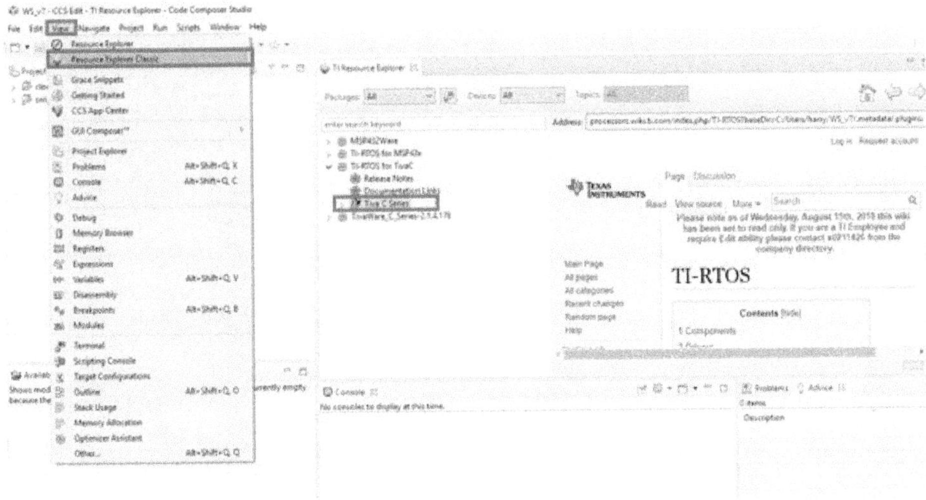

FIGURE 5.5 Open Resource Explorer.

2. Pick Uart Echo Project and import it into the workspace (Figure 5.6).

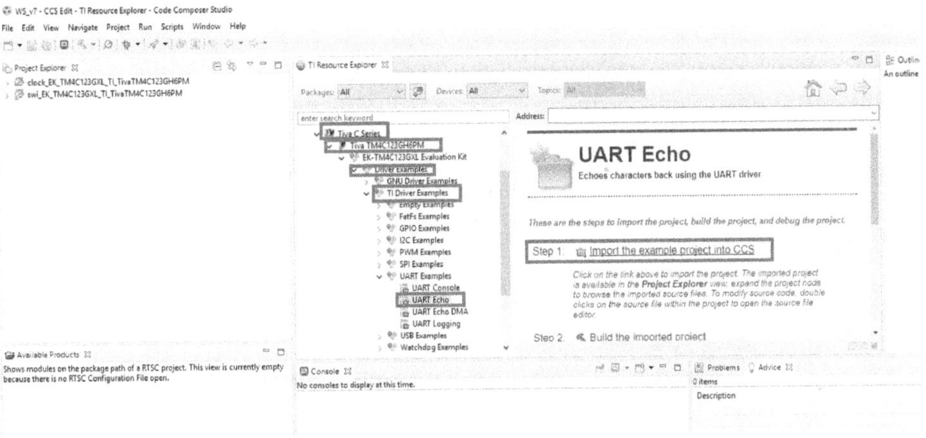

FIGURE 5.6 Select a Project in the Resource Explorer.

3. Click on Build Project button (Figure 5.7).

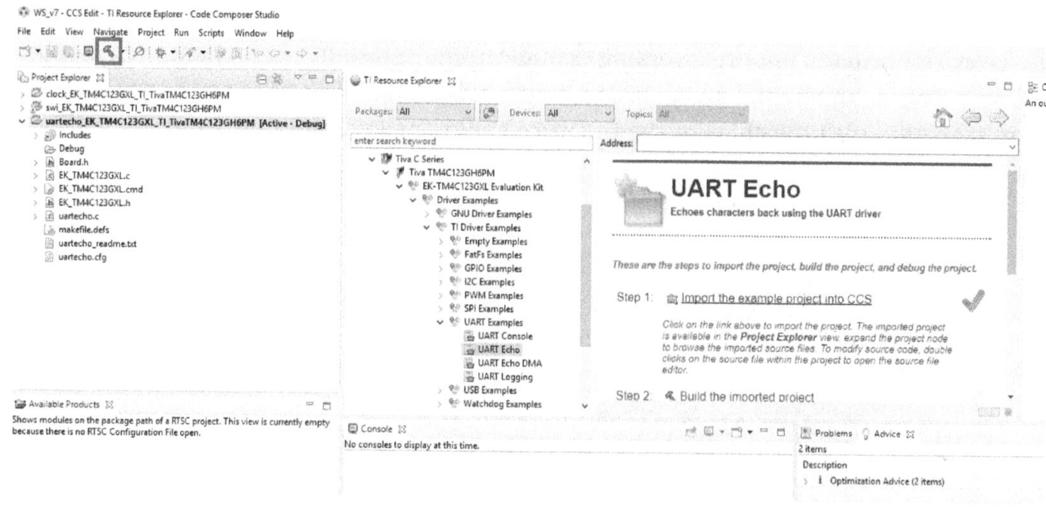

FIGURE 5.7 Pick Project UART Echo.

4. After building the project and finding no errors, click on Debug (Figure 5.8).

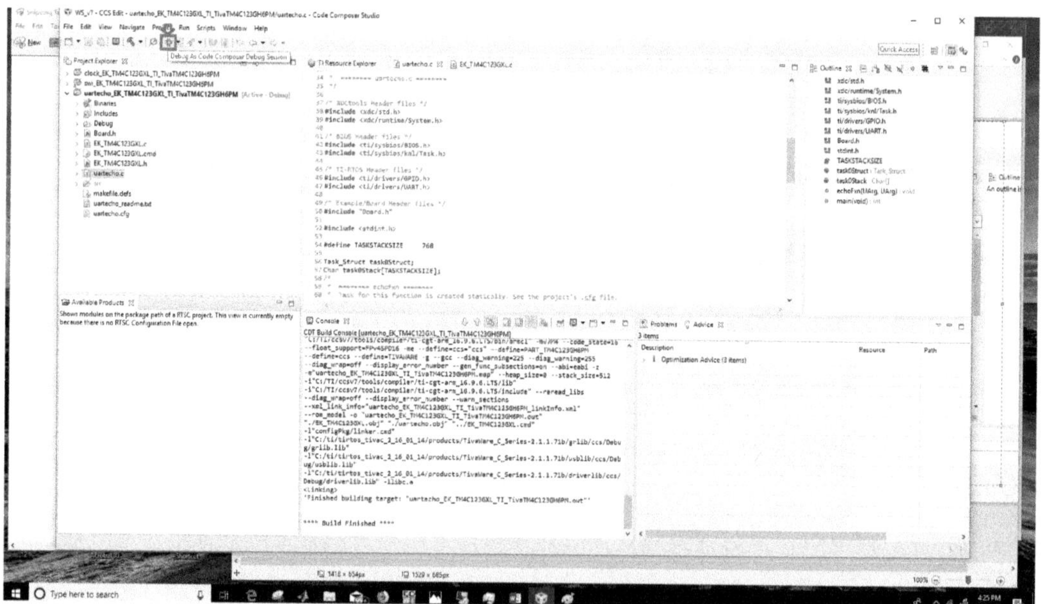

FIGURE 5.8 Enter Debug Mode and Flash the Program.

5. Double-click on the Tera Term icon to create a serial terminal to communicate with the launchpad via the UART port. Select the right baud rate after selecting setup from the menu (Figure 5.9).

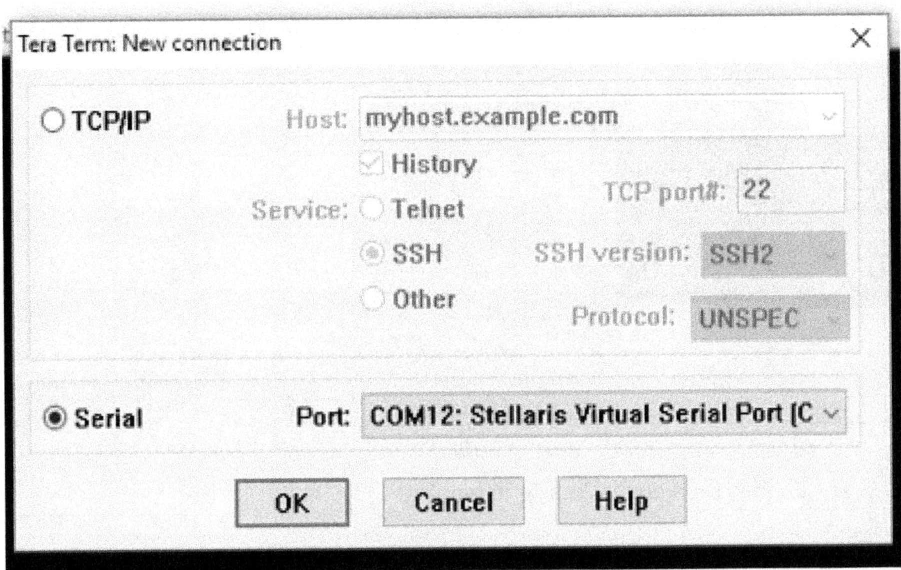

FIGURE 5.9 Set up a Tera Term terminal.

6. After clicking on the Debug button, you can now run the program by clicking on the icon next to the small arrow shown in Figure 5.10. The big arrow points to several options, such as stepping into a line of code in the program, stepping over a line, or returning from a line.

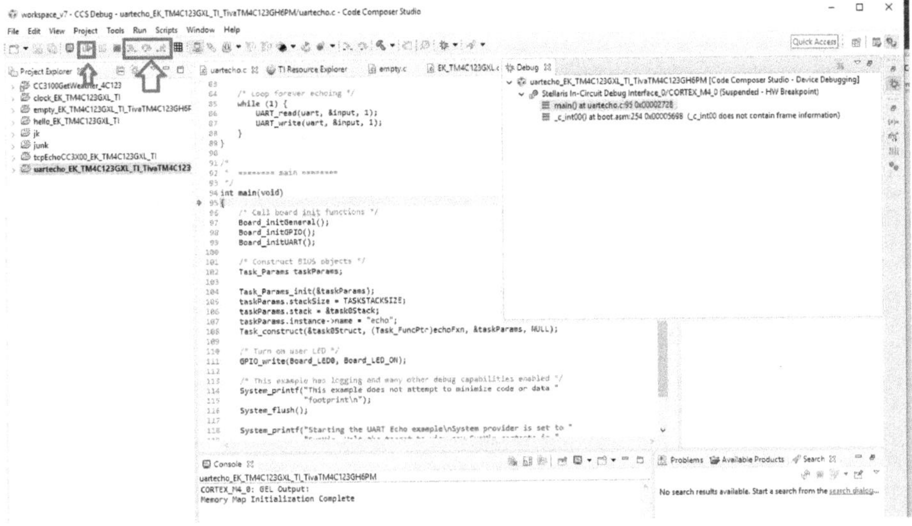

FIGURE 5.10 Stepping into the Program.

7. Type in the Tera Term window to see characters being echoed back on the terminal screen (Figure 5.11).

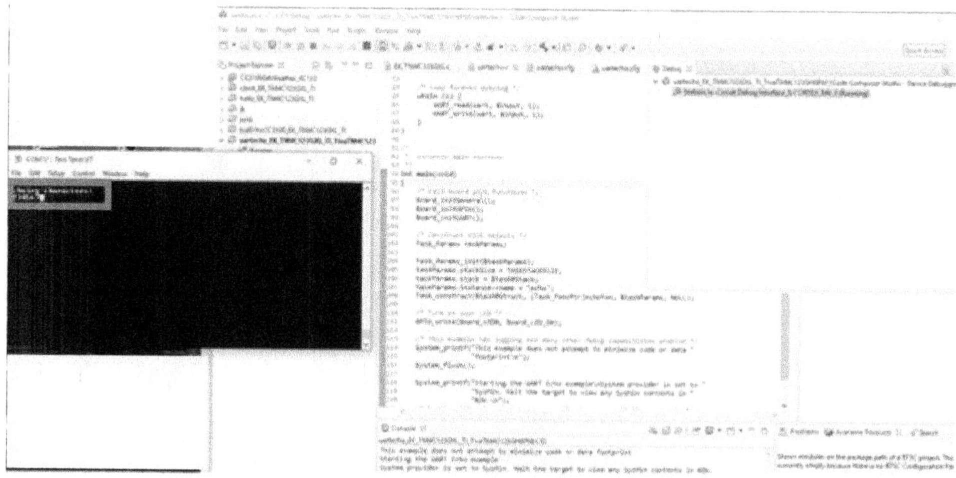

FIGURE 5.11 Echoed Data on the Tera Term terminal.

8. We can view the system configuration by right-clicking on the project config file and opening it with XGCONF to get a picture (see Figure 5.12). You can click on any block to learn more about the structure of the project.

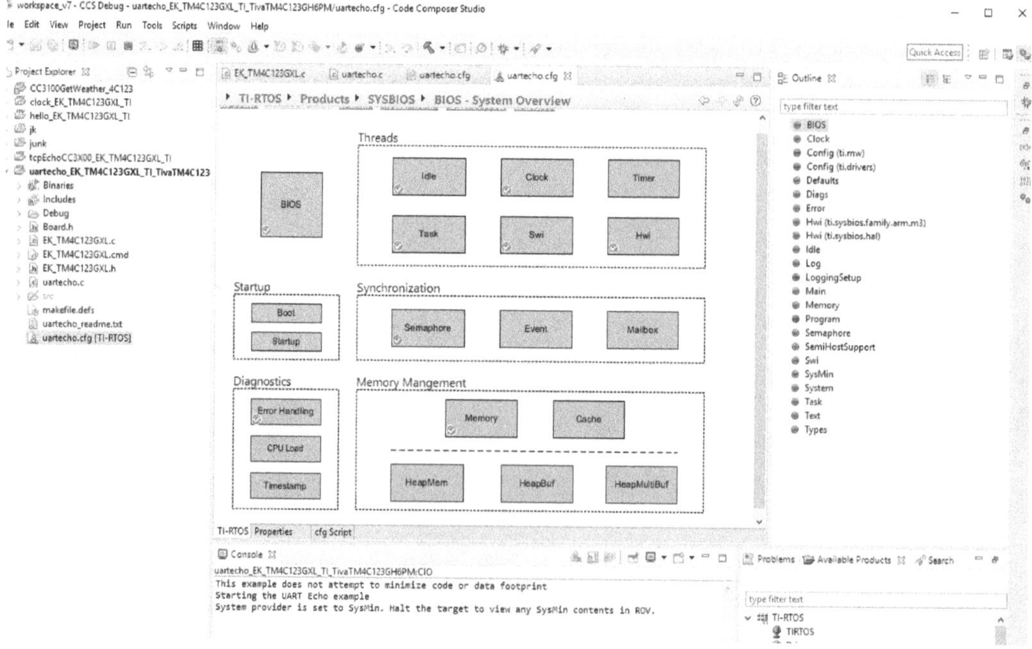

FIGURE 5.12 The System Configuration.

Creating a new project with CCS 6.2

Instead of using Keil, we can use another developing system from TI called Code Composer Studio (CCS) and one of its stable versions is version 6.2. There are newer versions, but this version 6.2 should work fine with the Tiva C evaluation board. In the following figures, we will show you how to open a new CCS project.

1. Project -> New CCS Project

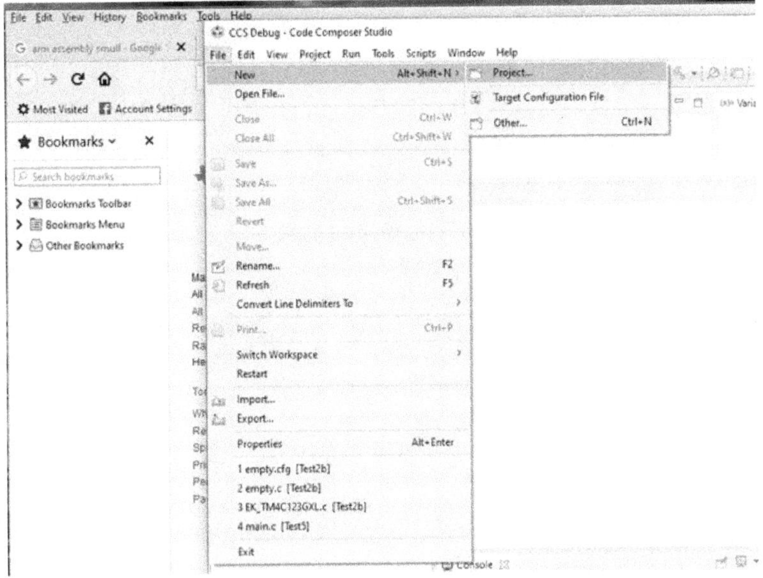

FIGURE 5.13 New Project.

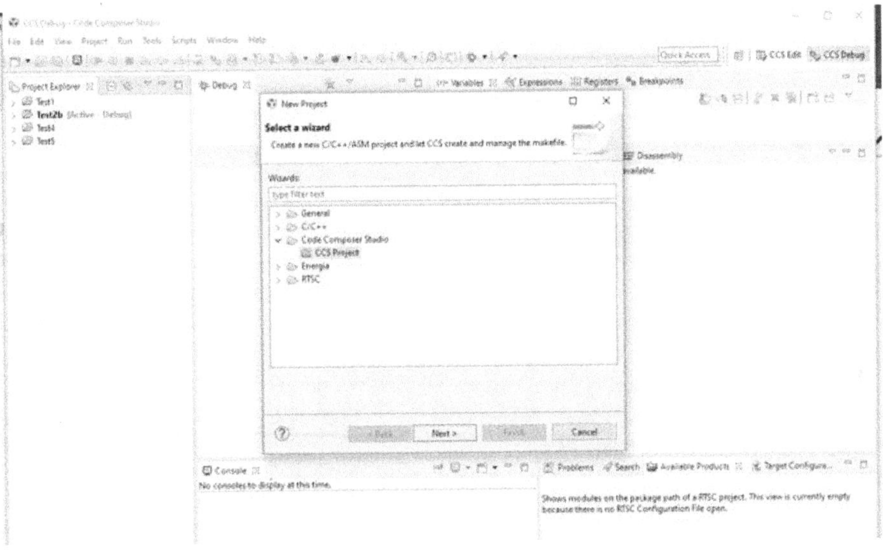

FIGURE 5.14 New CCS Project.

2. Target: select Tiva TM4C123GH6PM
   Connection: Stellaris In-Circuit Debug Interface
   Project name: Test
   Project Templates -> Empty Project (with main.c)
   Finish

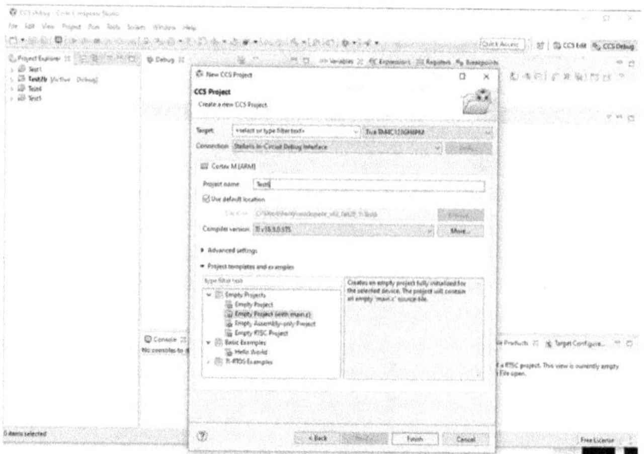

FIGURE 5.15 Parameters for the New CCS Project.

3. Right Click on Project Test -> Property -> Linked Resources -> New -> Name : TIVAWARE_INSTALL,
   Location: C:\TI\tirtos_tivac_2_16_01_14\products\TivaWare_C_Series-2.1.1.71b, Folder
   OK

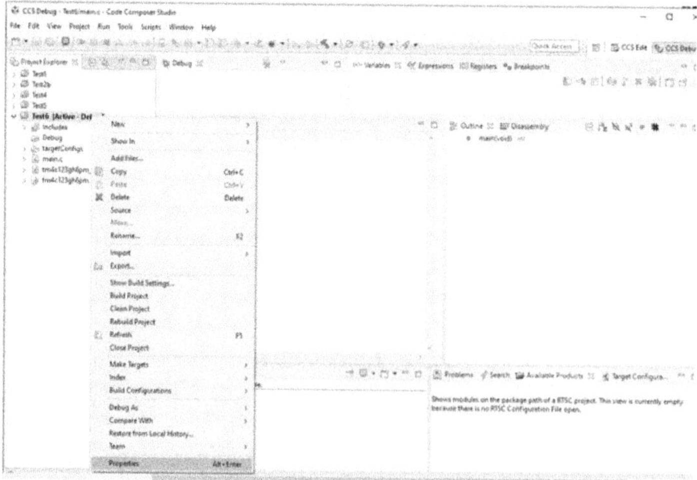

FIGURE 5.16 Project Properties.

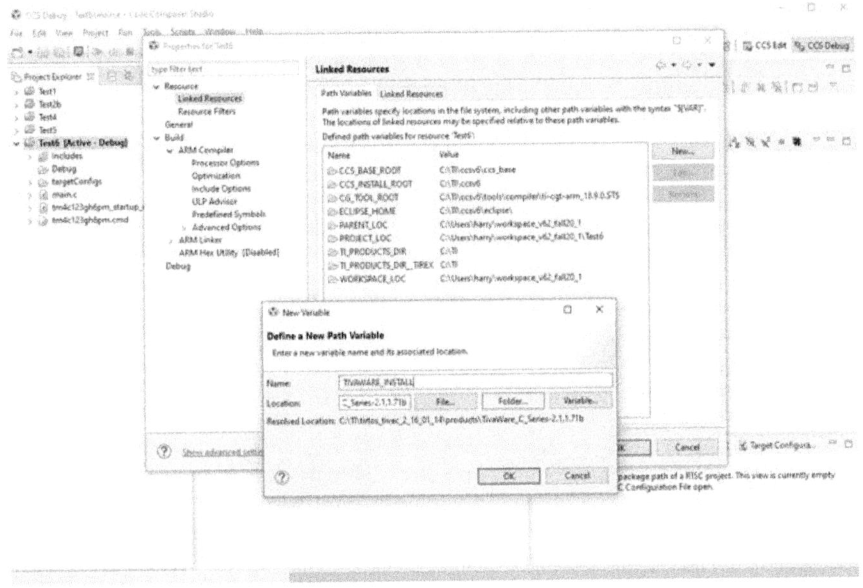

FIGURE 5.17 Set up TIVAWARE INSTALL.

4. Right click on project Test -> add files
   -add C:\TI\tirtos_tivac_2_16_01_14\products\TivaWare_C_Series-2.1.1.71b\driverlib\ccs\Debug\driverlib.lib
   Linked to files
   Create link relative to TIVAWARE_INSTALL
   OK

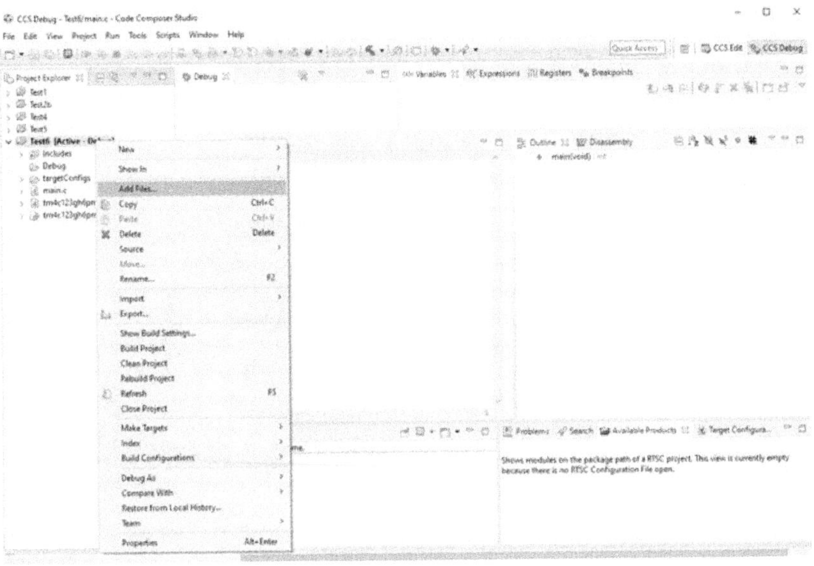

FIGURE 5.18 Add Files.

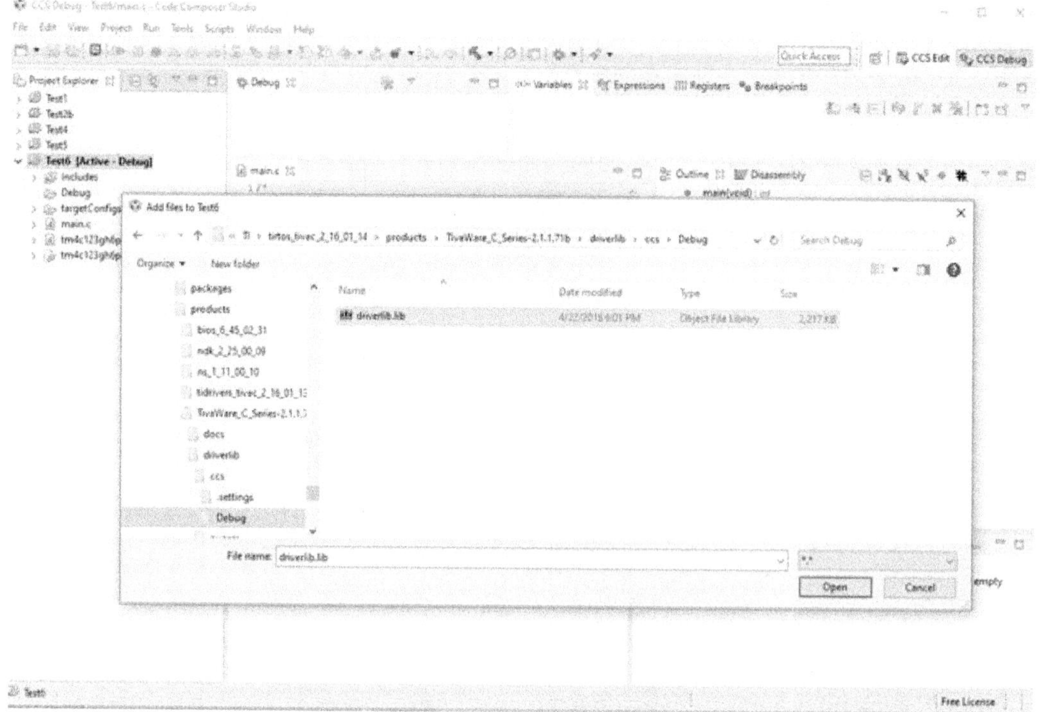

FIGURE 5.19 Adding TI Library.

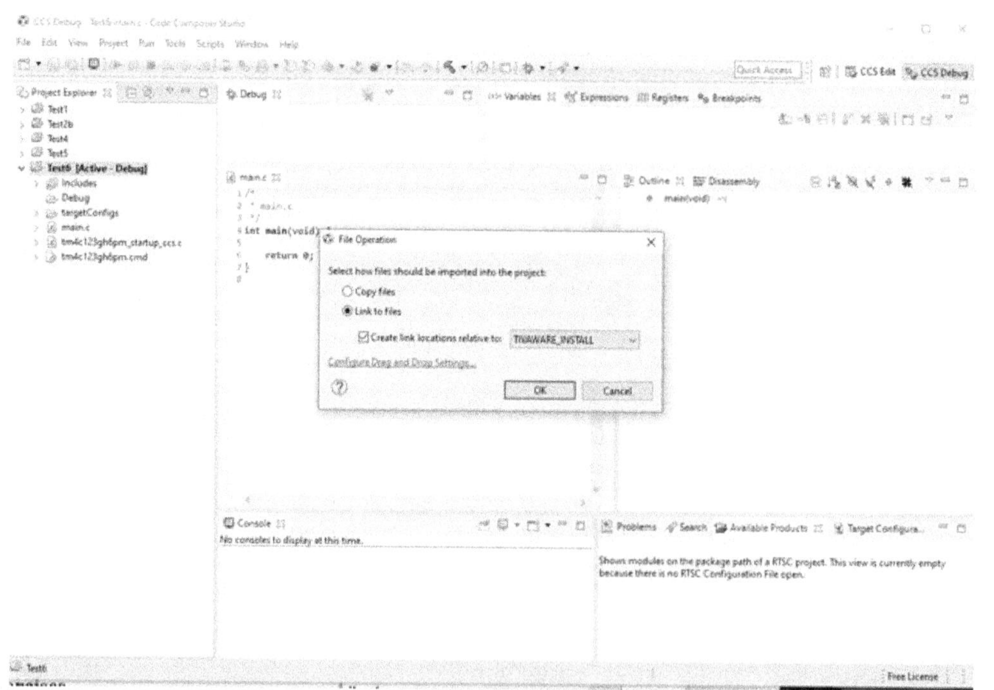

FIGURE 5.20 Set up Link to the TI Library.

5. Build

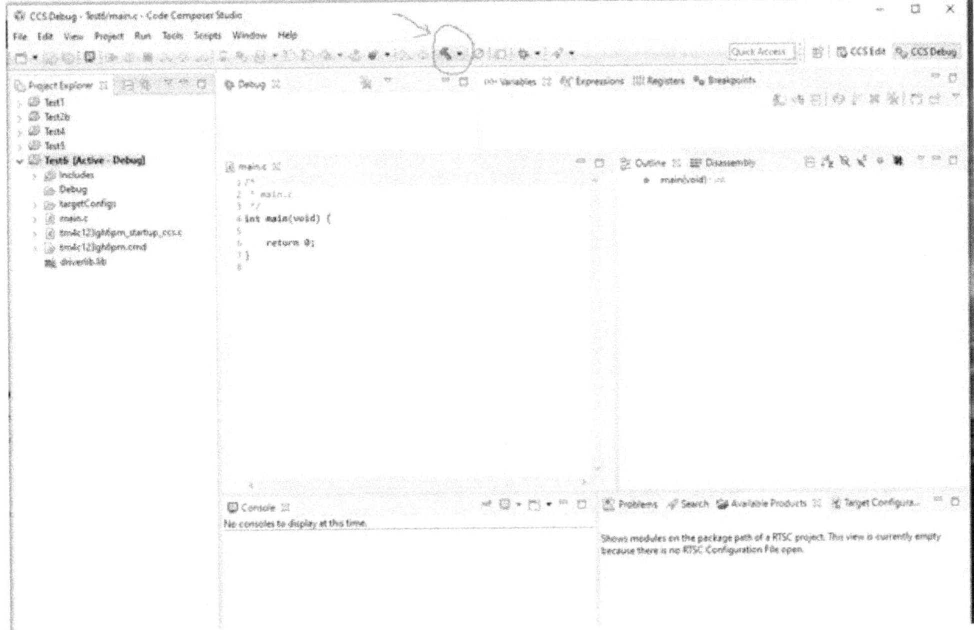

FIGURE 5.21 Build the Project.

6. Debug

FIGURE 5.22 Flash the Program and Enter Debug Mode.

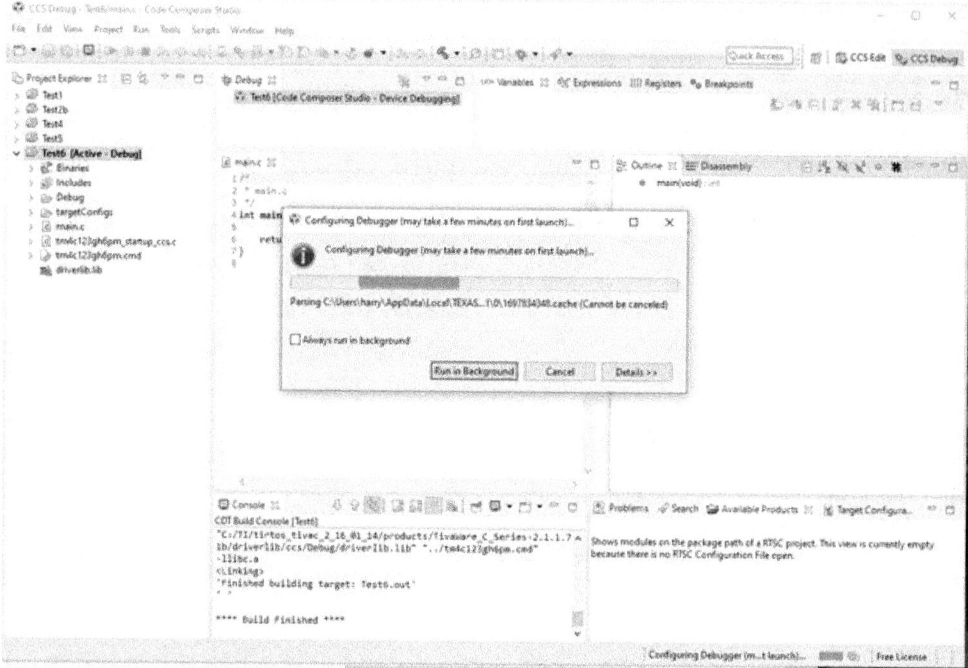

FIGURE 5.23 Flashing the Tiva C.

7. The program is ready to run or step through.

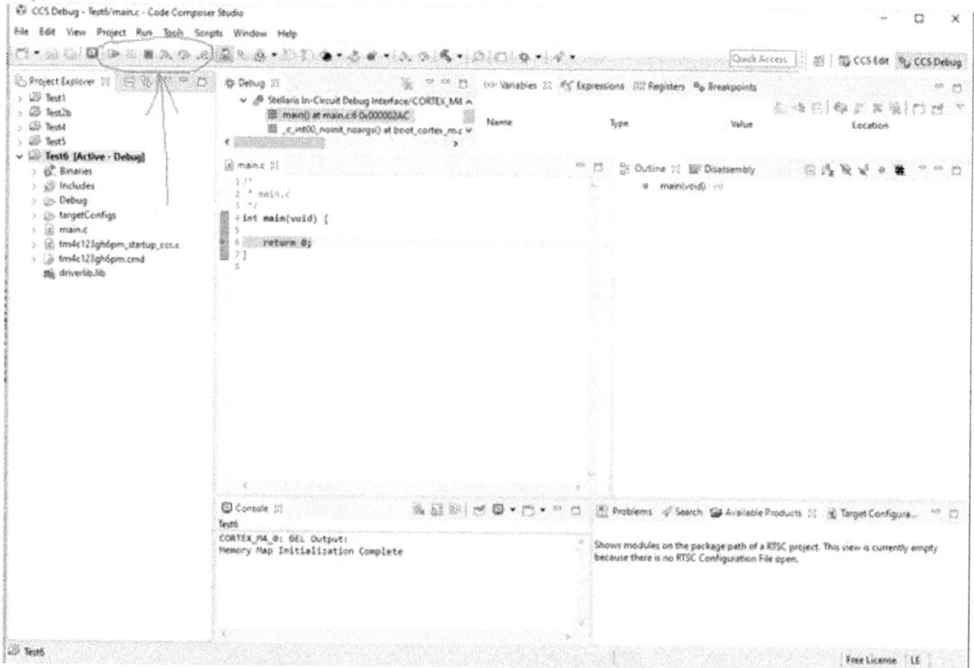

FIGURE 5.24 Ready to Run.

EXERCISES

1. Write a simple C program to display the message "Hello."

2. Write a C program to create an array of one hundred elements. Initialize the array, with each element having a value equal to the index of the element. Write a loop to calculate the sum of all the array elements.

3. Solve Problem 2 using the pointer instead of array index.

4. Write a C program to configure Pin 0–3 of Port A of the TivaC to be inputs and Pin 4–7 to be outputs. Hints: You need to use the following macros:

```
#define SYSCTL_RCGC2_R         (*((volatile uint32_t *)0x400FE108))

#define GPIO_PORTA_AFSEL_R    (*((volatile uint32_t *)0x40004420))

#define GPIO_PORTA_DIR_R      (*((volatile uint32_t *)0x40004400))

#define GPIO_PORTA_DEN_R      (*((volatile uint32_t *)0x4000451C))

#define GPIO_PORTA_AMSEL_R    (*((volatile uint32_t *)0x40004528))

#define GPIO_PORTA_PCTL_R     (*((volatile uint32_t *)0x4000452C))
```

5. Assume the bus clock is 50MHz, and use UART1 Port B to communicate at 9,600 bits/sec, 8-bit data, one start bit, and one stop bit, with no parity with the BlueSMURF Bluetooth module RN42. Write a C program to configure port UART1.

Credits

Fig. 5.12: Copyright © by Texas Instruments Incorporated.

Fig. 5.13: Copyright © by Texas Instruments Incorporated.

Fig. 5.14: Copyright © by Texas Instruments Incorporated.

Fig. 5.15: Copyright © by Texas Instruments Incorporated.

Fig. 5.16: Copyright © by Texas Instruments Incorporated.

Fig. 5.17: Copyright © by Texas Instruments Incorporated.

Fig. 5.18: Copyright © by Texas Instruments Incorporated.

Fig. 5.19: Copyright © by Texas Instruments Incorporated.

Fig. 5.20: Copyright © by Texas Instruments Incorporated.

Fig. 5.21: Copyright © by Texas Instruments Incorporated.

Fig. 5.22: Copyright © by Texas Instruments Incorporated.

Fig. 5.23: Copyright © by Texas Instruments Incorporated.

Fig. 5.24: Copyright © by Texas Instruments Incorporated.

Chapter 6

Introduction to Peripheral Modules

1. GPIO[1]

The GPIO module supports six different GPIO ports (Port A, B, C, D, E, F), each of which has eight pins that can be mapped to various functions. Depending on which ports are used, the GPIO module can provide support of up to 43 programmable I/O pins. The following are some of the features of the GPIO module:

- It is 5V tolerant when configured as input pins, except pins PD4, PD5, PB0, and PB1, which are limited to 3.6V.
- To configure pins of a GPIO port, we need to enable the port's clock using register SYSCTL_RCGCGPIO_R advanced peripheral bus (APB) address = 0x400FE608), where each bit is mapped to a port. For instance, bit 0 is used to enable Port A's clock, and bit 5 is used to enable Port F's clock.
- The direction of a pin of a port, say Port A, is configured by writing a "1" for output or a "0" for input to the corresponding bit of register GPIO_PORTA_DIR_R (Figure 6.1). For example, a value of 0xF0 written to this register means Port A Pins 0–3 are inputs and Pins 4–7 are outputs.
- A pin of a port, say Port A, can also be programmed to be an analog or digital pin using register GPIO_PORTA_AMSEL_R (analog pins) or GPIO_PORTA_DEN_R (digital pins) (Figure 6.1). For example, to make Pins 0–1 of Port A analog pins and Pins 4–7 digital pins, we need to write "0x03" and "0xF0" to registers GPIO_PORTA_AMSEL_R and GPIO_PORTA_DEN_R, respectively.
- The pins are configured as general-purpose input pins after reset, but depending on the configuration and ports, the pins can be configured to support GPIO, general-purpose timers (GPTMs), ADCs, UARTs, SSI, CAN, PWM, USB, quadrature encoder interface, and so forth. To map an alternate function to a pin of a port (e.g., Port A), we need to use registers GPIO_PORTA_AFSEL_R and GPIO_PORTA_PCTL_R. Each bit of register GPIO_PORTA_AFSEL_R is used to enable the alternate function for that corresponding

---

1 Texas Instruments Incorporated, *Tiva™ TM4C123GH6PM Microcontroller Data Sheet* (Austin: Texas Instruments), 649–703.

pin. For example, if bit 2 of this register is set, it means Pin PA2 is no longer a regular GPIO pin, but it has an alternate function. We need the bit field PCM2 of register GPIO_PORTA_PCTL_R to tell us what alternate function Pin 2 is mapped to. Each PCM nibble of register GPIO_PORTA_PCTL_R is used to map a particular alternate function to the corresponding pin (e.g., value of PCM0 is used to map Pin 0, PCM7 is used to map Pin 7). Referring back to the previous example, if PCM2 is equal to 2, from Table 6.1, we can see that Pin PA2 is mapped to Pin SSI0Clk (SSI 0 clock pin). The example program that follows will show you how to map a pin to an alternate function.

- The ports can be accessed via the APB or the AHB.
- The pins can be configured to support edge-triggered or level-triggered interrupts. The example code at the end of this section illustrates the use of PortA Interrupt registers to configure interrupts.
  - Each bit of the first eight bits of the Interrupt Sense register GPIO_PORTA_IS_R corresponds to a pin of Port A. When a bit is set, the corresponding pin is configured to detect a level. When a bit is reset, the pin is to detect edges. For example, if bit 2 is a "0," Pin 2 of Port A is edge sensitive.
  - Similarly, the Interrupt Both Edges register GPIO_PORTA_IBE_R also has eight bits and each bit when set ("1") configures the corresponding pin to detect both rising and falling edges. Only one edge is detected by a pin if the corresponding bit is reset ("0"). For example, if bit 1 is set, pin 1 triggers a local interrupt on both edges.
  - Register GPIO_PORTA_IEV_R works together with register GPIO_PORTA_IS_R to configure a rising or a falling edge/level. For example, if bit 4 of register GPIO_PORTA_IS_R is reset ("0") and bit 4 of register GPIO_PORTA_IEV_R is set ("1"), Pin 4 of Port A will trigger a local interrupt on a rising edge. Another example: if bit 3 of register GPIO_PORTA_IS_R is set ("1") and bit 3 of register GPIO_PORTA_IEV_R is reset ("0"), Pin 3 of Port A is configured to detect a low level.
  - Each bit of register GPIO_PORTA_IM_R when set is to enable a local interrupt on a pin. For example, if bit 7 is set ("1"), local interrupt on Pin 7 of Port A is enabled.
  - A bit of register GPIO_PORTA_RIS_R indicates the status of the local interrupt status on the corresponding pin. For example, if bit 6 is set, a local interrupt condition on Pin 6 of Port A has happened.
  - Each bit of register GPIO_PORTA_ICR_R when set is used to clear the local interrupt status of the corresponding pin. For example, if bit 3 is set ("1"), the local interrupt status of Pin 3 Port A is cleared. If bit 3 is not set ("0"), Pin 3's local interrupt status is not affected.
  - Figure 6.1 in the following shows the local interrupt registers for Port A. Other ports have similar registers except that they are located at different base addresses. Here are the base addresses of all the GPIO local interrupt registers:
    - GPIO_PORTA_IS_R @0x40004404
    - GPIO_PORTB_IS_R @0x40005404
    - GPIO_PORTC_IS_R @0x40006404
    - GPIO_PORTD_IS_R @0x40007404

- GPIO_PORTE_IS_R @0x40024404
- GPIO_PORTF_IS_R @0x40025404

Register	31-8	7-0	Address
GPIO_PORTA_IS_R	Reserved	IS	0x4000_4404
GPIO_PORTA_IBE_R	Reserved	IBE	0x4000_4408
GPIO_PORTA_IEV_R	Reserved	IEV	0x4000_440C
GPIO_PORTA_IM_R	Reserved	IM	0x4000_4410
GPIO_PORTA_RIS_R	Reserved	RIS	0x4000_4414
GPIO_PORTA_ICR_R	Reserved	ICR	0x4000_441C

FIGURE 6.1 GPIO Port A Interrupt Registers.

- Address lines can be used to mask bits in either read or write operations.
- When configured as inputs, the pins are Schmitt triggered.
- Weak pull-up or pull-down resistors on GPIO pins can be programmed.
- The pins can be programmed to be open drain, digital I/O, or analog.

Register	31-8	7-0	Address
GPIO_PORTA_DATA_R	Reserved	Data	0x4000_4000
GPIO_PORTA_DIR_R	Reserved	DIR	0x4000_4400
GPIO_PORTA_DEN_R	Reserved	DEN	0x4000_451C
GPIO_PORTA_AFSEL_R	Reserved	CMPA	0x4000_4420

Register	31-28	27-24	23-20	19-16	15-12	11-8	7-4	3-0	Address
GPIO_PORTA_PCTL_R	PCM7	PCM6	PCM5	PCM4	PCM3	PCM2	PCM1	PCM0	0x4000_452C

FIGURE 6.2 General-Purpose Port A Registers.

Since pin PD[7] and PF[0] are mapped to nonmaskable interrupt (NMI) signals, to reprogram these pins; you have to unlock them first by using register GPIOLOCK and GPIOCR (more details later).

TABLE 6.1 **ALTERNATE FUNCTIONS ENCODING**

		Alternate Functions (GPIOPCTL PMCx Encoding)										
I/O	Analog Function	1	2	3	4	5	6	7	8	9	14	15
PA0		U0Rx							CAN1Rx			
PA1		U0Tx							CAN1Tx			
PA2			SSI0CLK									
PA3			SSI0Fss									
PA4			SSI0Rx									
PA5			SSI0Tx									
PA6				I2C1SCL		M1PWM2						
PA7				I2C1SDA		M1PWM3						
		Alternate Functions (GPIOPCTL PMCx Encoding)										
I/O	Analog Function	1	2	3	4	5	6	7	8	9	14	15
PB0	USB0ID	U1Rx						T2CCP0				
PB1	USB0VBUS	U1Tx						T2CCP1				
PB2				I2C0SCL				T3CCP0				

PB3				I2C0SCDA				T3CCP1				
PB4	AIN10		SSI2CLK		M0PWM2			T1CCP0	CAN0Rx			
PB5	AIN11		SSI2Fss		M0PWM3			T1CCP1	CAN0Tx			
PB6			SSI2Rx		M0PWM0			T0CCP0				
PB7			SSI2Tx		M0PWM1			T0CCP1				
PC0		TCLK SWCLK						T4CCP0				
PC1		TMS SWDIO						T4CCP1				
PC2		TDI						T5CCP0				
PC3		TDO SWO						T5CCP1				
PC4	C1-	U4Rx	U1Rx		M0PWM6		IDX1	WT0CCP0	U1RTS			
PC5	C1+	U4Tx	U1Tx		M0PWM7		PhA1	WT0CCP1	U1CTS			
PC6	C0+	U3Rx					PhB1	WT1CCP0	USB0EPEN			
PC7	C0-	U3Tx						WT1CCP1	USB0EPFLT			
PD0	AIN7	SSI3CLK	SSI1CLK	I2C3SCL	M0PWM6	M1PWM0		WT2CCP0				
PD1	AIN6	SSI3Fas	SSI1Fas	I2C3SDA	M0PWM7	M1PWM1		WT2CCP1				
PD2	AIN5	SSI3Rx	SS1Rx		M0FAULT0			WT3CCP0	USB0EPEN			

(continued)

TABLE 6.1 ALTERNATE FUNCTIONS ENCODING (*CONTINUED*)

		Alternate Functions (GPIOPCTL PMCx Encoding)										
PD3	AIN4	SSI3Tx	SS1Tx				IDX0	WT3CCP1	USB0EPFLT			
PD4	USBD0DM	U6Rx						WT4CCP0				
PD5	USBD0DP	U6Tx						WT4CCP1				
PD6		U2Rx			M0FAULT0		PhA0	WT5CCP0				
PD7		U2Tx					PhB0	WT5CCP1	NMI			
PE0	AIN3	U7Rx										
PE1	AIN2	U7Tx										
PE2	AIN1											
PE3	AIN0											
PE4	AIN9	U5Rx		I2C2SCL	M0PWM4	M1PWM2			CAN0Rx			
PE5	AIN8	U5Tx		I2C2SDA	M0PWM5	M1PWM3			CAN0Tx			
PF0		U1Rx	SS1Rx	CAN0Rx		M1PWM4	PhA0	T0CCP0	NMI	C0o		
PF1		U1Tx	SS1Tx			M1PWM5	PhB0	T0CCP1		C1o	TRD1	
PF2			SSI1CLK		M0FAULT0	M1PWM6		T1CCP0			TRD0	
PF3			SSI1Fas	CAN0Tx		M1PWM7		T1CCP1			TRCLK	
PF4						M1FAULT0	IDX0	T2CCP0	USB0EPEN			

1.1. Example Code

In the following sections, we will show you how to configure GPIO pins to carry out different functions, such as GPIO, UART, PWM, and ADC.

GPIO Pins

The following code is used to configure Port F Pin 0 and Pin 4 as inputs connected to Switch SW2 and SW1, respectively. Port F Pins 1–3 are also configured as outputs to drive the three LEDs of the Tiva C microcontroller kit.

a. Enable Port F clock

```
LDR R0, =SYSCTL_RCGCGPIO_R

LDR R1, [R0]

ORR R1, R1, #0x20

STR R1, [R0]

NOP; delays to allow the clock to stabilize

NOP
```

b. Unlock Port F since Port F Pin 0 is multiplexed between the important NMI pin and other pins.

```
LDR R0,= GPIO_PORTF_LOCK_R ; unlock portF

LDR R1,= 0x4C4F434B ; special number to unlock

STR R1, [R0]

LDR R0,= GPIO_PORTF_CR_R

MOV R1, #0xFF

STR R1, [R0]
```

c. Change Port F Pin 4 and 0 to inputs and Port F Pin 3–2 to outputs.

```
LDR R0, = GPIO_PORTF_DIR_R;

LDR R1, [R0]

BIC R1, R1, #0x11; clear bit 0 and 4
```

```
ORR R1, R1, #0xE; output portF pin 3-1

STR R1, [R0]
```

d. Put a pull-up resistor on Pin 4 and Pin 0 to prevent the pins from floating if the switches are not closed.

```
LDR R0, =GPIO_PORTF_PUR_R

LDR R1, [R0]

ORR R1, R1, #0x11; pullup

STR R1, [R0]
```

e. Make sure Pins 4–0 are not analog pins; they are digital pins.

```
LDR R0, =GPIO_PORTF_AMSEL_R

LDR R1, [R0]

BIC R1, R1, #0x1F

STR R1, [R0]

LDR R0, =GPIO_PORTF_DEN_R

LDR R1, [R0]

ORR R1, R1, #0x1F

STR R1, [R0]
```

f. Make sure Pins 4–0 are not mapped to any alternate functions.

```
LDR R0, =GPIO_PORTF_AFSEL_R

LDR R1, [R0]

BIC R1, R1, #0x1F

STR R1, [R0]

LDR R0, =GPIO_PORTF_PCTL_R

LDR R1, [R0]

LDR R2, =0xFFF00000
```

```
AND R1, R1, R2 ;

STR R1, [R0]
```

Program 6.1: Configuring a GPIO Pin

Mapping Pins to Alternate Functions

The following code is used to map Port A Pin 0 and Pin 1 to the UART0 Rx and UART0 Tx pins, respectively.

1. Enable Port A's clock. Make sure to wait at least two clock cycles to let the clock become stable before proceeding.

```
LDR R0, = SYSCTL_RCGCGPIO_R

LDR R1, [R0]

ORR R1, R1, #0x01

STR R1, [R0]

NOP

NOP
```

2. Change Port A Pin 0 to input and Pin 1 to output.

```
LDR R0, = GPIO_PORTA_DIR_R;

LDR R1, [R0]

BIC R1, R1, #0x1; clear bit 0

ORR R1, R1, #0x2; set bit 1

STR R1, [R0]
```

3. Make sure Pins 1–0 are not analog pins; they are digital pins.

```
LDR R0, = GPIO_PORTA_AMSEL_R

LDR R1, [R0]

BIC R1, R1, #0x3

STR R1, [R0]
```

```
LDR R0, = GPIO_PORTF_DEN_R
LDR R1, [R0]
ORR R1, R1, #0x3
STR R1, [R0]
```

4. Make sure Pins 1–0 are mapped to UART0 alternate functions.

```
LDR R0, = GPIO_PORTA_AFSEL_R
LDR R1, [R0]
ORR R1, R1, #0x3
STR R1, [R0]
LDR R0, = GPIO_PORTF_PCTL_R
LDR R1, [R0]
LDR R2, = 0xFFFFFF00
AND R1, R1, R2
ORR R1, R1, 0x00000011
STR R1, [R0]
```

Program 6.2: Mapping GPIO Pins to an Alternate Function

GPIO Interrupts

The following code sets up interrupts for Port F Pin 0 and Pin 4. These pins are connected to switches SW2 and SW1, respectively. Anytime a switch is pressed, an interrupt happens and the interrupt service routine (ISR) is executed checking to see which switch is pressed and then toggles either the Red or Blue LED of the Tiva C launchpad.

```
        AREA Block1, DATA, READWRITE, ALIGN=2
cnt  DCD 0x0102
        AREA Ex1, CODE, READONLY, ALIGN=2
```

1. Include macro definitions of addresses of NVIC and port F registers

```
NVIC_ST_CTRL_R      EQU 0xE000E010

NVIC_ST_RELOAD_R    EQU 0xE000E014

NVIC_ST_CURRENT_R   EQU 0xE000E018

NVIC_SYS_PRI3_R     EQU 0xE000ED20  ; Sys. Handlers 12 to 15
Priority

NVIC_PRI17_R        EQU 0xE000E444

NVIC_PRI7_R         EQU 0xE000E41C

NVIC_EN0_R          EQU 0xE000E100

NVIC_EN1_R          EQU 0xE000E104


GPIO_PORTF_LOCK_R  EQU 0x40025520

GPIO_PORTF_CR_R    EQU 0x40025524

GPIO_PORTF_AMSEL_R EQU 0x40025528

GPIO_PORTF_PCTL_R  EQU 0x4002552C

GPIO_LOCK_KEY      EQU 0x4C4F434B

GPIO_PORTF_DATA_R  EQU 0x400253FC

GPIO_PORTF_DIR_R   EQU 0x40025400

GPIO_PORTF_AFSEL_R EQU 0x40025420

GPIO_PORTF_PUR_R   EQU 0x40025510

GPIO_PORTF_DEN_R   EQU 0x4002551C

GPIO_PORTF_IBE_R   EQU 0x40025408

GPIO_PORTF_IEV_R   EQU 0x4002540C

GPIO_PORTF_IM_R    EQU 0x40025410
```

```
GPIO_PORTF_RIS_R   EQU 0x40025414

GPIO_PORTF_ICR_R   EQU 0x4002541C

GPIO_PORTF_IS_R    EQU 0x40025404

DELAY              EQU 8000000 ; delay 0.5sec
(=8000,000*1/16MHz)


SYSCTL_RCGCGPIO_R  EQU 0x400FE608


        EXPORT Start

        EXPORT SysTick_Handler

        EXPORT      GPIOPortF_Handler

        ENTRY
```

2. Main program

```
Start

        BL Port_Init

        BL PF_Int_Init

LoopS

        WFI

        B LoopS
```

3. Initialization routines for port F
   PF_Int_Init

```
MOV R2, #0x1

MSR PRIMASK, R2;    store 1 to PRIMASK register to disable
the global interrupt

LDR R0, =GPIO_PORTF_IS_R ; loading port F Interrupt Sense
register
```

```
MOV R1, #0x00               ; select Edge detect

STR R1, [R0]

LDR R0, =GPIO_PORTF_IBE_R; loading port F Both Edges Inter-
rupt register

MOV R1, #0x00               ; choose 1 Edge

STR R1, [R0]

LDR R0, =GPIO_PORTF_IEV_R; loading port F Interrupt Event
register

MOV R1, #0x00               ; choose Falling Edge detect

STR R1, [R0]

LDR R0, = NVIC_PRI7_R           ; loading NVIC priority reg-
ister 7 controlling priority of

LDR R1, =0xFF0FFFFF                ; SysCtl, FlahCtl and port
F interrupts

; clearing out bits 20-23

LDR R2, [R0]

AND R2, R2, R1

LDR R1, =0x00A00000              ; set port F interrupt prior-
ity to 5 (bits 23-21)

ORR R2, R2, R1

STR R1, [R0]

LDR R0, = NVIC_EN0_R     ; enable port F interrupt (bit 30 of
register NVIC_EN0_R)

LDR R1, =0x40000000

LDR R2, [R0]

ORR R2, R2, R1

STR R2, [R0]
```

```
LDR R0, =GPIO_PORTF_IM_R ; Enable port F interrupt (pin 0 and
pin 4)

MOV R1, #0x11

STR R1, [R0]

MOV R2, #0x0

MSR PRIMASK, R2;    store 0 to PRIMASK register to enable the
global interrupt

BX LR


; Port F interrupt Service Routine

      GPIOPortF_Handler

      PUSH {LR}                  ; save Link Register before
jumping to a subroutine

      BL Check_PF               ; jump to subroutine Check_PF to
see which switch (1 or 0)

      POP {LR}                   ;that has been pressed.

; Clearing old interrupts

      LDR R0, =GPIO_PORTF_ICR_R ;loading interrupt status
clear register

      MOV R1, #0x11

      STR R1, [R0]

;updating cnt, the number of getting to this ISR

      LDR R0, =cnt

      LDR R1, [R0]

      ADD R1, R1, #1

      STR R1, [R0]

      BX LR


;Checking interrupts of port F switches
```

```
Check_PF

        LDR R0, =GPIO_PORTF_RIS_R ;loading port F Raw Inter-
rupt Status register

        LDR R1, [R0]

        ANDS R2, R1, #0x01 ;checking port F pin 0 (SW1)

        BNE B_PF0

        ANDS R2, R1, #0x10 ;checking port F pin 4 (SW0)

        BNE B_PF4

        BX LR

B_PF0

; Toggling the red LED

        LDR R4, = GPIO_PORTF_DATA_R

        LDR R5,  [R4]

        AND R5, R5, #0x2

        EOR R5, R5, #0x2

        STR R5, [R4]

        BX LR

B_PF4

; Toggling the blue LED

        LDR R4, = GPIO_PORTF_DATA_R

        LDR R5,  [R4]

        AND R5, R5, #0x4

        EOR R5, R5, #0x4

        STR R5, [R4]

        BX LR
```

Program 6.3: Set up Interrupts for Port F Pin0 and Pin 4

2. Clocks and Phase Locked Loop (PLL)[2]

To configure the clock for the Tiva C microcontroller, you need to use either the Run-Mode Clock Configuration 2 (RCC2) register or the Run-Mode Clock Configuration (RCC) register. Registers RCC2 and RCC have similar fields, but some of register RCC2's fields have more bits. The fields in register RCC2 override similar fields in register RCC when bit USERCC2 bit (bit 31) of register RCC2 is set. There are four different input clock sources for a Tiva C microcontroller version, such as TM4P123GH6PM. They can be either one of the following oscillators:

- *Precision internal oscillator (PIOSC):* Provides a 16-MHz clock with about 1 percent accuracy after calibration. This is an on-chip oscillator that provides a clock for the microcontroller during and after a power-on reset. Another divided-by-four version of this clock is also available as a clock source.
- *Main oscillator (MOSC):* Supports a crystal oscillator or a single-ended clock source. If the PLL is used, the crystal value must be a value between 5 and 25 MHz, as specified in Table 6.2. The XTAL field (bit [10:6]) of the RCC register specifies the XTAL frequency (see Table 6.4). If the PLL is not used, the frequency of the crystal can be any of those supported from 4 to 25 MHz.
- *Low-frequency internal oscillator (LFOSC):* Used in deep-sleep, power-saving modes.
- *Hibernation module clock source:* Clocked by a 32.768-kHz oscillator. This clock is the real-time clock source.

To choose one of the aforementioned clock sources, you have to program the OSCSRC2 field (bit 6-4) of register RCC2, as in Table 6.2 or the OSCSRC field (bits 5:4) of register RCC in Table 6.3.

TABLE 6.2 **OSCRC2**

Register RCC2 OSCSRC2[6:4]	Selected Clock Source
0x0	MOSC
0x1	PIOSC
0x2	PIOSC/4
0x3	LFIOSC
0x7	32.768 kHz

TABLE 6.3 **OSCSRC**

Register RCC OSCSRC[5:4]	Selected Clock Source
0x0	MOSC
0x1	PIOSC
0x2	PIOSC/4
0x3	LFIOSC

2 Texas Instruments, *Tiva*™ *TM4C123GH6PM*, 219–62.

2.1. Clock Configuration

If we want to use register RCC2, which has more expanded bit fields than register RCC, the USERCC2 bit (bit 31) of register RCC2 needs to be set. To set up the Tiva C to use the PLL to generate the system clock, you need to take the following steps (you can find the controls of the various register bits on the clock by using Figure 6.3):

- To configure the PLL, first, we need to bypass the PLL and the system clock divider by writing "1" to the BYPASS bit (bit 11) and "0" to the USESYSDIV bit (bit 22) of register RCC/RCC2. The microcontroller is now running on a non-PLL raw system clock to allow the PLL configuration to proceed. When it's done, and the PLL is stable, the system clock can be switched to the PLL system clock.

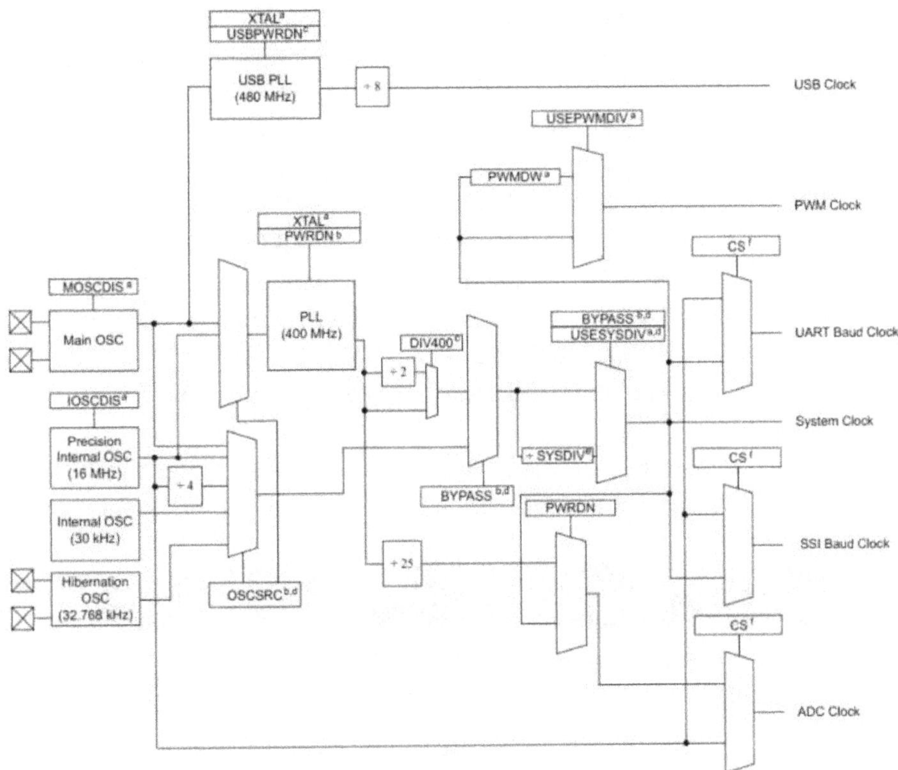

FIGURE 6.3 The Main Clock Tree.

- Configure the XTAL value (bit 10-6) and the oscillator source (OSCSRC bit 5-4) of register RCC or set the XTAL value of register RCC (see Table 6.4) and the oscillator source (OSCSRC2 bit 6-4) of register RCC2. Reset bit PWRDN (bit 13) of register RCC2/RCC to start the PLL circuit (Figure 6.4).

	31	30	29	28-23	22	21-60	SS0
SYSCTL_RCC2_R	USERCC2	DIV400	Reserved	SYSDIV2	SYSDIV2LSB	Reserved	0x400F_E070

	15	14	13	12	11	10-7	6-4	3-0	
SYSCTL_RCC2_R (cont.)	Reserved	USBPWND	PWRDN2	Reserved	BYPASS2	Reserved	SYSDIV2LSB	Reserved	0x400F_E070

	31-28	27	26-23	22	21	20	19-17	16	
SYSCTL_RCC_R	Reserved	ACG	SYSDIV	USESYSDIV	Reserved	USEPWMDIV	PWMDIV	Reserved	0x400F_E060

	15-14	13	12	11	10-6	5-4	3-1	0	
SYSCTL_RCC_R (cont.)	Reserved	PWRDN	Reserved	BYPASS	XTAL	OSCRC	Reserved	MOSCDIS	0x4000_E060

FIGURE 6.4 Run-Mode Configuration Registers.

- Set the value of the SYSDIV bits (bits 26–23) and set bit USESYSDIV (bit 22) of register RCC. The values of the SYSDIV bits set the system clock's frequency, which is equal to 200/(SYSDIV + 1) (see Table 6.3). On the other hand, if you want to use SYSDIV2 bits (6 bits instead of 4 bits like in register RCC) and the 200 MHz PLL output, you can select the values of the SYSDIV2 bits (bits 28–23) of the register RCC2. The system clock's frequency is equal to 200/(SYSDIV2 +1) (see Table 6.4). However, if you want to use register RCC2 and the 400 MHz PLL, you need to set bit DIV400 (bit 30) and select the values of the SYSDIV2 bits (bits 28–23) and bit SYSDIV2LSB (bit 22) of register RCC2. The SYSDIV2 bits and SYSDIV2LSB bit are combined to become a 7-bit divisor to the 400 MHz PLL to create the system clock, of which frequency is equal to 400/({SYSDIV2, SYSDIV2LSB} +1) (see Tables 6.5, 6.6, and 6.7).
- Wait for the PLL to lock by polling bit PLLRIS (bit 6) of register raw interrupt status (at address 0x400F_E050).
- When the PLLRIS bit is set, we can enable the PLL system clock by resetting bit BYPASS (bit 11) of register RCC/RCC2.

TABLE 6.4 **XTAL VALUES**

XTAL Values	Crystal Frequency not Using the PLL	Crystal Frequency Using the PLL
0x00-0x05	Reserved	
0x06	4 MHz	Reserved
0x07	4.096 MHz	Reserved
0x08	4.9152 MHz	Reserved
0x09	5 MHz	

0x0A	5.12 MHz
0x0B	6 MHz
...	...
0x15	16 MHz
...	...
0x18	20 MHz
...	...
0x1A	25 MHz

TABLE 6.5 **SYSTEM CLOCK FREQUENCY USING SYSDIV BITS (= 200 MHZ/(SYSDIV + 1))**

SYSDIV	Divisor	System Clock Frequency (Bypass = 0)	System Clock Frequency (Bypass = 1)
0x0	÷1	Reserved	Raw clock source frequency/1
0x1	÷2	Reserved	Raw clock source frequency/2
0x2	÷3	66.67 MHz	Raw clock source frequency/3
0x3	÷4	50 MHz	Raw clock source frequency/4
0x4	÷5	40 MHz	Raw clock source frequency/5
0x5	÷6	33.33 MHz	Raw clock source frequency/6
0x6	÷7	28.57 MHz	Raw clock source frequency/7
0x7	÷8	25 MHz	Raw clock source frequency/8
0x8	÷9	22.22 MHz	Raw clock source frequency/9
.....	.....	.....	.....
0xE	÷15	13.33 MHz	Raw clock source frequency/15
0xF	÷16	12.5 MHz (default)	Raw clock source frequency/16

TABLE 6.6 SYSTEM CLOCK FREQUENCY USING SYSDIV2 BITS (= 200 MHZ/(SYSDIV2 + 1))

SYSDIV2	Divisor	System Clock Frequency (Bypass2 = 0)	System Clock Frequency (BYPASS2 = 1)
0x0	÷1	Reserved	Raw clock source frequency/1
0x1	÷2	Reserved	Raw clock source frequency/2
0x2	÷3	66.67 MHz	Raw clock source frequency/3
0x3	÷4	50 MHz	Raw clock source frequency/4
0x4	÷5	40 MHz	Raw clock source frequency/5
0x5	÷6	33.33 MHz	Raw clock source frequency/6
0x6	÷7	28.57 MHz	Raw clock source frequency/7
0x7	÷8	25 MHz	Raw clock source frequency/8
0x8	÷9	22.22 MHz	Raw clock source frequency/9
.....	.....	.....	.....
0x3E	÷63	3.175 MHz	Raw clock source frequency/15
0x3F	÷64	3.125 MHz (default)	Raw clock source frequency/16

TABLE 6.7 **SYSTEM CLOCK FREQUENCY USING SYSDIV2 BITS AND BIT SYSDIV2LSB WITH THE DIV400 BIT SET (= 400 MHZ/({SYSDIV2, SYSDIV2LSB} + 1))**

SYSDIV2	SYSDIV2LSB	Divisor	System Clock Frequency (BYPASS2 = 0)[a]
0x0	Reserved	÷2	Reserved
0x1	0	÷3	Reserved
	1	÷4	Reserved
0x2	0	÷5	80 MHz
	1	÷6	66.7 MHz
0x03	0	÷7	Reserved
	1	÷8	50 MHz
0x04	0	÷9	44.44 MHz
	1	÷10	40 MHz
.....	.....	.....	.....
0x3F	0	÷127	3.15 MHz
	1	÷128	3.125 MHz (default)

Note that DIV400 and SYSDIV2LSB are only valid when BYPASS2 = 0

Set Up the PLL for a System Clock of 80 MHz (Maximum Running Frequency of the Tiva C)

a. Set up the macro-definition for bit fields of the RCC and RCC2 registers. (These macros are already defined in the TI file tm4c123gh6pm.h, and we do not have to redefine them here; I listed them just for illustration purposes.)

```
#include <stdint.h>

#include "PLL.h"

#include "tm4c123gh6pm.h"
```

```
#define SYSCTL_RCC_XTAL_M         0x000007C0  // Crystal Value

#define SYSCTL_RCC_XTAL_8MHZ      0x00000380  // 8 MHz

#define SYSCTL_RCC_XTAL_16MHZ     0x00000540  // 16 MHz

#define SYSCTL_RCC2_USERCC2       0x80000000  // Use RCC2

#define SYSCTL_RCC2_DIV400        0x40000000  // Divide PLL as
400 MHz vs. 200

                                              // MHz

#define SYSCTL_RCC2_SYSDIV2_M     0x1F800000  // System Clock
Divisor 2

#define SYSCTL_RCC2_SYSDIV2LSB    0x00400000  // Additional
LSB for SYSDIV2\

#define SYSCTL_RCC2_PWRDN2        0x00002000  // Power-Down
PLL 2

#define SYSCTL_RCC2_BYPASS2       0x00000800  // PLL Bypass 2
(bit 11)

#define SYSCTL_RCC2_OSCSRC2_M     0x00000070  // Oscillator
Source 2

#define SYSCTL_RCC2_OSCSRC2_MO    0x00000000  // MOSC

#define SYSCTL_RCC2_OSCSRC2_IO    0x00000010  // PIOSC

#define SYSCTL_RCC2_SYSDIV2_S     23

#define FREQ_80MHZ  (4<<22)
```

b. Bypass the PLL to start the configuration process.

```
SYSCTL_RCC2_R |= SYSCTL_RCC2_BYPASS2; //Bit
```

c. Set up to use register RCC2 with expanded bit fields and more features, like using 400 MHz for the PLL (Figure 6.3).

```
SYSCTL_RCC2_R |= SYSCTL_RCC2_USERCC2; //Bit 31 (Figure 6.3)
```

d. Select the 16 MHz crystal by first clearing the crystal field before updating it (Figure 6.3).

```
SYSCTL_RCC_R &= ~SYSCTL_RCC_XTAL_M;          // Clear the Crys-
tal Field

SYSCTL_RCC_R += SYSCTL_RCC_XTAL_16MHZ; // Pick 16 MHz Crystal
(bit[10:6]=0x15)
```

e. Select the MOSC as the clock source by clearing the oscillator source bit fields before updating it.

```
// Clear the oscillator source bit field  (bits 6-4)

            SYSCTL_RCC2_R &= ~SYSCTL_RCC2_OSCSRC2_M;// clear
oscillator source field

            //Updating the oscillator bit field to pick the
MOSC as the clock source

SYSCTL_RCC2_R += SYSCTL_RCC2_OSCSRC2_MO;
```

f. Use the 400 MHz PLL.

```
SYSCTL_RCC2_R |= SYSCTL_RCC2_DIV400;
```

g. Choose 80 MHz as the system clock by clearing the divider field before updating its value to four (system clock frequency = PLL clock frequency/(divider value + 1) = 400 MHz/5 = 80 MHz)

```
// Clear system clock divider2 bit field and the divider2 LSB

SYSCTL_RCC2_R = (SYSCTL_RCC2_R &  ~(SYSCTL_RCC2_SYSDIV2_M+
SYSCTL_RCC2_SYSDIV2LSB );

//Update the divider2 and the divider2 LSB bit field

SYSCTL_ RCC2_R |=  FREQ_80MHZ;
```

h. Activate the PLL by clearing the PWRDN2 bit.

```
SYSCTL_RCC2_R &= ~SYSCTL_RCC2_PWRDN2;
```

i. Wait until the PLL is locked by checking its status.

```
while((SYSCTL_RIS_R & SYSCTL_RIS_PLLLRIS)==0){};
```

j. After the PLL has been locked, remove the BYPASS2 bit.

```
SYSCTL_RCC2_R &= ~SYSCTL_RCC2_BYPASS2; //Bit 11
```

The system clock is now set up and running at 80 MHz, which is the maximum system clock frequency of the Tiva C microcontroller.

Program 6.4: Configuration of the PLL for an 80 MHz System Clock

Set Up the PLL for a System Clock of 40 MHz Without Using the 400 MHz PLL Setting

The following is an example of how to set up the PLL to generate a system clock of 40 MHz without the need to run the PLL at 400 MHz. The program looks similar to the previous program, except for a few steps. First, we need to define a new SYSDIV2 macro for 40 MHz without using 400 MHz PLL. Since we are not using bit 30, DIV400, bit 22, SYSDIV2LSB, of register SYSCTL_RCC2_R, is ignored. Only bits 28–23 of register RCC2 are used for SYSDIV2.

```
#define FREQ_40MHZ_200      (4<<23)  //use with 200MHz PLL
```

Only Step c and Step d need to be changed as follows. The rest of the steps are not changed:

```
Step c: SYSCTL_RCC2_R &= ~SYSCTL_RCC2_DIV400;

Step d:

// Clear system clock divider2 bit field and the divider2 LSB

SYSCTL_RCC2_R = (SYSCTL_RCC2_R &  ~(SYSCTL_RCC2_SYSDIV2_M |
SYSCTL_RCC2_SYSDIV2LSB );

//Update the divider2 and the divider2 LSB bit field

SYSCTL_ RCC2_R |=  FREQ_40MHZ_200;
```

3. GPTMs

In the Tiva C TM4CGH6PM, there are six 16/32-bit GPTM blocks (block0-block5) and six 32/64-bit GPTM blocks, each of which has two timers/counters called Timer A and Timer B. The 16/32 timers/counters can operate independently or be combined to run as a 32-bit timer or a 32-bit real-time clock. The 32/64-bit timers/counters can also run independently or be concatenated to run as a 64-bit timer/counter. The following are operation features of the timers/counters:

- They can be used as either two half-width timers/counters or a full-width timer/counter.
- In 16/32-bit mode, the timer/counter can be configured as a 16-bit timer/counter with an 8-bit prescaler. For the 32/64-bit mode, it can be a 32-bit timer/counter with a 16-bit prescaler.
- The timers/counters can be configured to run in one-shot or continuous timer mode as half-width or full-width timers. In continuous mode, the timer/counter keeps counting after it reaches the upper limit (counting up) or zero (counting down), whereas in one-shot mode, the timer/counter stops counting when it reaches zero (counting down) or the load value (counting up).

- They can be used as counters for event capture. They can count the time between events or the number of events. The events can be configured as positive edge, negative edge, or both edges. They can also work as PWM generators.
- They can also be set up as interrupt generators. Similar to the event capture, interrupts can be generated when an event is captured or a configured number of events have been captured.
- They can be configured to synchronize timers.
- They can be used in transfers involved with the ultra-direct memory access (uDMA).
- They can be used to trigger ADC events.

Registers of Timer 2A are detailed in the following description and Figure 6.5. Registers of other timers (0–5) have similar specifications.

- The values of bit 2-0 of register TIMER2_CFG_R configures operation of the timer as follows:
  - 0x0: for a 16/32-bit timer, 32-bit timer configuration is selected. For a 32/64-bit wide timer, 64-bit timer configuration is selected
  - 0x1: for a 16/32-bit timer, 32-bit real time clock (RTC) counter configuration is selected. For a 32/64-bit timer, 64-bit real time clock (RTC) counter configuration is selected.
  - 0x2–0x3: reserved
  - 0x4: for a 16/32-bit timer, 16-bit timer configuration is selected. For a 32/64-bit wide timer, 32-bit timer configuration is selected
  - 0x5–0x7: reserved.
- Register TIMER2_CTL_R is used together with register TIMER2_CFG_R and TIMER2_TAMR_R to fine tune the configuration of the timer 2A.

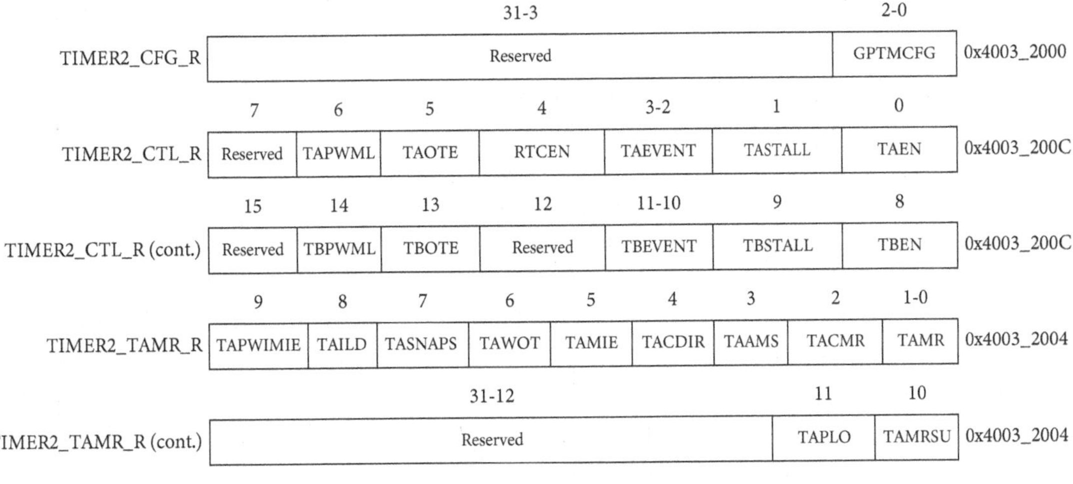

FIGURE 6.5 Timer2A registers.

    - Bit 0 (TAEN) Timer A Enable:
        - 0: disable Timer A.
        - 1: enables Timer A.
    - Bit 1 (TASALL) Timer A Stall Enable:
        - 0: Timer A keeps on counting while the processor is halted.
        - 1: Timer A freezes counting during the time the processor is halted by the debugger.
    - Bit 2:1 (TAEVENT): Timer A Event Mode.
        - 0x0 Positive Edge
        - 0x1 Negative Edge
        - 0x2 Reserved
        - 0x3 Both edges.
    - Bit 4 (RTCEN): the RTC Stall Enable. The meaning of the bit's value is opposite to bit 1, but it applies to the RTC.
    - Bit 5 (TAOTE) Timer A Output Trigger Enable is used to enable (1) or disable (0) the output Timer ADC trigger. This bit is valid only if the timer is configured in one-shot or periodic mode.
    - Bit 6 (TAPWML) when set, Timer A PWM Output Level inverts output.
    - Bit 7: reserved.
    - Bit 8, 9, 11–10, 13, 14: have similar meanings like those of bit 0, 1, 3–2, 5, 6, respectively, except that they apply to Timer B.
    - Bit 31–15: reserved.
- Register TIMER2_TAMR_R configures Timer A when it operates independently. When Timer A and Timer B are concatenated, this register configures the modes for both Timer A and Timer B and register TIMER2_TBMR_R is ignored.
    - Bit 1–0 (TAMR) control operation mode of Timer A.
        - 0x0 Reserved
        - 0x1 One-shot timer mode
        - 0x2 Periodic Timer mode
        - 0x3 Capture mode
    - Bit 2 (TACMR): Timer A Capture Mode
        - 0 Edge-Count mode
        - 1 Edge-Time mode
    - Bit 3 (TAAMS) Timer A Alternate Mode Select
        - 0 Capture or compare mode
        - 1 PWM mode. To use PWM mode, bit 1 (TACMR) must be cleared (Edge-Count mode) and Timer A is configured as one-shot or periodic (TAMR must be 0x1 or 0x2).
    - Bit 4 (TACDIR) Timer A Count Direction controls the direction of Timer A. 1 for countup and 0 for countdown.
    - Bit 5 (TAMIE) Timer Match Interrupt Enable
        - 0: The match interrupt is disabled.

- 1: In One-Shot or Periodic mode, an interrupt is generated when the value of register TIMER2_TAMATCHR_R matches that of counter Timer2A.
- Bit 6 (TAWOT) Timer2A Wait-on Trigger
  - 0: Counter Timer2A starts counting when it is enabled.
  - 1: When Timer2A is enabled, it starts counting only when it's triggered from the previous counter in the daisy chain. This feature only works for one-shot, periodic, and PWM modes.
- Bit 7 (TASNAPS) Timer2A Snap-shot mode
- Bit 8 (TAILD) Time2A Load Write
- Bit 9 (TAPWMIE) Timer2A Interrupt PWM Enable
  - 0: disable Capture event interrupt
  - 1: enable Capture event interrupt
- Bit 10 (TAMRSU) Timer2A Match Register update
  - 0: update register Time2_TAMATCHR_R register on the next cycle
  - 1: update register Time2_TAMATCHR_R register on the next timeout.
- Bit 11 (TAPLO) Timer2A PWM Legacy Operation
  - 0: CCP pin is driven Low when register TIMER2_TAILR_R is reloaded after the timer reaches 0.
  - 1: CCP pin is driven High when register TIMER2_TAILR_R is reloaded after the timer reaches 0.
- Bit 31:12 Reserved.

- As shown in Figure 6.6, register TIMER2_TAMATCHR_R is a 32-bit R/W register that contains a value to be compared with register TIMER2_TAR_R to create a match event.

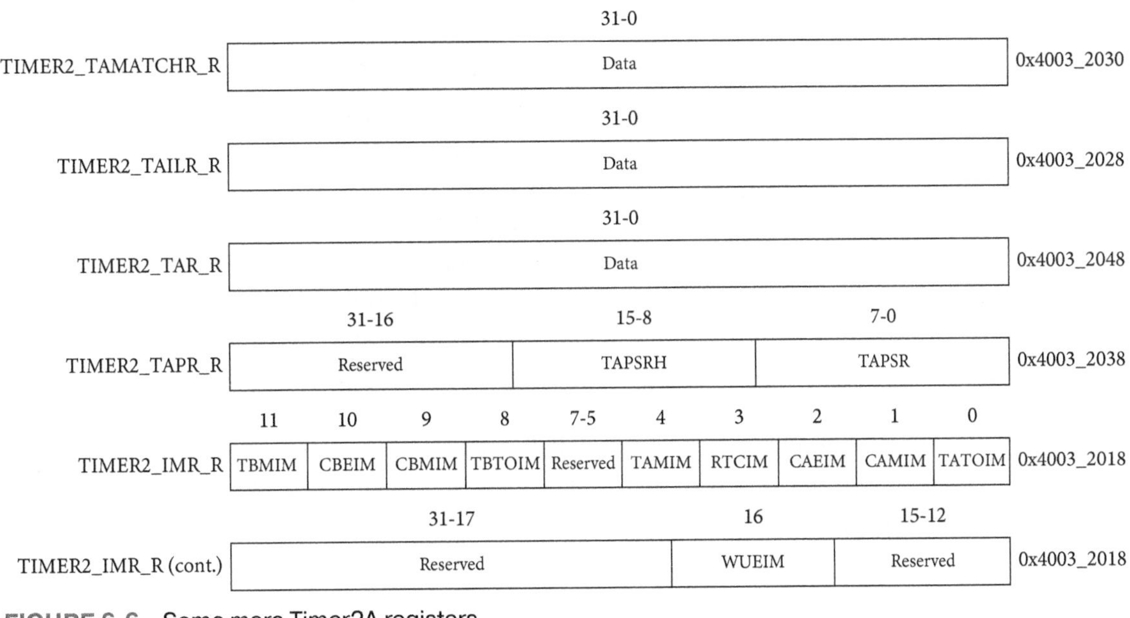

FIGURE 6.6 Some more Timer2A registers.

- Register TIMER2_TAILR (Timer 2A Load Interval register) is a 32-bit R/W register that is used to reload timer 2A if the timer is counting down. It is used as the upper bound for timeout event when the timer is counting up.
- Register TIMER2_TAR_R (at address 0x4003_20048) is an RO register that shows the current value of Timer2A counter when it's not in Edge Count or Edge Time mode.
- Register TIMER2_TAPR_R is an R/W Timer 2A Pre-scale register that when used individually in one-shot or periodic countdown mode, counts down to zero before the value of register TIMER2_TAR_R or TIMER2_TAV_R is changed. In other individual/split modes, this register holds bits 23:16 in the 16-bit mode of the 16/32-bit Timer and bits 47:32 in the 32-bit modes of the 32/64-bit Wide General Purpose Timer.
- Register TIMER2_IMR_R is the Timer2 Interrupt Mask Register that is used to enable (set to 1) or disable (cleared to 0) various event interrupts of timer A and B as follows:
  - Bit 0 (TATOIM): Timer 2A Time-Out Interrupt Mask.
  - Bit 1 (CAMIM): Timer 2A Capture Mode Match Interrupt Mask.
  - Bit 2 (CAEIM): Timer 2A Capture Mode Event Interrupt Mask.
  - Bit 3 (RTCIM) Timer 2A RTC Interrupt Mask.
  - Bit 4 (TAMIM): Timer 2A Match Interrupt Mask.
  - Bit 5–7: Reserved.
  - Bit 8 (TBTOIM): Timer 2B Time-Out Interrupt Mask.
  - Bit 9 (CBMIM): Timer 2B Capture Mode Match Interrupt Mask.
  - Bit 10 (CBEIM): Timer 2B Capture Mode Event Interrupt Mask.
  - Bit 11 (TBMIM): Timer 2B Match Interrupt Mask.
  - Bit 12–15: Reserved.
  - Bit 16 (WUEIM): 32/64-bit Wide Timer Write Update Error Interrupt Mask.
  - Bit 31–15: Reserved.
- Register TIMER2_RIS_R (located at address 0x4003_201C) shows the status of internal interrupts of Timer 2. Its bit field looks exactly like that of register TIMER2_IMR_R. For example, bit 3 shows the status of the RTC interrupt or bit 4 shows the Timer 2A timeout interrupt.
- Register TIMER2_ICR_R (located at address 0x4003_2024) is the Timer 2 Interrupt Clear register that is used to clear the status bits in register TIMER2_RIS_R. Their bit field looks exactly the same. For example, writing 1 to bit 8 of register TIMER2_ICR_R clears the raw status bit 8 (Timer 2B timeout interrupt status) of register TIMER2_RIS_R.

3.1. Block Diagram[3]

Figure 6.7 in the following shows the block diagram of a timer block consisting of Timer A and Timer B. To make it easy to follow the effects of the timer's registers, the following are some example codes that illustrate the setup of a timer in various timer modes.

---

3 Texas Instruments, *TivaTM TM4C123GH6PM*, 705.

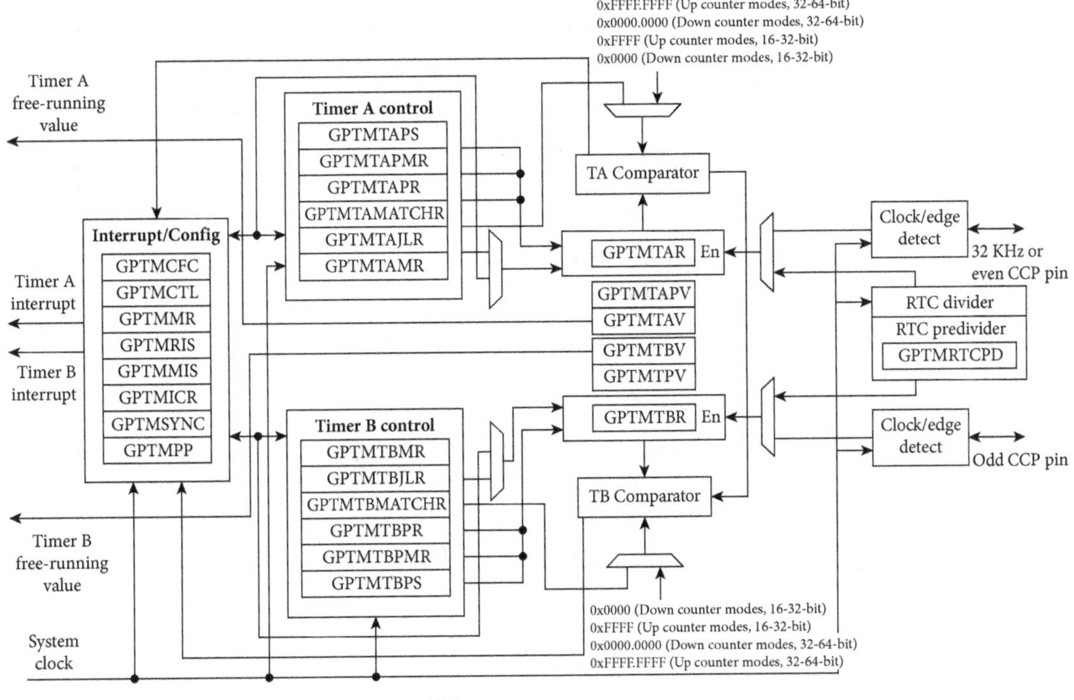

FIGURE 6.7 Block Diagram of the GPTM.

1. Set Up Timer 2A for Event-Counting Capture

In the following, we will set up Timer 2A to count the number of Switch 1 presses of the Tiva C kit.

a. Disable Timer 2A to prevent any changes from causing Timer 2A to react.

```
TIMER2_CTL_R &= ~0x01;
```

b. Select a 16-bit timer for a 16/32-bit timer or a 32-bit timer for a 32/64-bit mode.

```
TIMER2_CFG_R   |= 0x00000004;
```

c. Set Timer 2A to count up (TACDIR = 1), edge count mode (TACMR = 0), and capture mode (TAMR = 3).

```
TIMER2_TAMR_R |= 0x0013; //Edge Count, Capture mode, count up
```

d. Set Timer 2A to count the negative-edged event (TAEVENT = 0x01), which freezes counting when the processor is halted in debug mode (TASTALL = 1).

```
TIMER2_CTL_R |= 0x06; //TAEVENT=1 negative edge, TASTALL=1
```

e. In up-count mode, the timer TIMER 2A counts up to the values of TIMER2_TAMATCHR_R and TTIMER2_TAPMR_R registers. The values of TIMER2_TAPR_R and TIMER2_TAILR_R registers must be greater than TTIMER2_TAMATCHR_R and TTIMER2_TAPMR_R registers for the up counting to take place.

```
TIMER2_TAMATCHR_R = 0x8;
TIMER2_TAILR_R = 0x10;
```

f. Enable the capture event interrupt, which happens when the values of TIMER2_TAPR_R and TIMER2_TAR_R register equal to those of TTIMER2_TAPMR_R and TTIMER2_TAMATCHR_R registers.

```
TIMER2_IMR_R  |= 0x02; //CAMIM Capture Mode Event Interrupt
```

g. Clear all remaining interrupts.

```
TIMER2_ICR_R  |= 0x02; //CBEIM Capture Mode Event Interrupt
```

h. Set priority and enable TIMER 2A and the global interrupts.

```
NVIC_PRI5_R = (NVIC_PRI5_R&0x0FFFFFFF)|0x40000000;//Tim-
er1B=priority 2
NVIC_EN0_R = 0x1 << 23;  //Timer 2A iRQ 23, Interrupt number
39
EnableInterrupts();
```

i. Enable TIMER 2A.

```
TIMER2_CTL_R  |= 0x01; //Enable Timer 2A
Uint32_t delay;
SYSCTL_RCGCTIMER_R |=0x04; //Timer 2
 delay = SYSCTL_RCGCTIMER_R;
 TIMER2_CTL_R &= ~0x01;
 TIMER2_CFG_R  |= 0x00000004; //16 bit timer
  TIMER2_TAMR_R |= 0x0013; //Edge Count, Capture mode, count
up
  TIMER2_CTL_R |= 0x06; //TAEVENT=1 negative edge, TASTALL=1
  TIMER2_TAMATCHR_R = 0x8;
   TIMER2_TAILR_R = 0x10;
```

```
   TIMER2_IMR_R  |= 0x02; //CAMIM Capture Mode Event
Interrupt

   TIMER2_ICR_R  |= 0x02; //CBEIM Capture Mode Event
Interrupt

   NVIC_PRI5_R = (NVIC_PRI5_R&0x0FFFFFFF)|0x40000000;  //Tim-
er1B=priority 2

   NVIC_EN0_R = 0x1 << 23;     //Timer 1B iRQ 23, Interrupt
number 39

   EnableInterrupts();

   TIMER2_CTL_R  |= 0x01; //Enable Timer 2A
```

Program 6.5: Configuring Timer 2A for Event Counting Capture

2. Set up Timer 1B to Generate a Square Wave Running at a Frequency of 128Hz

Need to include files startup.s and tm4c123gh6pm.h with the following file Prog6.6. We can change the frequency by changing the value of parameter DELAY below. For example, if you want to create a square wave of 128Hz. This program runs with a default system frequency of 16MHz.

```
// Prog6-6ProgTimer1B-Ints. Producing a square wave output at
PB7 running at a frequency of 128Hz

// Flashing the Red LED at a frequency of about 14Hz


#include "tm4c123gh6pm.h"

#include <stdint.h>


void DisableInterrupts(void); // Disable interrupts

void EnableInterrupts(void);  // Enable interrupts

void GPIO_Init(void);

void Timer1B_Init(uint16_t delay);
```

```
//Producing a square wave output on portB pin 7 (PB7) with a
frequency of 128Hz.

//Creating a delay of (16000000/256) system clocks to obtain
a frequency of 256Hz.

//By toggling PB7 every Timer 1B interrupts, we create a
128Hz at PB7

#define DELAY (16000000/256)

//debug code

int main(void){

	DisableInterrupts();

	GPIO_Init();

	Timer1B_Init(DELAY);

	EnableInterrupts();


	while(1){

	}

}

void GPIO_Init(void) {

	uint8_t tp1;

	SYSCTL_RCGCGPIO_R |= 0x22;  // activate port F, port B

	//Delay for a few clock cycles

	tp1 = SYSCTL_PRGPIO_R;

	tp1 = SYSCTL_PRGPIO_R;

	GPIO_PORTF_LOCK_R = 0x4C4F434B;//  unlock GPIO Port F

	GPIO_PORTF_CR_R = 0x0F;// allow changes to PF0-3
```

```
    //Configure port B
    GPIO_PORTB_DIR_R |= 0x80;    // make PB-7 output (PF2
built-in LED)
    GPIO_PORTB_AFSEL_R &= ~0x80;// disable alt funct on
PB-7
    GPIO_PORTB_DEN_R |= 0x80;    // enable digital I/O on
PB-7
    GPIO_PORTB_PCTL_R = 0x00000000; //reset PCTL register
    GPIO_PORTB_AMSEL_R &= ~0x80;      // disable analog
functionality on PB-7


    //Configure port F
    GPIO_PORTF_DIR_R |= 0x0E;    // make PF1-3 output (PF2
built-in LED)
    GPIO_PORTF_AFSEL_R &= ~0x0E;// disable alt funct on
PF3-1
    GPIO_PORTF_DEN_R |= 0x0E;    // enable digital I/O on
PF1-3
    GPIO_PORTF_PCTL_R = 0x00000000; //reset PCTL register
    GPIO_PORTF_AMSEL_R &= ~0x0E;      // disable analog
functionality on PF1-3
}


void Timer1B_Init(uint16_t delay){
    uint8_t tp;
    //Disable global interrupts during configuration
    DisableInterrupts();
```

```
        //Enable Timer1

        SYSCTL_RCGCTIMER_R |= 0x02;    // 0) activate TIMER1

        //Wait for the Timer block to become stable

        tp = SYSCTL_RCGCTIMER_R;

        TIMER1_CTL_R = 0x00000000;     //  Disable Timer1 during
setup

        TIMER1_CFG_R = 0x00000004;     //  Set up Timer1 for
16-bit mode

        TIMER1_TBMR_R = 0x00000002;    //  Periodic mode, count
down

        TIMER1_TBILR_R = delay;        //  Program reload value
to register TIMER1

        TIMER1_ICR_R = 0x00000100;     //  Remove TIMER1B time-
out flag

        TIMER1_IMR_R = 0x00000100;     //  Enable Timer1B
interrupt

        NVIC_PRI5_R = (NVIC_PRI5_R&0xFF0FFFFF)|0x00800000; //
priority 4

        // interrupts enabled in the main program after all
devices initialized

        // vector number 38, interrupt number 22

        NVIC_EN0_R = 1<<22;            // 9) enable IRQ 22 in
NVIC

        TIMER1_CTL_R = 0x00000100;     // 10) enable TIMER1B

        //Enable the global interrupts

        EnableInterrupts();

}
```

```
void Timer1B_Handler(void){
        static uint32_t tp1 = 0x80;
        static uint32_t tp2 = 0x2;
        TIMER1_ICR_R = TIMER_ICR_TBTOCINT;// acknowledge
timer1B timeout
        //Flashing the Red LED of the launchpad
        GPIO_PORTF_DATA_R = tp2 & 0x02;
        if (tp2 == 0x80000) { tp2 = 0x2;}
        else {tp2 = tp2 << 1;}
        //Generate a square wave on port B pin 7
        GPIO_PORTB_DATA_R = tp1 & 0x80;
        if (tp1 == 0x80) { tp1 = 0x0;}
        else {tp1 = 0x80;}
}
```

Program 6.6: Creating a Square Wave Using Timer1B

4. ADC[4]

There are two identical 12-bit ADC modules in the Tiva C. They use the successive approximation method to convert an analog signal to a 12-bit digital value. Each ADC module can handle twelve analog inputs and an internal temperature sensor. The analog inputs are multiplexed with other functions and the GPIO pins through the configuration of the AFSEL, PCTL, DEN, and AMSEL registers (see the GPIO section). An ADC module has four sequencers, which can be programmed to support various combinations of priority, trigger events, and interrupt generation. Each ADC module also has eight digital comparators that can be used to compare an ADC conversion value with two user-defined values to determine the signal's operational range. The analog input and the trigger source can be used with different modules or with the same two ADC modules. The following are features of ADC module 0 (module 1 has similar features and use registers ADC1_xxxxxx):

4 Texas Instruments, *Tiva™ TM4C123GH6PM*, 799–892.

- *Twelve shareable analog input channels and an internal temperature sensor:* Register ADC0_SSMUXn_R (n = 0 – 3) has 8 nibbles (MUX0–7), each of which is associated with a sample of a sequence. For example, nibble MUX0 (bit 3–0), associated with the first sample, specifies which analog input (or the temperature sensor) is used for this sample. For example, if MUX0 is equal to two, that corresponds to AIN2, which is Pin 1 of Port E (PE1) (see Table 6.1 in the GPIO section).
- *Four sequencers (SS0–SS3):* Sequencer SS3 can capture one sample and has a one-deep FIFO. Sequencer SS1 and SS2 can capture a maximum of four samples each and has a four-deep FIFO. Sequencer SS0 can capture a maximum of eight samples and has an eight-deep FIFO. Bits 3–0 of register ADC0_ACTSS_R (Figure 6.8) correspond to the enable/disable of Sequencer SS3–SS0, respectively. Bit 16 of this register shows the status of the ADC0, busy (= 1) or idle (= 0).

	31-14	13-12	11-10	9-8	7-6	5-4	3-2	1-0	SS0
ADC0_SSPRI_R		SS3		SS2		SS1		SS0	0x4003_8020

	31-16	15-12	11-8	7-4	3-0	
ADC0_EMUX_R	Reserved	EM3	EM2	EM1	EM0	0x4003_8014

	31-17	16		3	2	1	0	
ADC0_ACTSS_R	Reserved	BUSY		ASEN3	ASEN2	ASEN1	ASEN0	0x4003_8000

	31-4	3	2	1	0	
ADC0_SSTL3_R	Reserved	TS0	IE0	END0	D0	0x4003_80A4

	31-17	16		3	2	1	0	
ADC0_RIS_R	Reserved	INRDC		INR3	INR2	INR1	INR0	0x4003_8004

FIGURE 6.8 ADC0 Registers.

- *Differential or single-input configurations:* Register ADC0_SSCTLn_R (n = 0 – 3) has up to 8 nibbles, each of which corresponds to a sample and each of which has four bits associated with temperature measurement, interrupt enable for this sample completion, indicator of the last sample of the sequence or differential input, respectively. For example, in register ADC0_SSTL3_R (Figure 6.8), Sequencer 3 of module ADC0, if the binary value of nibble 0 (bit 3-0) is 0110, it means the temperature measurement is disabled (bit 3 = 0), raw interrupt bit 0 is asserted at the end of the first sample completion (bit 2 = 1), the first sample is the last sequence of the sequence (bit 1 = 1), and analog input is single ended, not differential input (bit 0 = 0). Register ADC0_SSCTL0_R is associated with Sequencer 0, which has eight samples, so it has eight nibbles. Similarly, ADC0_SSTL1_R and ADC0_SSTL2_R have four nibbles and register ADC0_SSTL3_R has 1 nibble.
- *Sample rate ranges from 125 Kbits/sec to 1 Mbits/sec:* Values of bits 3–0 of register ADC0_PC_R specify the sampling rate of the ADC0 module: one for 125 Kb/s, three for 250 Kb/s, five for 500 Kb/s, and seven for 1 Mb/s. Other values are reserved.

- *ADC trigger source:* Module ADC0/1 has multiple trigger sources, such as processor (software start), analog comparators, timer, PWM generators, or continuously sampling. Register ADC0_EMUX_R (Figure 6.8) has four nibbles, EM3-EM0 associated with Sequencer 3 to Sequencer 0, respectively. Each nibble specifies the trigger source for a sequencer. For example, if the value of EM3 is equal to zero, then the trigger source for Sequencer 3 is software (processor): one for Analog Comparator 0, four for external GPIO, five for the timer, and so on. The following are the configurations for the trigger source of a sequencer based on the value of its nibble:
  - 0x0: Processor (software).
  - 0x1: Analog Comparator 0.
  - 0x2: Analog Comparator 1.
  - 0x3: Reserved.
  - 0x4: External (GPIO pins).
  - 0x5: Timer. Besides, the trigger must be enabled with bit TAOTE (Timer A Output Trigger Enable) or TBOTE of register TIMERn_CTL_R (n = 0–5).
  - 0x6: PWM generator 0.
  - 0x6: PWM generator 1.
  - 0x6: PWM generator 2.
  - 0x6: PWM generator 3.
  - 0xA–0xE: reserved.
  - 0xF: Always (continuously sampled).
- *Optional programmable phase shift in sample time:* Values of bits 3–0 of register ADC0_SPC_R specify the sample phase difference in increments of 22.5° (0 to 337.5°) from the standard sample time.
- *Register ADC0_RIS_R lists all raw interrupt status of Sequencer 3–0:* Bits 3–0 of register ADC0_IM_R enable raw interrupts of Sequencer SS3-SS0 and bits 19–16 enable a raw interrupt from the digital comparator to be sent on interrupt line SS3-SS0, respectively. Register ADC0_ISR_R has similar bit format as register ADC0_RIS_R and it's used to reset raw interrupt status bit of register ADC0_RIS_R. For example, a '1' written to bit 0 of register ADC0_ISC_R will reset the interrupt status bit 0 (Sequencer 0) of register ADC0_RIS_R. A '0' written to any bit of register ADC0_ISC_R will not do anything. Bit 16 of register ADC0_RIS_R indicates a raw comparator interrupt has happened.
- The RO (Read Only) 12-bit register ADC0_SSFIFO0_R is used to read out conversion results of the ADC0 sequencer 0, which has eight samples. By reading this register repeatedly, we obtain values of sample 0, then sample 1, and so on, until the FIFO is empty. Similarly, the RO 12-bit register ADC0_SSFIFO1_R is associated with the ADC0 sequencer 1 and register ADC0_SSFIFO2_R, ADC0_SSFIFO3_R with ADC0 sequencer 2 and 3, respectively. As a reminder, sequencer 0 has eight samples. Sequencer 1 and 2 have four samples each and sequencer 3 has only one sample.
- Register ADC0_SSFSTATn (n = 0–3) shows the FIFO status of the ADC0 Sequencer n (n = 0–3) (Figure 6.9). Bits 3-0 contain the value of the current tail pointer, which points to the next entry to be read. Bits 7-0 are the head pointer, which points to the next entry

to be written. Bit 8 and bit 12 show the FIFOn (n=0-3) Empty or Full status, respectively. The values of the tail pointer and head pointer of the Sequencer 0 range from 0 to 7, 0 to 3 for Sequencers 1 and 2, and 0 for Sequencer 3.

Register ADC0_SSPRI_R specifies the priorities of the four sequencers (Figure 6.9). The priority of the sequencers ranges from zero (highest) to three (lowest). The sequencers cannot be assigned with the same priority. Figure 6.8 shows the bit fields for the sequencers' priorities.

	31-13	12	11-9	8	7-4	3-0	SS0
ADCO_SSFSTAT0_R	Reserved	FULL	Reserved	EMPTY	HPTR	TPTR	0x4003_804C

	31-13	12	11-9	8	7-4	3-0	
ADCO_SSFSTAT1_R	Reserved	FULL	Reserved	EMPTY	HPTR	TPTR	0x4003_806C

	31-13	12	11-9	8	7-4	3-0	
ADCO_SSFSTAT2_R	Reserved	FULL	Reserved	EMPTY	HPTR	TPTR	0x4003_808C

	31-13	12	11-9	8	7-4	3-0	
ADCO_SSFSTAT3_R	Reserved	FULL	Reserved	EMPTY	HPTR	TPTR	0x4003_80AC

	31-14	13-12	11-10	9-8	7-6	5-4	3-2	1-0	
ADCO_SSPRI_R	Reserved	SS3	Reserved	SS2	Reserved	SS1	Reserved	SS0	0x4003_8020

FIGURE 6.9 ADC0 SSFSTAT*n* (*n* = 0–3) and SSPRI registers.

4.1. Starting an ADC Conversion with Software Using ADC0 Sequencer 3

The following example shows ways to set up the ADC for conversions with a software start. Every time the SysTick Timer times out, its ISR makes a software request of an ADC conversion. We'll use Sequencer 3 with only one sample per conversion.

1. Set up Port E Pin 2 (PE2) as input analog Channel 1.
2. Set up the SysTick timer.
3. Enable module ADC0.

```
SYSCTL_RCGADC_R = 0x01;
```

4. Wait for 10 ms.

```
Delay1(2000);
```

5. Set the ADC sampling rate to 125 samples/sec.

```
ADC0_PC_R = 0x01; //125 KHz
```

6. Set the priority of Sequencer 3–0 to 0–3, respectively, with Sequencer SS3 at the highest priority of 0.

```
ADC0_SSPRI_R = 0x0123;
```

7. Disable Sequencer 3 to start the ADC configuration.

```
ADC0_ACTSS_R &= ~0x08;
```

8. Set the conversion trigger source for Sequencer 3 for a software start.

```
ADC0_EMUX_R &= ~0xF000;
```

9. Choose Port E Pin 2 or analog Channel 1 as the analog input of Sequencer 3.

```
ADC0_SSMUX3_R = (ADC0_SSMUX3_R & 0xFFFFFFF0) + 1; //Ain1
(PE2)  SS3 field
```

10. Configure the first sample by disabling the temperature measurement, enabling the raw interrupt for the first sample completion, changing the first sample to the last sample, and choosing the analog signal input so that it is single ended (not differential ended).

```
ADC0_SSCTL3_R = 0x06; //IE0, END0
```

11. Enable the ADC interrupt for Sequencer 3.

```
ADC0_IM_R |= 0x08;
```

12. Enable the NVIC interrupt for Sequencer 3 of module ADC0.

```
NVIC_EN0_R |= 0x1 << 17; //IRQ 17, Interrupt number 33
```

13. Set the NVIC interrupt priority for Sequencer 3 of module ADC0.

```
NVIC_PRI4_R = (NVIC_PRI4_R & 0xFFFF0FFF) | 0x00004000;
```

14. Enable Sequencer 3.

```
ADC0_ACTSS_R |= 0x08; //enable ADC0 sample sequence 3
```

15. Enable the global interrupt.

```
EnableInterrupts();
```

The SysTick Timer ISR set a software start for Sequencer 3.

```
void SysTick_Handler(void) {

        ADC0_PSSI_R = 0x08; //start conversion

}
```

The ISR of Sequencer 3 of module ADC: Get the conversion data from Sequencer 3 one-deep FIFO and then reset the ADC0 interrupt.

```
void ADC0Seq3_Handler(result) {

        int32_t result;

result = ADC0_SSFIFO3_R & 0xFFF;

        ADC0_ISC_R = 0x08;

}
```

Program 6.7: ADC Conversion Using Sequencer 3

4.2. Starting an ADC Conversion with Software Using ADC0 Sequencer 1

As we know, after a conversion, Sequencer 1 provides four samples instead of one like Sequencer 3. We can average these samples to reduce measurement noises. The complete program is listed as program 6.7 in Appendix D.

4.3. Triggering an ADC Conversion with a Timer

We can modify the previous example to change the trigger source for the ADC module from software start to a timer by changing Step 8 to the following.

Set the conversion trigger source for Sequencer 3 to be the GPTM 2A.

```
ADC0_EMUX_R |= 0x5000;
```

But we also have to add the initialization of Timer 2A, as shown in Section 3. The complete program is listed in Appendix D.

5. UARTs

In the *Tiva C TM4C123GH6PM*, there are eight UARTs (0–7), each of which can perform like a parallel-to-serial or a serial-to-parallel converter and has similar functionality as a standard 16C550 UART, but its registers are not compatible with the 16C550. We are using UART0 registers to illustrate the following features:

- To generate a desired programmable baud rate, we have to load a 22-bit number, 16-bit integer, and 6-bit fractional numbers into register UARTn_IBRD_R and register UART*n*_FBRD_R (n = 0–7), respectively. For instance, for a baud rate of 115,200 bauds/s and with a system clock of 50 MHz, the numbers are calculated as follows:

  ```
  the integer IBRD = int (50,000,000 / (16*115200)) =
  int(27.1267) = 27

  the fractional FBRD = int ((0.1267*64) +0.5) = 8
  ```

- UART control register, UART0_CTL_R, is used to enable or disable UART0 and control other miscellaneous functions as described in the following (all other UART*n*, *n* = 0–7, control registers operate the same way):
  - Bit 0 (UARTEN) when set enables the UART0 and disables the UART0 when it is cleared
  - Bit 1 (SIREN) when set enables the IrDA SIR (Serial Infrared Interface) block allowing the UART0 to transmit and receive data using the SIR protocol
  - Bit 2 (SIRLP) when set enables the UART0 to operate in IrDA SIR low power mode
  - Bit 7 (LBE) enables the UART loop back (UART Tx is connected to UART Rx)
  - Bit 8 (TXE) enables the Transmit logic of the UART when set
  - Bit 9 (RXE) enables the Receive logic of the UART when set
- Register UARTn_LCRH_R (line control register) specifies a programmable number of data bits (5–8), even or odd parity, 1 or 2 stop bits, FIFO enabled or not. Flow control signals RTS and clear to send (CTS) are also handled by this register.
  - Bit 7 (SPS): UART Stick Parity Select. When this bit is cleared, stick parity is disabled. When bit 1 (parity enabled), bit 2 (even parity), and bit 7 (stick parity) are set, the parity bit is sent and checked as a 0. When bit 1 and 7 are set and bit 2 is cleared, the parity bit is sent and checked as a 1.
  - Bits 6–5 (WLEN): UART Word Length
    - WLEN = 0x0, 5 bits
    - WLEN = 0x1, 6 bits
    - WLEN = 0x2, 7 bits
    - WLEN =0x3, 8 bits
  - Bit 4 (FEN): UART FIFO Enable
  - Bit 3 (STP2): when set, 2 stop bits are transmitted at the end of a frame. When cleared, one stop bit is transmitted at the end of a frame.
- UART Flag register UART*n*_FR_R (*n* = 0–7) indicates the status of the Transmit and Receive FIFO as well as the busy state of the UART*n*.
  - Bit 0 (CTS) is only implemented for UART1 and it is a reserved bit in UART 0
  - Bit 1-2: Reserved
  - Bit 3 (BUSY) is set when the transmit FIFO becomes nonempty (even if the UART is not enabled)
  - Bit 4 (RXFE) is the UART Receive FIFO empty status
  - Bit 5 (TXFF) is the UART Transmit FIFO full status
  - Bit 6 (RXFF) is the UART Receive FIFO full status
  - Bit 7 TXFE UART Transmit FIFO empty
  - Bit 31:8 Reserved
- UART Interrupt Mask register UART*n*_IM_R (*n* = 0–7) enables or disables UART Transmit or Receive interrupts as shown in the following:
  - Bit 4 (RXIM) when set allows Receive interrupts (indicated by bit RXRIS in register UART*n*_RIS_R) to be sent to the interrupt controller

  - Bit 5 (TXIM) when set allows Transmit interrupts (indicated by bit TXRIS in register UART*n*_RIS_R) to be sent to the interrupt controller.
- Each UART has two 16-byte FIFOs, one of which is the transmit FIFO and the other the receiver FIFO, which has an additional four status bits per character. The UART Data register (UARTn_DATA_RO is used to access either of the FIFO's. If the UART*n* is enabled and data is written into the transmit FIFO, the busy bit in the UART flag register UART*n*_FR_R (*n* = 0–7) is asserted and a data frame is transmitted. The busy bit stays asserted until the transmit FIFO is empty. Figure 6.9 shows a UART data frame, which includes a start bit, 5–8 data bits, parity bits (if enabled), and 1–2 stop bits. The parameters used with the data frame are specified by register UART*n*_LCRH_R, as mentioned earlier.

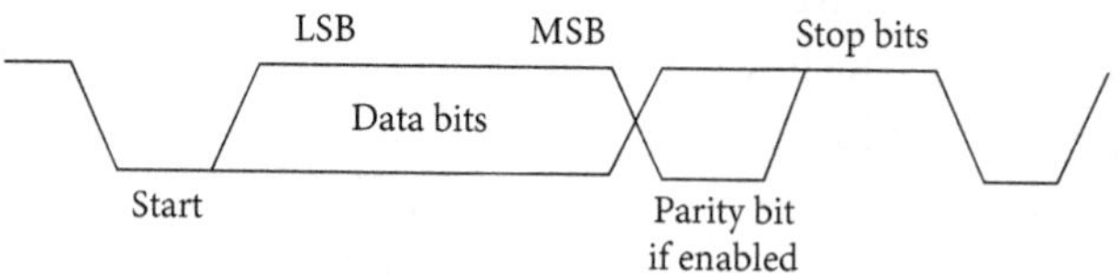

FIGURE 6.10 UART Data Frame.

As shown in Figure 6.11, register UART0 Interrupt FIFO Level (UART0_IFLS_R) defines a FIFO level for the receive and the transmit FIFO level, separately. Bits 0–2 are used to set the Transmit Interrupt FIFO level and bits 3–5 for the Receive Interrupt FIFO level.

TXIFLSEL	Description
0x0	FIFO ≤ 7/8 empty
0x1	FIFO ≤ ¾ empty
0x2	FIFO ≤ ½ empty (default)
0x3	FIFO ≤ ¼ empty
0x4	FIFO ≤ 1/8 empty
0x5–0x7	Reserved

RXIFLSEL	Description
0x0	FIFO ≥ 1/8 full
0x1	FIFO ≥ 1/4 full
0x2	FIFO ≥ ½ full (default)
0x3	FIFO ≥ 3/4 full
0x4	FIFO ≥ 7/8 full
0x5–0x7	Reserved

For example, if the value of register UART0_IFLS_R is 0x1A, that means the FIFO Receive Interrupt level is greater or equal to ¾ full and the FIFO Transmit Interrupt level is less than or equal to ½ empty since TXIFSEL = 0x2 and RXIFSEL = 0x3. The interrupts for the

Transmit or Receive FIFO are generated based on the transition through the trigger levels. For example, if the receive FIFO level is set at ½ full—that is, eight characters—the interrupt happens when the eighth character is received.

- UART Raw Interrupt Status register UART*n*_RIS_R ($n = 0–7$), as shown in Figure 6.11 below, when read, indicates the raw status value of the corresponding interrupts like TXRIS or RXRIS.
  - Bit 4 (RXRIS) is the UART Receive Raw Interrupt Status. When set, it means the Receive FIFO level has crossed the receive level threshold defined in register UART*n*_IFLS_R. It will be cleared when writing a "1" to bit RXIC of register UART*n*_ICR_R or by reading data from the Receive FIFO until its level is less than the trigger level defined by register UART*n*_IFLS_R if the Receive FIFO is enabled. Otherwise, it is cleared after reading a single byte.
  - Bit 5 (TXRIS) is the UART Transmit Raw Interrupt Status. When set, it means the TransmitFIFO level has crossed the transmit level threshold defined in register UART*n*_IFLS_R. It will be cleared when writing a "1" to bit TXIC of register UART*n*_ICR_R or by writing data to the Transmit FIFO until its level is greater than the trigger level defined by register UART*n*_IFLS_R if the Transmit FIFO is enabled. Otherwise, it is cleared after writing a single byte.
- UART*n*_ICR_R ($n = 0–7$) is the interrupt clear register. Writing 1 to bit 4 (RXIC) clears bit 4 (RXRIS) of register UART*n*_RIS_R. It is similar for bit 5 (TXIC)—writing 1 clears bit 5 (TXRIS) of register UART*n*_RIS_R.
- UART*n*_DR_R ($n = 0–7$) is the UART Data Register. If the Transmit FIFO is enabled, a write to this register will push data onto the Transmit FIFO. If not, data is put onto the transmitter holding register, which is the bottom byte of the transmit FIFO. If the Receive FIFO is enabled, received data together with its 4-bit status (Overrun, Break, Parity, Framing) are pushed onto the Receive FIFO. Otherwise, the received data and its status are stored in the receiving holding register. Reading this register retrieves the received data.

		9	8	7				0	
UART0_CTL_R		RXE	TXE	LBE		SIRLP	SIREN	UARTEN	0x4000_C030

	31-6	5-3	2-0	
UART0_IFLS_R	Reserved	RXIFSEL	TXIFSEL	0x4000_C034

	31-8	7	6-5	4	3	2	1	0	
UART0_LCRH_R	Reserved	SPS	WPEN	FEN	STP2	EPS	PEN	BRK	0x4000_C02C

	31-8	7	6	5	4	3	2-1	0	
UART0_FR_R	Reserved	TXFE	RXFF	TXFF	RXFE	BUSY	Reserved	CTS	0x4000_C018

	31-13		5	4		
UART0_IM_R	Reserved		TXIM	RXIE		0x4000_C038

FIGURE 6.11 Some UART0 Registers.

The following are some example codes using UART with and without FIFO and/or with and without UART interrupts.

5.1 Using UART with Busy-Wait Approach (Without Interrupts) to Echo a Character Input

In the following, we will set up UART0 to receive a character and echo it back on the serial terminal. We are not using the interrupt to receive or transmit data. Instead, we will use the busy-wait approach to receive and transmit ASCII data.

1. The main program calls a subroutine, UART_Init, to initialize the UART.

   ```
   void UART_Init (void) {
   ```

2. Enable UART0.

   ```
   SYSCTL_RCGCR1_R |= 0x01;
   ```

3. Disable UART0 to start configuring it. We don't want UART0 to start acting when the configuration is not complete yet.

   ```
   UART0_CTL_R &= ~0x01;
   ```

4. We are using the default system clock frequency, which is 16 MHz, after a power-on reset. The UART0 baud rate will be set at 115,200 bauds.

   ```
   The integer IBRD = int (16,000,000/(16*115,200)) = int(8.681)

   The fraction FBRD = int (0.681*64 + 0.5) = 44

   UART0_IBRD_R = 8;

   UART0-FBRD_R = 44;
   ```

5. Set 8 data bits, 0 parity bit, 1 stop bit, FIFO not enabled.

   ```
   UART0_LCRH_R = 0x60;
   ```

6. Enable UART0.

   ```
   UART0_CTL_R |= 0x01;
   ```

7. Clear receive and transmit interrupt before using the UART.

   ```
   UART0_ICR_R = 0x30;
   ```

8. Enable and map Port A Pin 0 and Pin 1 to UART0 receive and UART0 transmit, respectively (see the GPIO section).

9. Main program:

```
char chr1;

int main(void){

        UART_Init();                // initialize UART

        UART0_ICR_R = 0x10;         //Clear Receive Flag

        while (1) {

        //while the Receive FIFO is empty stays here

              while ((UART0_FR_R & 0x10) != 0) {};

        //if the Receive FIFO is not empty, read a character

              chr1 = UART0_DR_R & 0xFF; //UART input

        //Clears FIFO Receive flag

              UART0_ICR_R = 0x10;

        //Check to see if the Transmit FIFO is full

              While ((UART0_FR_R & 0x20) != 0) {}; //FIFO
Transmit full

        //If not, send out the receive character

              UART0_DR_R = chr1;

        }

}
```

Program 6.8: Using UART0 with Busy-Wait Approach and Interrupt Disabled

5.2. Using UART with the Receive Interrupt to Echo a Character Input

Steps 1–8 are similar to those of Program 6.8. The following program is different from the previous one, as the receive interrupt is enabled.

1. Enable UART0 receive interrupt.

```
UART0_IM_R |=  0x10;              //Receive Interrupt
```

2. Enable NVIC interrupt and NVIC interrupt priority.

```
NVIC_PRI1_R |= 0x4000; //priority = 2 (bit 15-13)

NVIC_EN0_R |= 0x20; //IRQ 5, Interrupt Number 21
```

3. Enable the global interrupt.

```
EnableInterrupts();
```

4. Set up the UART0 ISR.

```
Void UART0_Handler (void) {

        char1 = UART0_DR_R;

        flag = 1;

        UART0_ICR_R |= 0x30;

}
```

5. Main program:

```
void main (void) {

        UART_Init();

        while (1) {

                while (flag == 0) {};

                UART0_DR_R = char1;

                flag = 0;

        }

}
```

Program 6.9: UART0 with Receive Interrupt and FIFO Disabled

5.3. Using UART0 with FIFO and Interrupt Enabled

1. Include file tm4c123gh6pm.h because it contains all the necessary macro-definitions of register names.

```
#include "tm4c123gh6pm.h"

#include <stdint.h>
```

2. Define the FIFO size and declare the FIFO array.

```
#define FIFO_SIZE 16

char static FIFO[FIFO_SIZE];
```

3. Function prototypes:

```
void EnableInterrupts(void);

void UART0_Handler(void);

void UART_Init(void);

void FIFO_input(void );

void FIFO_output(void );
```

4. Variable declaration:

```
int flag;

int static rdptr;

int static wrptr;
```

5. Variable wwrap and rwrap are used to signal that a wrap action has been taken for index wptr or rdptr, respectively. To find out if the FIFO is full or empty, we can use the following logical equation:

```
FIFO empty condition = (wptr == rdptr) && (wwrap == rwrap);

FIFO full condition = (wptr == rdptr) && (wwrap != rwrap);

uint8_t wwrap, rwrap;
```

6. Main program: flag is high (= 1) when there are data in the FIFO to output to the UART.

```
int main(void){

        UART_Init();                    // initialize UART

                while (1) {

                        if (flag) {

                        FIFO_output();
```

```
                flag = 0;
            }
        }
    }
```

7. Use a subroutine to output data to the UART when there are data in the FIFO array.

```
void FIFO_output(void) {
        char data;
        while (((UART0_FR_R & UART_FR_TXFF) == 0)  &&
                (!((rdptr == wrptr) && (wwrap == rwrap))) ){ //
FIFO is not empty
                data = FIFO[rdptr];
        UART0_DR_R = data;
        if (rdptr == FIFO_SIZE - 1) {
                rdptr = 0;
                rwrap = ~rwrap;
                }
                else {
                        rdptr += 1;
                }
        }
}
```

8. Subroutine to initialize the UART and map Port A Pins 0 and 1 to the UART alternate function (see section GPIO).

```
void UART_Init(void){
  SYSCTL_RCGC1_R |= 0x01; // activate UART0 module
  SYSCTL_RCGCGPIO_R |= 0x01; // activate port A module
```

```
  UART0_CTL_R &= ~0x01;      // disable UART module

 //For 16MHz System Clock

  UART0_IBRD_R = 8;                    // IBRD =
int(16,000,000 / (16 * 115,200)) = int(8.681)

  UART0_FBRD_R = 44;                     // FBRD = int(0.681 *
64 + 0.5) = 44

 // 8 data bit, no parity bits, one stop bit, FIFO enabled

  UART0_LCRH_R = 0x70;

      UART0_IFLS_R = UART_IFLS_RX4_8 | UART_IFLS_TX4_8;
      //0x24, FIFO 1/8 full

      //UART0_IFLS_R = 0x24; // >= 7/8

  UART0_IM_R |= 0x10;           //Receive Interrupt

  UART0_CTL_R |= 0x301;       // enable UART

  GPIO_PORTA_AFSEL_R |= 0x03;          // enable alt funct
on PA1-0

  GPIO_PORTA_DEN_R |= 0x03;            // enable digital I/O
on PA1-0

  NVIC_PRI1_R |= 0x4000; //priority = 2 (bit 15-13)

  NVIC_EN0_R |= 0x20; //IRQ 5, Interrupt Number 21

 // configure PA1-0 as UART

  GPIO_PORTA_PCTL_R =
(GPIO_PORTA_PCTL_R&0xFFFFFF00)+0x00000011;

  GPIO_PORTA_AMSEL_R &= ~0x03;         // disable analog
functionality on PA

  UART0_ICR_R = 0x30;

  EnableInterrupts();

      wwrap = 0;

      rwrap = 0;

}
```

9. Use UART ISR when there is a UART character.

```
void UART0_Handler(void) {
        if (UART0_RIS_R & UART_RIS_RXRIS) {
                UART0_ICR_R = UART_ICR_RXIC;
                FIFO_input();
        }
}
```

10. Use a subroutine to collect incoming UART characters and put them in an FIFO array.

```
void FIFO_input(void) {
    char data;
        while ((UART0_FR_R & UART_FR_RXFE) == 0) {//while the
UART FIFO is not empty
                data = UART0_DR_R;
                FIFO[wrptr] = data;
                if (wrptr == FIFO_SIZE - 1) {
                        wrptr = 0;
                        wwrap = ~wwrap;
                }
                else {
                        wrptr += 1;
                }
        }
        flag = 1; //signal the main program there are data in
the FIFO
}
```

Program 6.10: Using UART0 with FIFO and Interrupt Enabled

6. PWM[5]

Compared to the ADC technique (Section 4), PWM is another method for encoding an analog signal digitally. It is used to create a square wave signal whose duty cycle is proportionate to the analog signal level. We can find common applications using PWM signals in audio amplifiers, telecommunication, motor control, or switching power supplies.

There is a total of sixteen PWM outputs inside two PWM modules in a Tiva C TM4C123H6PM microcontroller. Each PWM module has four PWM generator blocks and a control block. The following are features of a PWM generator:

- There are two output signals for each PWM generator block, and they share the same timer. They can be configured to be a pair of complementary signals or programmed to behave independently.
- The PWM generator block's outputs, pwmA and pwmB, are going through various or no changes at the control block before becoming device pins, such as MnPW0, MnPWM1, ..., MnPWM3 (n = 0–3).
- There is an input dedicated to fault handling to generate a low latency shutdown, preventing damage to the device under control.
- Each PWM generator has a 16-bit counter that can operate in down or up/down mode. The load value of the counter determines the output frequency, and the counter can generate an output signal at zero and load values.
- There are two comparators per a PWM generator that can generate single-clock output pulses: cmpA and cmpB. Figure 6.12 shows four different events (zero count, count loading, matching comparator A's value, and matching comparator B's value) in the countdown mode that you can use to create your PWM output signal.

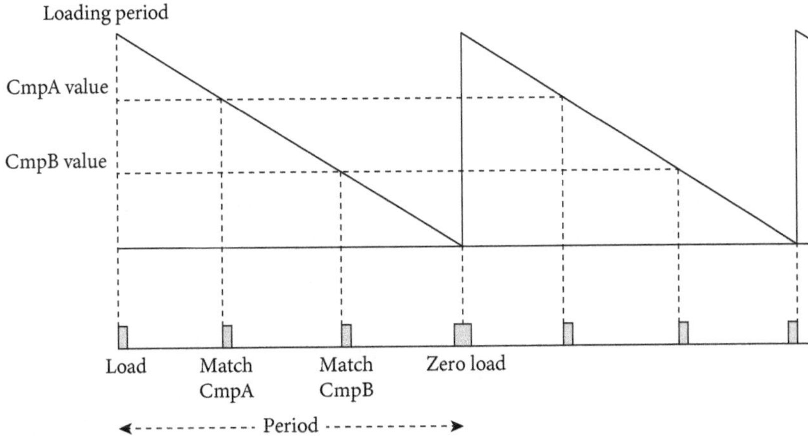

FIGURE 6.12 PWM Countdown Mode.

5 Texas Instruments, *Tiva™ TM4C123GH6PM*, 1230–1304.

- In the case of count-up/-down mode, from the six different pulses of the load, zero, cmpA, cmpB events, and the direction signal in Figure 6.13, we can program the PWM output signals to fit various combinations of positions and duty cycles. For example, we can create signal pwmA, as in the example code in Figure 6.18. We can also use those four or six events of load, zero, cmpA, and cmpB to generate an interrupt or to trigger an ADC conversion.

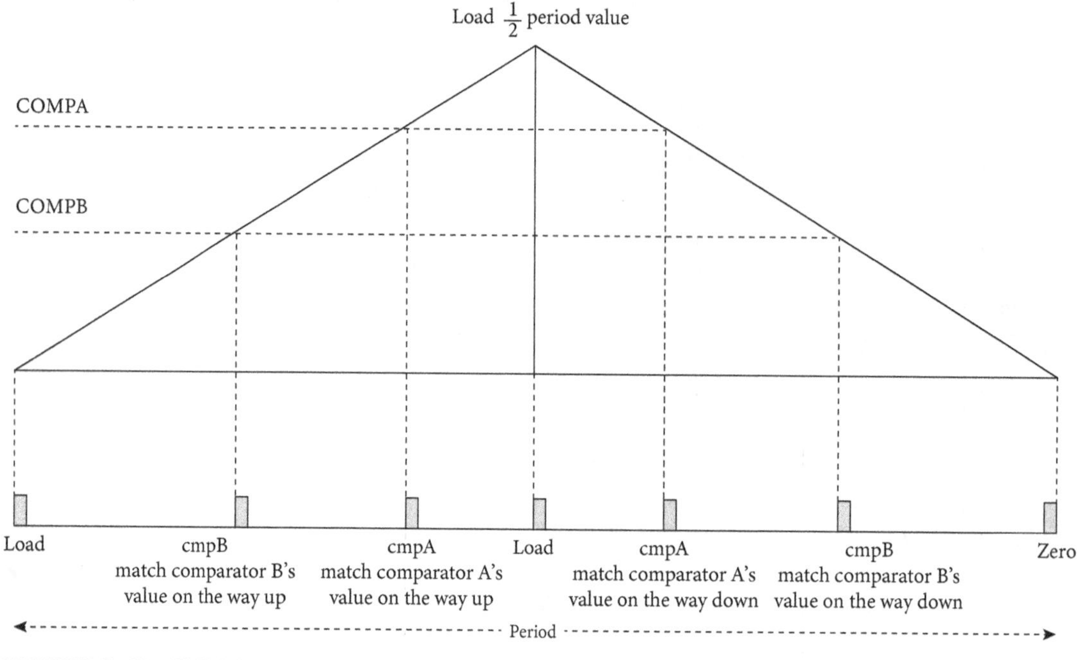

FIGURE 6.13 PWM Count-Up/-Down Mode.

- In the following, we use module PWM0 and Generator A to program the previously mentioned events using register PWM0_0_GENA_R, as listed in Figure 6.14. For example, if you want to use the up/down counter mode and you want signal pwm0A to go high when the timer count matches Comparator A on the way up, and it goes low when matching Comparator A's value on the way down. Bits 5–4 (ATCMPAU) of register PWM0_0_GENA_R are set to three and bits 7–6 (ACTCMPAD) are set to two. Bit 1 (mode) of register PWM0_0_CTL_R needs to be set to one for the up/down count mode in which the counter counts up from zero to a load value and counts down to zero and repeats. The load value can be entered using register PWM0_0_LOAD_R. Register PWM0_0_CMPA_R and PWM0_0_CMPB_R are used to enter the Comparator A's and Comparator B's value, respectively. It should be noted that all the counters and comparators used in PWM modules are 16-bits long, so be careful when loading values into comparators. They should not be greater than 2^{16}-1 or 65,535.
- To pass signal pwm0A to the chip's output Pin M0PWM0, we can use bit 0 of register PWM0_ENABLE_R (Figure 6.15). Similarly, signal pwm0B can be enabled to pass to pin M0PWM1 using bit 1 of the register. Remember that each generator has two outputs,

	31-10	9-8	7-6	5	4	3	2	1	0	
PWM0_0_CTL_R	-----	GENBUPD	GEN2UPD	CMPBUPD	CMPAUPD	LOADUPD	Debug	Mode	ENABLE	0x4002_8040

	31-12	11-10	9-8	7-6	5-4	3-2	1-0	
PWM0_0_GENA_R	Reserved	ACTCMPBD	ACTCMPBU	ACTCMPAD	ACTCMPAU	ACTLOAD	ACTZERO	0x4002_8060

	31-16	15-0	
PWM0_0_LOAD_R	Reserved	LOAD	0x4002_8050

	31-16	15-0	
PWM0_0_CMPA_R	Reserved	CMPA	0x4002_8058

	31-16	15-0	
PWM0_0_CMPB_R	Reserved	CMPB	0x4002_805C

FIGURE 6.14 Some Registers of Module PWM0 Generator 0.

so for module PWM0, Generator 1 has signals pwm1A and pwm1B, which are mapped to Pins M0PWM2 and M0PWM3.

- To enable one of the four events (for countdown mode) or six events (for up-down count mode) mentioned earlier to generate interrupts or triggers for ADC modules, we can use register PWM*n*_*m*_INTEN_R, where $n = 0–1$ and $m = 0–3$. Figure 6.15 shows the bit fields of register PWM0_0_INTEN_R. The names of the bits are self explained. For example, bit 1 of this register enables a raw interrupt when the counter's value is equal to the load value or bit 12, when set, generates an ADC trigger pulse when the counter matches the value of the Comparator B while the counter is counting up.
- Register PWM*n*_*m*_RIS_R ($n = 0–1$, $m = 0–3$) can be used to check the raw status of a PWM interrupt. For example, bit 0 (INTCNTZERO) of register PWM0_0_RIS_R shows the status of the counter-equal-to-zero interrupt event of module PWM0 Generator 0. Register PWM0_0_RIS_R has six status bits matching those six least significant enable bits of register PWM0_0_INTEN_R.

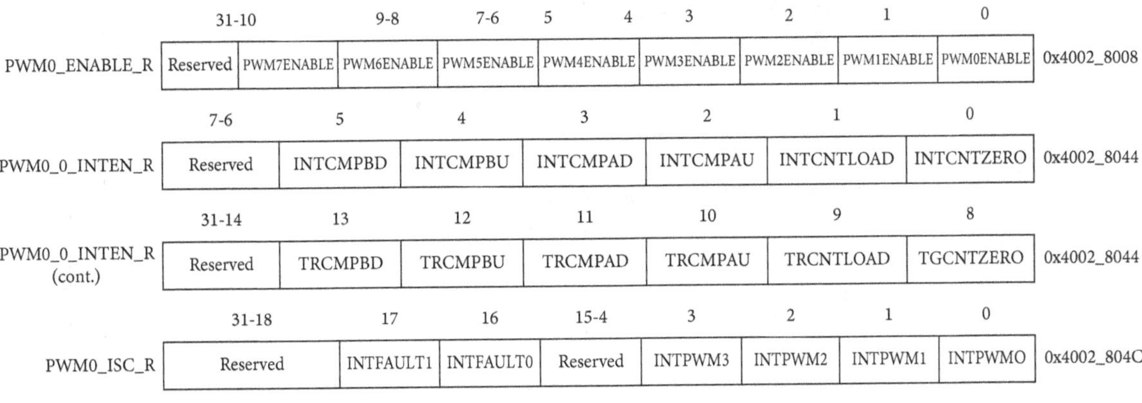

	31-10	9-8	7-6	5	4	3	2	1	0	
PWM0_ENABLE_R	Reserved	PWM7ENABLE	PWM6ENABLE	PWM5ENABLE	PWM4ENABLE	PWM3ENABLE	PWM2ENABLE	PWM1ENABLE	PWM0ENABLE	0x4002_8008

	7-6	5	4	3	2	1	0	
PWM0_0_INTEN_R	Reserved	INTCMPBD	INTCMPBU	INTCMPAD	INTCMPAU	INTCNTLOAD	INTCNTZERO	0x4002_8044

	31-14	13	12	11	10	9	8	
PWM0_0_INTEN_R (cont.)	Reserved	TRCMPBD	TRCMPBU	TRCMPAD	TRCMPAU	TRCNTLOAD	TGCNTZERO	0x4002_8044

	31-18	17	16	15-4	3	2	1	0	
PWM0_ISC_R	Reserved	INTFAULT1	INTFAULT0	Reserved	INTPWM3	INTPWM2	INTPWM1	INTPWM0	0x4002_804C

FIGURE 6.15 More Registers of Module PWM0 Generator 0.

- Register PWMn_ISCR_R (n=0–1), is used to clear a PWM interrupt.
- To clear an interrupt, write "1" to the corresponding bit. For instance, to clear Comparator B down interrupt, write "1" to bit 5.
- A dead-man generator is used to generate nonoverlapping signal pwmA and pwmB from signal pwmA to prevent a shoot-through current in an H-bridge circuit, avoiding damaging the motor under control, as shown in Figure 6.16.
- The PWM generators can operate independently with other generators in an unsynchronized mode, or they can be used in a synchronized mode with other generators.
- The following are some example codes using PWM modules.

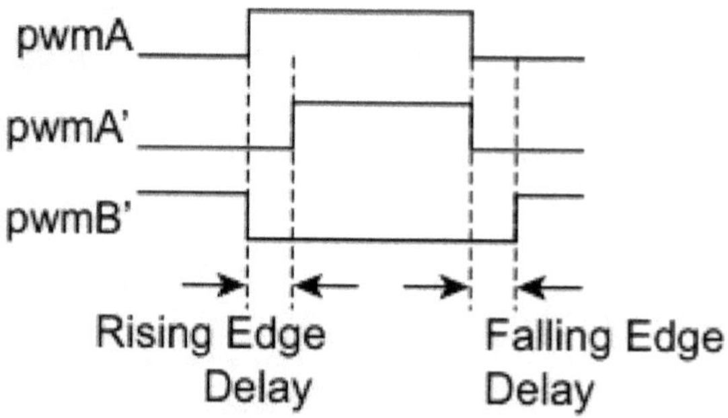

FIGURE 6.16 Dead-Man Generator.

6.1. Creating a PWM Signal Using Either Count-Up/Down or Countdown Mode

1. Countdown mode using Comparator A: we want to generate a PWM signal with a frequency of 1 KHz and a duty cycle of 25 percent. The microcontroller is running at the system clock's frequency default value of 16 MHz (period = 62.5 ns). One period of the PWM clock is 1/1 KHz = 1ms, and it needs to run this many clock ticks (1ms/62.5ns = 16,000) to finish a period. Since the PWM is running in countdown mode, the load number to pack into register PWM0_0_GENA_R is 16,000 ticks (the counter runs from 15,999 (16,000 – 1) down to 0 to finish a PWM period). We'll use Comparator A to set pwmA (pwmA when enabled is connected to Pin M0PWM0 or Pin 6 of Port B) high when the counter matches Comparator A's value and set pwmA low when the counter reaches zero so that the number for Comparator A's value is 0.25*16,000 = 4,000.

```
int main(void){

        PWM0_Init(16000, 4000, 0);

        while(1){ }

}
```

Program 6.11: Creating PWM Signal Using either Count-Up/Down or Countdown Mode

Figure 6.17 illustrates the generation of signal pwmA in the countdown mode. Signal pwmA goes high when the counter counts down, matching the Comparator A's value, and it goes low when the count reaches zero.

2. Count-up/-down mode and using Comparator A. We want to generate a PWM signal with a frequency of 1 KHz and a duty cycle of 25 percent. The microcontroller is running at the system clock's frequency default value of 16 MHz (period = 62.5 ns). One period of the PWM clock is 1/1 KHz = 1 ms, and it needs to run this many clock ticks (1 ms/62.5 ns = 16,000) to finish a period. Since the PWM is running in count-up/-down mode, the reload number to load into register PWM0_0_GENA_R is 16,000/2 = 8,000 ticks (the counter runs from 0 to 8,000 and then from 8,000 down to 0 to finish a PWM period). We'll use Comparator A to set pwmA high on the way up and low on the way down so that the number for Comparator A's value is (100 – 25)*8,000 = 6,000.

```
int main(void){

        PWM0_Init(8000, 6000, 1);

        while(1){ }

        }
```

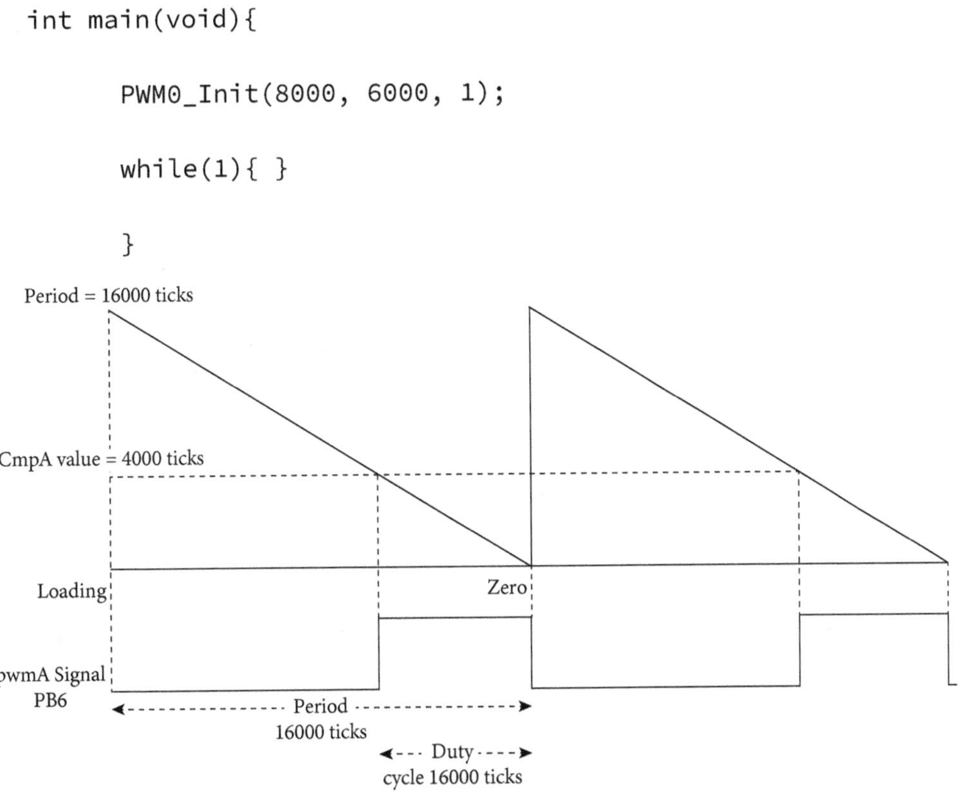

FIGURE 6.17 Countdown Mode of Signal PB6 Generation from the Previous Example.

Figure 6.18 shows how signal PB6 (pwmA) is generated in the count-up/-down mode. Signal pwmA is asserted high when the counter counts up and matches Comaparator A's value (6,000 ticks), and it's asserted low when the counter counts down and matches Comparator A's value.

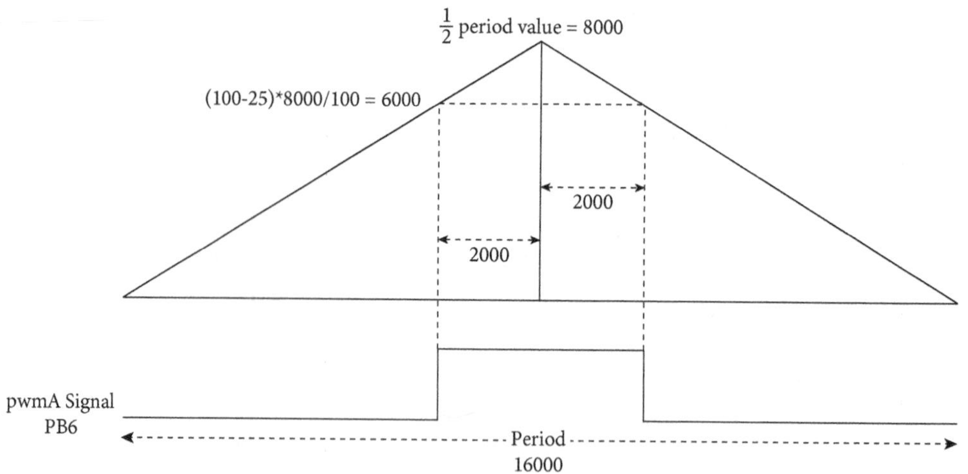

FIGURE 6.18 Count-Up/-Down Mode of Signal PB6 Generation from the Previous Example.

In this example, we only use Comparator A to generate signal pwmA. Of course, Comparator B can also be used alone or with Comparator A to create the PWM signals.

We can also change the PWM input clock to keep the period value within 16-bit range of the PWM modules if necessary. For example, instead of using the 80-MHz system clock, we can use a divide-by-four PWM input clock of 20 MHz (80 MHz/4) by using the following instructions:

```
SYSCTL_RCC_R |= SYSCTL_RCC_USEPWMDIV;    //Use a divided PWM
input clock

        SYSCTL_RCC_R &=  ~(SYSCTL_RCC_PWMDIV_M);  //Clear the
        PWM divider bit field

        SYSCTL_RCC_R |=  SYSCTL_RCC_PWMDIV_4;    // Update the
        PWM divider bit field

// Prog-6-12

//Modified from one of Valvano's programs

// Runs on TM4C123

// Use PWM0A/PB6 to generate PWM signal output.


/*
```

```
Copyright 2015 by Jonathan W. Valvano, valvano@mail.utexas.
edu

      You may use, edit, run or distribute this file

      as long as the above copyright notice remains

THIS SOFTWARE IS PROVIDED "AS IS". NO WARRANTIES, WHETHER
EXPRESS, IMPLIED

OR STATUTORY, INCLUDING, BUT NOT LIMITED TO, IMPLIED WARRAN-
TIES OF

MERCHANTABILITY AND FITNESS FOR A PARTICULAR PURPOSE APPLY TO
THIS SOFTWARE.

VALVANO SHALL NOT, IN ANY CIRCUMSTANCES, BE LIABLE FOR SPE-
CIAL, INCIDENTAL,

OR CONSEQUENTIAL DAMAGES, FOR ANY REASON WHATSOEVER.

For more information about my classes, my research, and my
books, see

http://users.ece.utexas.edu/~valvano/

*/

#include <stdint.h>

#include "tm4c123gh6pm.h"

void PWM0_Init(uint16_t period, uint16_t duty,
uint8_t updown);

void PWM0Generator0_Handler(void);

void  EnableInterrupts(void);

void  DisableInterrupts(void);


// change duty cycle of PB6

// duty is number of PWM clock cycles output is high
```

```
int main(void){

        //To use the Up-Down counting mode

        //clock period = 1/16MHz = 62.5ns, PWM clock freq
= 1KHz -> it takes 1ms/62.5ns = 16000 system clocks for 1
period of the PWM clock

        //This is up-down counting so period = 16000/2 = 8000

        // -> period = 8000. 25%duty cycle = (100-25%)*8000=
6000 since PWM signal goes high on cmpA up and goes down on
cmpA down

        //PWM0_Init(8000, 6000, 1);          //Up-down count-
ing, duty cycle = 25%

        //To use the Down counting mode

        //clock period = 1/16MHz = 62.5ns, PWM clock freq
= 1KHz -> it takes 1ms/62.5ns = 16000 system clocks for 1
period of the PWM clock

        // -> period = 16000. 75%duty cycle = 75%*16000= 12000

PWM0_Init(8000, 4000, 1);          //Up-down counting mode,
duty cycle = 50%

//PWM0_Init(8000, 6000, 1);        //Up-down counting mode,
duty cycle = 25%

        //PWM0_Init(16000, 4000, 0);         //Down counting
mode, duty cycle = 25%

        //PWM0_Init(16000, 12000, 0);        //Down counting
mode, duty cycle = 75%

//PWM0_Init(16000, 8000, 0);       //Down counting mode,
duty cycle = 50%

        EnableInterrupts();

while(1) {

}

}
```

```
// Output on PB6/M0PWM0

void PWM0_Init(uint16_t period, uint16_t duty,
uint8_t updown){

        //Activate PWM0

SYSCTL_RCGCPWM_R |= 0x01;

        //Activate port B and port F

SYSCTL_RCGCGPIO_R |= 0x22;

//Wait for the clock to port F and port B to be stable

while((SYSCTL_PRGPIO_R&0x22) == 0){};

        //Enable alt funct on PB6

GPIO_PORTB_AFSEL_R |= 0x40;

        //Configure PB6 as M0PWM2(PWM module 0, Generator 2)

GPIO_PORTB_PCTL_R &= ~0x0F000000;

GPIO_PORTB_PCTL_R |= 0x04000000;

        //Disable PB6 's ananlog function

GPIO_PORTB_AMSEL_R &= ~0x40;

        //Make PB6 a digital signal

GPIO_PORTB_DIR_R |= 0x40;

        //Make PB6 an out signal

GPIO_PORTB_DEN_R |= 0x40;

//Disable alt function on PF1

GPIO_PORTF_AFSEL_R &= ~0x02;

        //Disable alt function mapping on PF1

GPIO_PORTF_PCTL_R &= ~0x000000F0;

        //Disable analog functionality on PF1
```

```
GPIO_PORTF_AMSEL_R &= ~0x02;

      //Make PF1 an output signal

GPIO_PORTF_DIR_R |= 0x02;

//Up-down counting mode

GPIO_PORTF_DEN_R |= 0x02;

//Up-down counting mode

if (updown) {

      //Set PWM Generator 0 mode to Up-down counting mode and
disable the PWM Generator 0.

      //The counter counts up to the load value from 0 and
then from the load value counts down to 0

      //and then repeat.

      PWM0_0_CTL_R = 0x2;

//Pin PB6 is driven high when and after it matches the value
of comparator A while counting up (high on cmpA up)

      //PB6 is driven low on when and after it matches the
value of comapator A when counting down (low on cmpA down)

      PWM0_0_GENA_R = 0xB0;

      }

      //Count-down mode

      else {

            //Set PWM Generator 0 mode to Down counting mode
and diable the PWM Generator 0.

            //The counter counts down from the load value to
0 and then wraps back to the load value

            PWM0_0_CTL_R = 0x0;
```

```
//PB6 is driven low from the load value until the counter
matches the value of comparator A.

//Then it's driven high until the counter reaches zero.

            PWM0_0_GENA_R = 0xC2;

      }

//Load value for the PWM counter

PWM0_0_LOAD_R = period - 1;

//Value loaded to comparator A to be used to compare with the
PWM counter to generate signal cmpA

PWM0_0_CMPA_R = duty - 1;

      PWM0_INTEN_R = 0x01;

      if (updown) {

      PWM0_0_CTL_R |= 0x00000003;     // start PWM0, updown
counting mode

PWM0_0_INTEN_R = 0x000000002;   //INTCMPADU=1(bit 2)   Enable
PWM0 interrupt on cmpA down

//PWM0_0_INTEN_R = 0x00000000C; //INTCMPAD=1(bit 3), INTCM-
PADU=1(bit 2)      Enable PWM0 interrupt

      }

      else {

                  PWM0_0_CTL_R |= 0x00000001;    //start
PWM0, down counting mode

PWM0_0_INTEN_R = 0x000000009; //INTCMPAD=1(bit 3),
INTCNTZERO=1 (bit0)           Enable PWM0 interrupt

      }
```

```
PWM0_ENABLE_R |= 0x00000001;           // enable PB6/M0PWM0

        //Bit 23-21 of register NVIC_PRI2 set priority for PWM0
Generator 0 interrupt

        NVIC_PRI2_R |= 0x1 << 21; //priority 1

        //Bit 10 to enable PWM0 Generator 0 interrupt

        NVIC_EN0_R |= 0x01 << 10;

}


//Interrupt Service Handler (ISR) of PWM0 Generator 0

void PWM0Generator0_Handler (void) {

uint32_t pwm0_stat;

        static uint32_t red_led = 0x0;

        //Get the interrupt flag

pwm0_stat = PWM0_0_RIS_R;

        //Reset the interrupt status

PWM0_0_ISC_R |= pwm0_stat;

        //Flashing the Red LED at 1-Hz rate

        GPIO_PORTF_DATA_R = (red_led == 1000) << 1;

        if (red_led < 1000) {

              red_led = red_led + 1;

        }

        else {red_led = 0x0; }

}
```

Program 6.12: Creating PWM Signal Using either Count-Up/Down or Count-Down Mode

7. SysTick Timer[6]

The SysTick timer is a 24-bit timer running on the system clock. The timer counts down and wraps around to a 24-bit reload value contained in the SysTick reload register. When the timer reaches zero, it will set the count bit (bit 16) in the SysTick control/status register. The bit fields of the SysTick timer registers are shown in Figure 6.20:

- Bit 0 of register NVIC control/status register is to enable ("1") or disable ("0") the SysTick timer. Bit 1 is to enable or disable the SysTick timer interrupt. Bit 2 has to be set to "1" since in the normal operation, the only clock source for the SysTick timer is the system clock. As mentioned earlier, when the timer counts down and reaches zero, bit 16 or the count bit will be set. The bit will be cleared on a read of this register or if the SysTick current register is written with any value.
- The reload register contains the reload value, with which the timer will be reloaded when it reaches zero.
- The SysTick current register contains the current count of the timer. Writing with any value to this register will clear it.

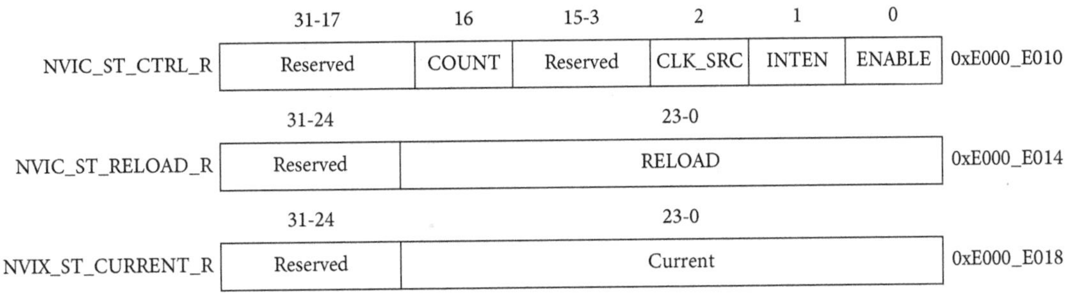

	31-17	16	15-3	2	1	0	
NVIC_ST_CTRL_R	Reserved	COUNT	Reserved	CLK_SRC	INTEN	ENABLE	0xE000_E010

	31-24	23-0	
NVIC_ST_RELOAD_R	Reserved	RELOAD	0xE000_E014

	31-24	23-0	
NVIX_ST_CURRENT_R	Reserved	Current	0xE000_E018

FIGURE 6.19 SysTick Timer Registers.

7.1. Using the SysTick Timer to Create a Delay

The following is an example of using the SysTick timer to delay 0.5 sec.

Assuming we are using the 16 MHz default value of the system clock, which has a period of 62.5 ns, to delay 0.5 seconds, we need 8000,000 clock ticks (8000,000 = 0.05 sec/62.5ns).

```
AREA Ex1, CODE, READONLY, ALIGN=2


GPIO_PORTF_DATA_R  EQU 0x400253FC

GPIO_PORTF_DIR_R   EQU 0x40025400

GPIO_PORTF_AFSEL_R EQU 0x40025420
```

6 Texas Instruments, *Tiva™ TM4C123GH6PM*, 137–41.

```
GPIO_PORTF_PUR_R   EQU 0x40025510

GPIO_PORTF_DEN_R   EQU 0x4002551C

GPIO_PORTF_AMSEL_R EQU 0x40025528

GPIO_PORTF_PCTL_R  EQU 0x4002552C

GPIO_PORTF_LOCK_R  EQU 0x40025520

GPIO_PORTF_CR_R    EQU 0x40025524

GPIO_LOCK_KEY      EQU 0x4C4F434B


NVIC_ST_CTRL_R     EQU 0xE000E010

NVIC_ST_RELOAD_R   EQU 0xE000E014

NVIC_ST_CURRENT_R  EQU 0xE000E018

DELAY             EQU 8000000 ; delay 0.5sec
(=8000,000*1/16MHz)


SYSCTL_RCGCGPIO_R  EQU 0x400FE608

       EXPORT Start

       ENTRY

Start

;Iniyialize port F

       BL Port_Init

;Initialize SysTick Timer

       BL SysTick_Init

;Turn on the Red LED

       LDR R4, = GPIO_PORTF_DATA_R

       MOV R5, #0x2
```

```
        STR R5, [R4]

LoopS

;Call SysTick_Delay with an input paramter of 8,000,000

;or 0.5 sec (=8000000*(1/16MHz))

        LDR R0,=DELAY

        BL SysTick_Delay

;After 0.5 second delay, toggle the red LED and

;repeat the delay

        LDR R4, = GPIO_PORTF_DATA_R

        LDR R5, [R4]

        AND R5, R5, #0x2

        EOR R5, R5, #0x2

        STR R5, [R4]

        B LoopS



SysTick_Init

;Disable the SysTick timer while doing configuration

        LDR R1, =NVIC_ST_CTRL_R

        MOV R0, #0

        STR R0, [R1]

;Load a max delay value into register NVIC_ST_RELOAD_R

        LDR R2, =0xFFFFFF;

        LDR R1, =NVIC_ST_RELOAD_R
```

```
        STR R2, [R1]
; Writing any value to CURRENT clears it
        LDR R1, =NVIC_ST_CURRENT_R
        MOV R0, #0
        STR R0, [R1]            ; clear counter
;Enable the SysTick Timer
        LDR R1, =NVIC_ST_CTRL_R
        MOV R0, #5
        STR R0, [R1]
        BX LR


SysTick_Delay
        SUBS R0, R0, #1
        LDR R1, = NVIC_ST_RELOAD_R
        STR R0, [R1] ; store delay
        LDR R1, = NVIC_ST_CURRENT_R
        STR R0, [R1] ; clear the Current register
Loop
        LDR R1, =  NVIC_ST_CTRL_R
        LDR R2, [R1]
        ANDS R2, R2, #0x010000 ; get the Count flag
        BEQ Loop
        BX LR
```

```
Port_Init

;Enable port F

        LDR R0, =SYSCTL_RCGCGPIO_R

        LDR R1, [R0]

        ORR R1, R1, #0x20

        STR R1, [R0]

;Wait for Port F's clock to be stable

        NOP

        NOP;


; Port F Init, port F pin 1

;Unlock Port F

        LDR R0,=GPIO_PORTF_LOCK_R ; unlock portF

        LDR R1,=0x4C4F434B

        STR R1, [R0]

        LDR R0,=GPIO_PORTF_CR_R

        MOV R1, #0x0F

        STR R1, [R0]

;Make Port F pin 1 an output

        LDR R0,=GPIO_PORTF_DIR_R

        LDR R1, [R0]

        ORR R1, R1, #0x2; output portF pin 1 (Red LED)

        STR R1, [R0]

;Disable analog functionality of PF1
```

```
        LDR R0, =GPIO_PORTF_AMSEL_R
        LDR R1, [R0]
        BIC R1, R1, #0x02
        STR R1, [R0]
;PF1 is a digital pin
        LDR R0, =GPIO_PORTF_DEN_R
        LDR R1, [R0]
        ORR R1, R1, #0x02
        STR R1, [R0]
;Turn off alternate function of PF1
        LDR R0, =GPIO_PORTF_AFSEL_R
        LDR R1, [R0]
        BIC R1, R1, #0x02
        STR R1, [R0]
;Turn off alternate function mapping of PF1
        LDR R0, =GPIO_PORTF_PCTL_R
        LDR R1, [R0]
        LDR R2, =0xFFFFFF0F
        AND R1, R1, R2;
        STR R1, [R0]
        BX LR

        ALIGN
        END
```

Program 6.13: Using SysTick Timer to Create a Delay

7.2. Using SysTick Timer to Create a Square Wave

The following program should be run with file Startup.s. It generate a 1-Hz square wave at PF1 using SysTick Timer interrupts

```
;Creating a 1-Hz square wave at PF1

        AREA Block1, DATA, READWRITE, ALIGN=2

cnt  DCD 0x0

        AREA Ex1, CODE, READONLY, ALIGN=2


NVIC_ST_CTRL_R      EQU 0xE000E010

NVIC_ST_RELOAD_R    EQU 0xE000E014

NVIC_ST_CURRENT_R   EQU 0xE000E018

NVIC_SYS_PRI3_R     EQU 0xE000ED20  ; Sys. Handlers 12 to 15
Priority


GPIO_PORTF_LOCK_R   EQU 0x40025520

GPIO_PORTF_CR_R     EQU 0x40025524

GPIO_PORTF_AMSEL_R  EQU 0x40025528

GPIO_PORTF_PCTL_R   EQU 0x4002552C

GPIO_LOCK_KEY       EQU 0x4C4F434B

GPIO_PORTF_DATA_R   EQU 0x400253FC

GPIO_PORTF_DIR_R    EQU 0x40025400

GPIO_PORTF_AFSEL_R  EQU 0x40025420

GPIO_PORTF_PUR_R    EQU 0x40025510

GPIO_PORTF_DEN_R    EQU 0x4002551C

DELAY               EQU 8000000 ; delay 0.5sec
(=8000,000*1/16MHz)
```

```
SYSCTL_RCGCGPIO_R  EQU 0x400FE608


        EXPORT Start

        EXPORT SysTick_Handler

        ENTRY

Start

;Initialize PF1

        BL Port_Init

;Initialize SysTick Timer

;Reload value = DELAY = 8000000 (=0.5 second delay)

        LDR R0,=DELAY

        BL SysTick_Init

LoopS

        B LoopS


;SysTick ISR

SysTick_Handler

;Toggle PF1 (flashing red LED at 1 Hz)

        LDR R4, = GPIO_PORTF_DATA_R

        LDR R5, [R4]

        AND R5, R5, #0x2

        EOR R5, R5, #0x2

        STR R5, [R4]

;Keep counting the number of SysTick interrupts

        LDR R0, =cnt
```

```
        LDR R1, [R0]

        ADD R1, R1, #1

        STR R1, [R0]

        BX LR


SysTick_Init

; Disable the global interrupt

        MOV R3, #1

        MSR    PRIMASK, R3

        ;CPSID  I                         ; mask all
(except faults)

        MOV R1, #1

        MSR    PRIMASK, R1

        LDR R1, =NVIC_ST_CTRL_R

        MOV R2, #0

        STR R2, [R1]

;Load the delay value into register NVIC_ST_RELOAD_R

        MOV R2, R0

        LDR R1, =NVIC_ST_RELOAD_R

        STR R2, [R1]

; Writing any value to CURRENT clears it

        LDR R1, =NVIC_ST_CURRENT_R

        STR R2, [R1]              ; clear counter

        ; set NVIC system interrupt 15 to priority 2

        LDR R1, =NVIC_SYS_PRI3_R

        LDR R2, [R1]
```

```
        AND R2, R2, #0x0FFFFFFF         ; R2 = R2&0x00FFFFFF
(clear interrupt 15 priority)

        ORR R2, R2, #0x40000000         ; R2 = R2|0x40000000
(interrupt 15's priority is in bits 31-29)

        STR R2, [R1]                    ; set SysTick to prior-
ity 2


        LDR R1, =NVIC_ST_CTRL_R

        MOV R0, #7

        STR R0, [R1]

; Enable the global interrupt

        MOV R3, #0

        MSR    PRIMASK, R3

        BX LR


Port_Init

;Enable port F

        LDR R0, =SYSCTL_RCGCGPIO_R

        LDR R1, [R0]

        ORR R1, R1, #0x20

        STR R1, [R0]

;Wait for Port F's clock to be stable

        NOP

        NOP;

;Unlock Port F
```

```
    LDR R0,=GPIO_PORTF_LOCK_R ; unlock portF
    LDR R1,=0x4C4F434B
    STR R1, [R0]
    LDR R0,=GPIO_PORTF_CR_R
    MOV R1, #0x0F
    STR R1, [R0]
;Make Port F pin 1 an output
    LDR R0,=GPIO_PORTF_DIR_R
    LDR R1, [R0]
    ORR R1, R1, #0x2; output portF pin 1 (Red LED)
    STR R1, [R0]
;Disable analog functionality of PF1
    LDR R0, =GPIO_PORTF_AMSEL_R
    LDR R1, [R0]
    BIC R1, R1, #0x02
    STR R1, [R0]
;PF1 is a digital pin
    LDR R0, =GPIO_PORTF_DEN_R
    LDR R1, [R0]
    ORR R1, R1, #0x02
    STR R1, [R0]
;Turn off alternate function of PF1
    LDR R0, =GPIO_PORTF_AFSEL_R
    LDR R1, [R0]
```

```
        BIC R1, R1, #0x02
        STR R1, [R0]
;Turn off alternate function mapping of PF1
        LDR R0, =GPIO_PORTF_PCTL_R
        LDR R1, [R0]
        LDR R2, =0xFFFFFF0F
        AND R1, R1, R2;
        STR R1, [R0]
        BX LR

        ALIGN
        END
```

Program 6.14: Using SysTick Timer to Create a 1-Hz Square Wave

7.3. C-based Program to Create a Square Wave Using SysTick Timer

```
#include <stdint.h>
#include "tm4c123gh6pm.h"

void DisableInterrupts(void);
void EnableInterrupts(void);
void SysTick_Init(uint32_t );
void GPIO_init(void);
void SysTick_Handler(void);
uint32_t reg_val;
//System clock's default frequency is 16 MHz
```

```
//Use SysTick to create a 1-Hz periodic waveform output on
PF2

//delay = 1/2 of 1-Hz period = 0.5 second = (0.5)/
(1/16000000) = 8000000

int main(void){

GPIO_init();

SysTick_Init(8000000);

while(1){

}

}

void SysTick_Init(uint32_t delay){

//Disable the global interrupt while configuring the SysTick
Timer

DisableInterrupts();

//Disable the SysTick Timer

NVIC_ST_CTRL_R = 0;

//Load reload value into the Reload register

NVIC_ST_RELOAD_R = delay - 1;

//Clear the Current Value register so the SysTick timer can
start counting from 0

NVIC_ST_CURRENT_R = 0;

//Enable the SysTick Timer, SysTick interrupt and select the
System Clock as SysTick clock source

NVIC_ST_CTRL_R = 0x7;

//Set the SysTick priority to 2 (bit 31-29 of
register NVIC_SYS_PRI3)

NVIC_SYS_PRI3_R |= 0x2 << 29; //priority 2
```

```
//Enable the global interrupt
EnableInterrupts();

}
void GPIO_init(void) {
int delay1;
SYSCTL_RCGCGPIO_R |= 0x20;  // activate port F and port B
delay1 = SYSCTL_RCGCGPIO_R;
//Configure port F pin 2 (blue LED)
//Make PF2 output (PF2 built-in LED)
GPIO_PORTF_DIR_R |= 0x04;
//Disable alt funct on PF2
GPIO_PORTF_AFSEL_R &= ~0x04;
//Enable digital functionality on PF2
GPIO_PORTF_DEN_R |= 0x04;
//Reset PCTL mapping register on PF2
GPIO_PORTF_PCTL_R &= ~0x00000F00;
//Disable analog functionality on PF2
GPIO_PORTF_AMSEL_R &= ~0x04;

}

void SysTick_Handler(void) {
static uint8_t tp = 0x04;
```

```
//reset the Count Flag status bit
reg_val = NVIC_ST_CTRL_R;
//Flashing PF2 at 1 Hz rate
GPIO_PORTF_DATA_R = tp & 0x04;
if (tp == 0x04) {tp = 0x0;}
else {tp = 0x04;}
}
```

Program 6.15: C-based Program Using SysTick Timer to Create a Square Wave

EXERCISES

1. Write an assembly program to configure Port F Pin 4 and 0 as inputs and Port F Pins 3–1 as outputs. Hint: unlock port F before using it.
2. Write an assembly program to configure Port C Pins 3–0 as inputs and Pins 7–4 as outputs.
3. Configure Port A Pins 6 and 7 to map to the I2C module Pins I2C1SCL and I2C1DA.
4. Write an assembly program to configure Port C Pin 4 to map to Pin M0PWM6 (PWM6 module 0).
5. Write a C program to configure Port B Pins 4–7 to map to the SSI module 2 Pins SSI2Clk, SSI2Fss, SSI2Rx, and SSI2Tx, respectively.
6. Write a C program to configure Port E Pin 4 to be an analog Channel 9 (AIN9).
7. Use the AMR assembly to write a program to set up the system clock to be 80, 50, 40, or 16 MHz, respectively.
8. Using a variable 3V DC power supply, connect it to an analog input of the Tiva C. Write a C program to convert the analog voltage to a digital number any time you press Switch SW1. You need to configure pins to interface the analog signal and Switch SW1. Write a version using software to trigger an ADC conversion and another version using a timer.

9. Write a C program to interface with an infrared distance sensor for measuring distance. Connect the sensor to an analog input pin on the ARM. Demonstrate functions that show proper operation of the sensors, including the ability to read the current distance.

10. Write a C program to generate a PWM signal with a frequency of 1 KHz and a duty cycle of 75 percent. Use the default system clock of 16 MHz, module PWM0, and Generator 0, and try with both count-up/down and countdown modes.

11. Write a C program to set up the system clock to be at the maximum value of 80 MHz to generate a PWM signal with a frequency of 1 KHz and a duty cycle of 25 percent. Use the module PWM0 Generator 0 and try with both count-up/-down and countdown modes.

12. Using the PLL frequency of 400 MHz, write a C program to set up the system clock to be at 50 MHz to generate a PWM signal with a frequency of 2 KHz and a duty cycle of 50 percent. Use the module PWM0 Generator 0 and try with both count-up/-down and countdown modes.

13. Using the PLL frequency of 200 MHz, write a C program to set up the system clock to be at 40 MHz to generate a PWM signal with a frequency of 4 KHz and a duty cycle of 75 percent. Use the module PWM0 Generator 0 and try with both count-up/-down and countdown modes.

14. Using the PLL frequency of 400 MHz, write a C program to set up the system clock to be at 40 MHz to generate a PWM signal with a frequency of 4 KHz and a duty cycle of 75 percent. Use the one-half PWM clock (PWM input clock's frequency is equal to one-half the system clock's), the module PWM3 Generator 0, and try with both count-up/-down and countdown modes.

15. Using the PLL frequency of 200 MHz, write a C program to set up the system clock to be at 20 MHz to generate a PWM signal with a frequency of 1 KHz and a duty cycle of 45 percent. Use the module PWM0 Generator 0 and try with both count-up/-down and countdown modes.

16. Write a device driver to use PWM signals to control the speed of a motor.

17. Write a C program to generate a PWM signal with a frequency of 5 KHz and a duty cycle of 25 percent. Use module PWM1 Generator 2 and try with both count-up/-down and countdown modes.

18. Write an ISR for Port F and configure Port F Pin 4 as input and Port F Pin 3-1 as outputs. Any time Switch SW1 is pressed, rotate blinking the LEDs from red to blue to green.

19. Write a C program using the SysTick timer interrupt to create a 10-KHz square wave output on Port B Pin 6.

20. Use Timer 1A to create a delay of 1 second assuming your Tiva C is running at a default frequency of 16MHz.

Credits

Chapter 7

Interrupts and Exceptions

1. Introduction

In general, a computer program is composed of a sequence of instructions, which is executed in series. However, to synchronize between the program execution and external hardware events, the flow of the program sequence needs to be interrupted either because of a certain event happening, or by being put into a waiting loop until a peripheral device responds. This synchronization happens quite frequently in embedded systems, where the software often interacts with the hardware-like input or output devices. For example, when a program needs to read data from an input device such as a temperature sensor, it can check the status of the sensor and loop itself while waiting for the sensor to respond. This scenario is called a busy wait or polling synchronization scheme. This is easy and simple to code, but during the time the processor is waiting, nothing productive happens. To avoid wasting time, a processor can continue executing its program, but it only pauses when being interrupted by a hardware event. Continuing with the previous example, instead of repeatedly polling the status register to check on whether the temperature sensor has data or not, the processor can keep on executing its program doing other things like calculations, and the like, and when the temperature data is available, an interrupt can happen, alerting the processor so that it can stop what it is doing to read the temperature data. After servicing the temperature sensor, the processor can return to the place in the program right after where it is interrupted.

2. ARM Interrupts and Exceptions

There are a couple of ways to configure ARM interrupts. The first way is to directly read and write to interrupts supporting registers, such as the NVIC registers. The second way is to use supporting libraries from the TI Tivaware Peripheral Library or Keil RTX Middleware CMSIS Core Library to configure the registers.

For an interrupt to happen, all of the following conditions must be met:

- The local enable bit of the source of the interrupt is set.
- The interrupt priority level must be lower than the interrupt level set in register BASEPRI. However, if register BASEPRI is set to zero, all interrupts are allowed to happen.

- The hardware associated with the interrupt happens, and that triggers the specific source interrupt flag.
- The global interrupt enable must be set (i.e., register PRIMASK bit 0 must be set to zero).
- When an interrupt happens, the following sequence of events will occur (Figure 7.1):
  - The current instruction completes.
  - The CPU execution is suspended and eight registers—R0–R3, R12, R14(LR), R15(PC), and PSR—are pushed onto the stack.
  - The Link Register (LR) is set to 0xFFFFFFF9.
  - IPSR is set to the interrupt number of the interrupting source.
  - PC is set to the ISR (interrupt service routine) starting address.
  - The ISR is executed.
  - The ISR clears the interrupt flag to acknowledge the interrupt and to avoid repeated interrupts except in the case of a SysTick interrupt since the system will automatically clear it.
  - It performs its intended functions.
  - It communicates with other threads or main programs through global variables.
  - The ISR is completed by executing BX LR.
  - The CPU pops eight registers from the stack and resumes executing the main program or whatever thread that was interrupted.

When the processor is executing an ISR, what will happen if another interrupt request comes along? If the new interrupt request is of a lower priority level than the current executing ISR, it will be ignored, but if the new request has a higher priority level, the system will pause the current ISR, and after all the proper registers have been pushed onto the stack, the system will let the new interrupt request start its ISR. This process is called interrupt nesting. ARM also supports a feature called tail chaining when there is back-to-back interrupt processing. The processor avoids the pop and then push of eight registers when exiting the current ISR to enter the next ISR since it will not affect the contents of the stack memory. Therefore, it saves the time consumed in pushing and popping eight registers when the system transitions from executing one ISR to another.

2.1 Interrupts and Exceptions in the ARM System

There can be three types of interrupts[1]: (1) internal interrupts, (2) external interrupts, and (3) software interrupts.

- Internal interrupts: Also called exceptions, these are synchronous events created by the processor when it encounters some abnormal conditions during its execution of instructions. For example, a divide by zero instruction can cause an exception.

---

1 Xiaocong Fan, *Real-time Embedded Systems: Design Principles and Engineering Practices* (Amsterdam: Elsevier, 2015), 86.

- External interrupts: Also called hardware interrupts, these are asynchronous events generated by peripheral devices to alert the microprocessor to a hardware's status change. For instance, a UART receiver that just receives a character can cause a UART interrupt if its interrupt registers are properly programmed.
- Software interrupts: Also called traps, these are synchronous events generated by special processor instructions.

2.2 ARM Cortex-M4 Interrupts and Exceptions

Inside the ARM Cortex-M4, there is a unit called a nested vectored interrupt controller (NVIC), which is used to control and process all maskable interrupts and exceptions. When an interrupt or exception happens, the NVIC executes the following sequence:

- An interrupt request is sent to the Cortex-M4 CPU.
- Depending on the content of the mask register PRIMASK and the interrupt priority level register BASEPRI, the interrupt will be processed or not. For every exception and interrupts to be enabled, the values of these registers must be zero.
- When the interrupt request is accepted to be processed, the related hardware module will provide the interrupt source number and the ISR entry address in a vector table.
- All other interrupts or exceptions are disabled while several registers, such as registers R0–R3, R12, Link Register (LR), PC, and the condition register (PSR), are pushed into the stack so that they can be restored later when the ISR is returned.
- The control will be given to the entry address of the ISR stored in the vector table. During this process, all other interrupts and exceptions are enabled to allow higher-level priority interrupts or exceptions to respond.
- When the ISR completes, all the previously saved registers (R0–R3, R12, LR, PC, and PSR) will be restored before control is returned to the main program to continue where it left off. All the interrupts and exceptions are enabled since they were accepted and processed in the previous step.

Figure 7.1 shows the interrupt sequence of events of a GPIO Port C interrupt.

The difference between an exception and an interrupt as an exception is generated by an event in the CPU, such as a system fault, while an interrupt is usually caused by an internal or external hardware module, such as a UART or a timer. In addition, an exception often has a higher priority than an interrupt. After an ISR completes, the system returns where it left off, but the program that causes an exception usually does not resume normally.[2]

2 Edward Ashford Lee and Sanjit Arunkumar Seshia, *Introduction to Embedded Systems—A Cyber-Physical Systems Approach* (Morrisville, NC: Lulu Press, 2013), 273.

PRIMASK 0
IPSR 0
BASEPRI 0
Before interrupt
Stack
During interrupt
PRIMASK 0
IPSR 18
BASEPRI 0
When the GPIO Port C interrupt happens, a context switch takes place:
1. Finish current instruction
2. PC is set to vector address 0x00000048 (which contains the starting address of the Port C ISR)
3. IPSR set to 18 (decimal) which is GPIO Port C interrupt number.
4. Registers R0-R3, R12, LR, PC and PSR are pushed on the stack. MSP is the stack pointer
5. LR set to 0xFFFFFFF9
6. Start executing the ISR program. When finishing the ISR, the processor restores registers R0-R3, R12, LR, PC, PSR. Return using the saved PC.
After interrupt
Old R0
Old R1
Old R2
Old R3
Old R12
Old LR
Old PC
Old PSR
Stack

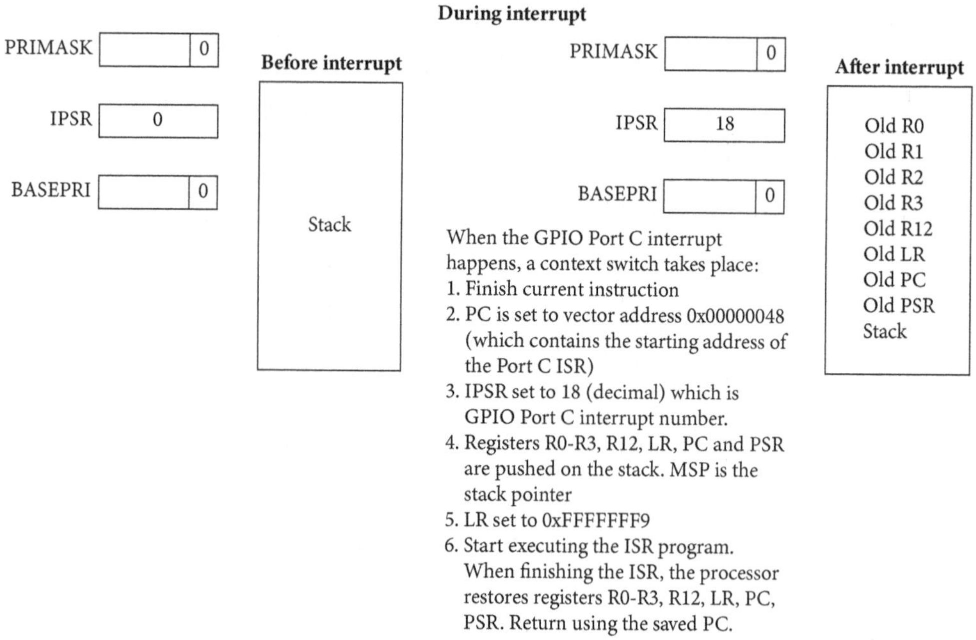

FIGURE 7.1 GPIO Port C Interrupt Sequences.

In the following example, we examine a GPIO Port F interrupt that happens due to either switch SW1 or SW2 being pressed. We will see how the registers are saved and later restored and we also discuss how the interrupt returns after the interrupt service routine of port F completes. Listing of this program is at the end of the chapter.

As we know, switch SW1 is connected to Port F pin 4, and switch SW2 is connected to Port F pin 0. Any time either switch SW1 or SW2 is pressed, a Port F falling edge interrupt happens. Inspecting Figure 7.2, we observe that the system is interrupted when executing the assembly code at address 0x000002A0 (or line 45 of the C program). The system will complete the current instruction, save registers R0–R3, R12, LR, PC, and the PSR before transitioning to the GPIOPortF_Handler program (PortF ISR). One way to confirm this observation is to look at the values of register R4, R5, and R6. Register R5 (current value = 0x12) is supposed to be updated to be 1 more than register R4 (current value = 0x11) and it is. That means the machine code at address 0x000002A0 (or line 46 of the assembly program) is completed. Meanwhile, the current value of register R6, 0x0C, is not equal to the current value of register R5 (0x12) plus 1. That means the machine code at address 0x000002A4 (or line 47 of the assembly program) is not executed yet. Another observation is that in the Disassembly windows of Figure 7.2, Keil highlights the most recently completed assembly instruction at address 0x000002A0 before going to a break point on the GPIOPortF_Handler program.

When the interrupt happens, the system saves registers R0–R3, R12, R14 (Link Register), R15 (PC), and the PSR in the stack memory. Figure 7.3 shows where the aforementioned registers are in the stack memory (they are saved in little endian format). Using the value of the Stack Pointer register, 0x200003E8, in Figure 7.2, we can find the values of register R0–R3,

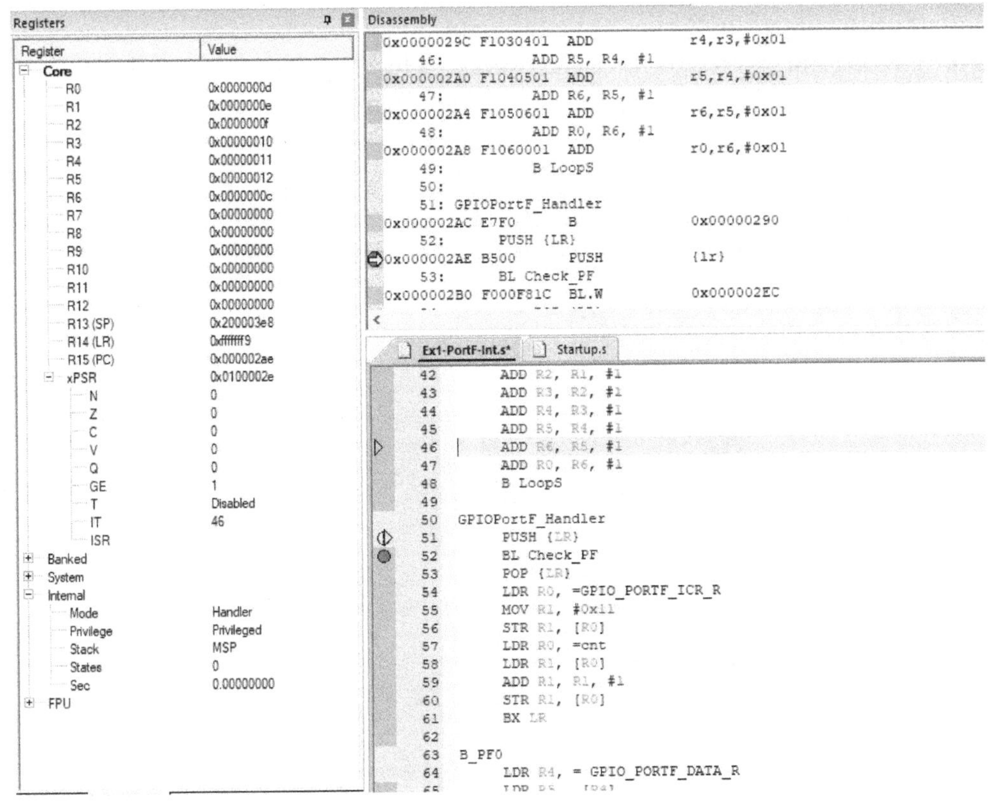

FIGURE 7.2 GPIO PortF Interrupt.

R12, LR, PC, and PSR as shown in Figure 7.3. The value of the PC register is 0x02A4 that corresponds to line 47 of the assembly program. This is the address of the next instruction to be executed when the system returns from the interrupt. In the lower left corner of Figure 7.2, you notice that the Internal Mode is Handler, the processor is in Privileged mode, and the Stack being used is MSP (instead of PSP). The microcontroller enters the Handler mode to process the interrupt and when it finishes, it should return to the Thread mode. You can also observe that the interrupt number is 46 and that corresponds to a Port F interrupt (see Figure 7.2 above).

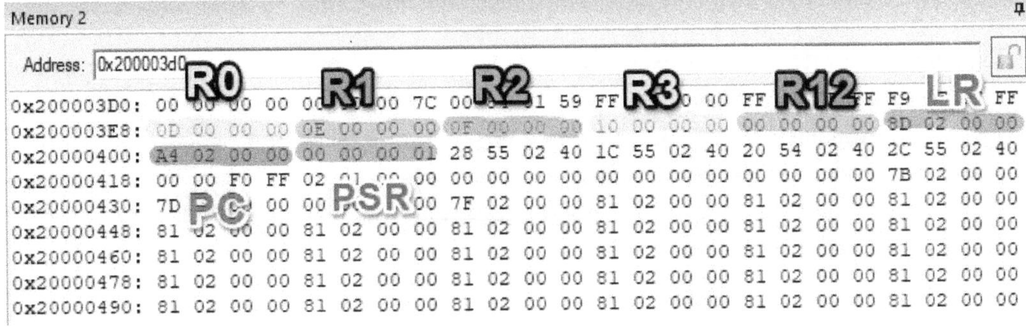

FIGURE 7.3 The System Stack during the Interrupt.

Once the program GPIOPortF_Handler completes, as shown in Figure 7.4, the system returns from the interrupt to the location pointed to by the PC register saved in the Stack memory, which is address 0x02A4 (line 53 of the assembly program). The yellow Keil-highlighted line of the Disassembly windows in Figure 7.4 is where the system returns to after the interrupt service routine of the GPIO Port F completes. You can notice in the left panel of Figure 7.4, there is no interrupt number since the microcontroller already exits the interrupt state and the internal Mode is now Thread mode instead of the Handler mode as shown in Figure 7.2.

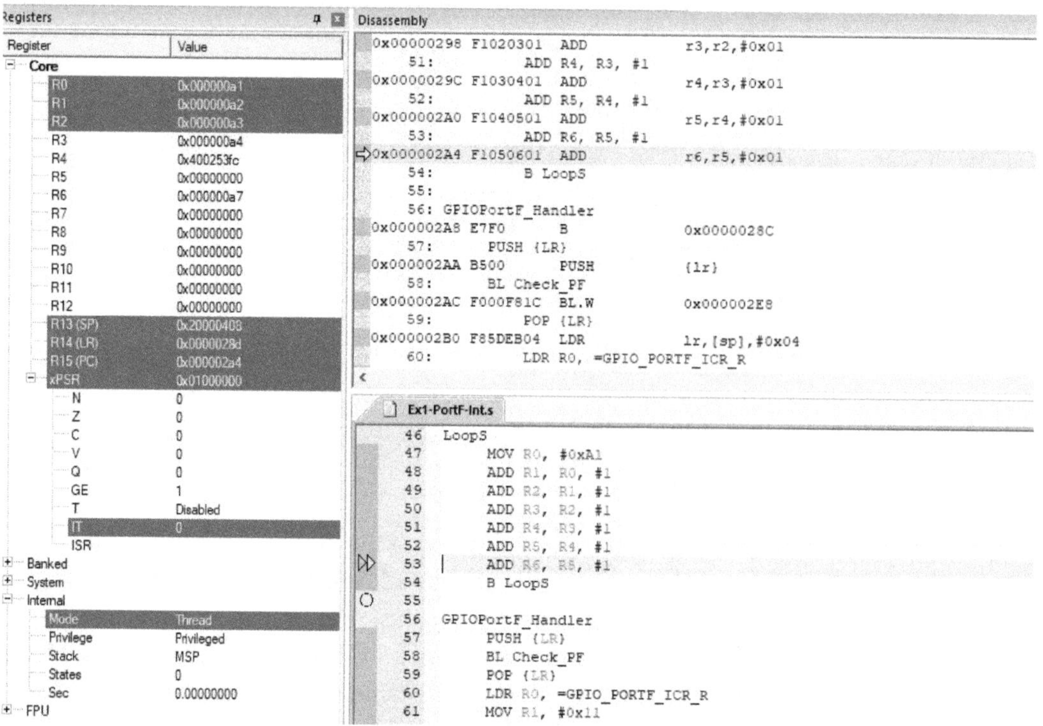

FIGURE 7.4 The System Status after Returning from the Interrupt.

The priorities of the exceptions, such as Reset, NMI, and Hard Fault, have priorities of negative values (i.e., they cannot be blocked by register BASEPRI). Table 7.1 lists the most popular exceptions and interrupts with their descriptions, priority levels, and types. For example, the SysTick Timer has a programmable priority level while Reset, NMI, and Hard Fault have the highest priorities and they cannot be masked.

TABLE 7.1 **INTERRUPT/EXCEPTION PRIORITY**[3]

Exception Number	Exception Type	Priority Level	Description
1	Reset	−3 (Highest)	Reset
2	NMI	−2	Non-Maskable Interrupt
3	Hard Fault	−1	Hardware Related Fault
4	Memory Manage Fault	Programmable	Memory Management Fault. MPU violations or program address faults
5	Bus Fault	Programmable	Bus Error
6	Usage Fault	Programmable	Program Error
7–10	Reserved	N/A	—
11	SVC	Programmable	Supervisor Call
12	Debug Monitor	Programmable	Debug related exceptions, such as breakpoints
13	Reserved	N A	—
14	PendSV	Programmable	Pendable Service Call
15	SYSTICK	Programmable	System Tick Timer
16	interrupt 0	Programmable	These interrupts can be generated by on-chip internal peripherals or external peripherals
17	Interrupt 1	Programmable	
18	Interrupt 3	Programmable	
...	...	...	
240	Interrupt 239	Programmable	

In Table 7.2, it can be seen that all exceptions and interrupts are considered IRQn with the emuneration (IRQn) column defining macros used for ISR in the Keil CMSIS core. Similarly, the exception handler column defines macros used in the TI Tivaware Library. When using the Tivaware Library, one needs to use the exact names in the exception handler column for ISRs. These macros are defined in the file "startup_TM4C123.s," so by modifying this file, they can be redefined if one wants to.

3 Bai, *Practical Microcontroller Engineering*, 301.

TABLE 7.2 **INTERRUPT/EXCEPTION HANDLERS**[4]

Exception Number	Exception Type	CMSIS Core Enumeration (IRQn)	Enumeration Value	Exception Handler
1	Reset		–	Reset_Handler
2	NMI	NonMaskableInt_IRQn	−14	NMI_Handler
3	Hard Fault	HardFault_IRQ	−13	HardFault_Handler
4	Memory Manage Fault	Memory Management_ IRQn	−12	MemManage_ Handler
5	Bus Fault	BusFault_IRQn	−11	BusFault_Handler
6	Usage Fault	UsageFault_IRQn	−10	UsageFault Handler
11	SVC	SVCall_IRQn	-5	SVC_Handler
12	Debug Monitor	DebugMonitor_IRQn	-4	DebugMon_Handler
14	PendSV	PendSV_IRQn	-2	PendSV_Handler
15	SYSTICK	SysTick_IRQn	−1	SysTick_Handler
16	Interrupt 0	(device-specified)	0	(device-specified)
17	Interrupt 1-239	(device-specified)	1~239	(device-specified)

NVIC Registers

The NVIC registers[5] can be used to support seventy-eight interrupts with a programmable priority level of 0–7 for each interrupt, which can be set statically or dynamically. The NVIC supports level-sensitive or pulse interrupts, stacked, or nested, interrupts, as well as tail chaining of interrupts. All NVIC registers (Table 7.3) and system debug registers are always little endian.

TABLE 7.3 **NVIC REGISTERS**[6]

Address	Name	Type	Reset	Description
0xE000E004	ICTR	RO	-	*Interrupt Controller Type Register, ICTR*
0XE000E100 - 0XE000E11C	NVIC_ISERO - NVIC_ISER7	RW	0X00000000	Interrupt Set-Enable Registers
0XE000E180 - 0E000XE19C	NVIC_ICER0 - NVIC_ICER7	RW	0X00000000	Interrupt Clear-Enable Registers
0XE000E200 - 0XE000E21C	NVIC_ISPRO - NVIC_ISPR7	RW	0X00000000	Interrupt Set-Pending Registers

4 Bai, 264.

5 Bai, 124.

6 ARM Limited, *Cortex-M4 Revision r0p1*, 6–4.

0XE000E280 - 0XE000E29C	NVIC_ICPR0 - NVIC_ICPR7	RW	0X00000000	Interrupt Clear-Pending Registers
0XE000E300 - 0XE000E31C	NVIC_IABR0 - NVIC_IABR7	RO	0X00000000	Interrupt Active Bit Register
0XE000E400 - 0XE000E4EC	NVIC_IPR0 - NVIC_IPR59	RW	0X00000000	Interrupt Priority Register
	0xE000EF00	Software Trigger Interrupt Register		

Interrupt Controller Type Register[6]

This is a read-only register showing the number of interrupts that the NVIC supports. Table 7.4 summarizes the decoding of the register bits. Even though in theory, it can support a maximum number of 240 external interrupts, in reality, the Tiva C TM4C123GH6PM only supports seventy-eight interrupts. This register resides at address 0xE000_E004 and in the Tiva C TM4C123GH6PM; a read of this register returns a value of 4.

TABLE 7.4 **INTERRUPT CONTROLLER TYPE REGISTER**[7]

Bits	**Name**	**Function**
[31:4]	-	Reserved
[3:0]	INTLINESNUM	Total number of interrupt lines in groups of 32:
		b0000 = 0...32
		b0001 = 33...64
		b0010 = 65...96
		b0011 =97...128
		b0100 = 129...160
		b0101 = 161...192
		b0110 = 193...224
		b0111 = 225...256[a]
a. The processor supports a maximum of 240 external interrupts.		

NVIC Registers[8]

- As shown in Figure 7.5, registers NVIC_ISER0-ISER7 are used to enable interrupt sources. Each bit of register NVIC_ISER0 enables one interrupt from IRQ0 (Interrupt Number 16) to IRQ31 (Interrupt Number 47). Similarly, each bit of register NVIC_ISER1 enables one interrupt from IRQ32 to IRQ63, and so on. For example, bit 0 of register NVIC_ISER7 enables IRQ255. These registers are also called NVIC_EN0_R to NVIC_EN7_R. The Tiva C TM4C23GH6PM only implements 2 registers NVIC_ISER0 and NVIC_ISER1 and they are renamed as registers NVIC_EN0_R and NVIC_EN1_R, respectively.

7 ARM Limited, 6–5.

8 Valvano, *Embedded Systems: Introduction to ARM Cortex-M3*, 355.

Address	31	30	29-7	6	5	4	3	2	1	0	Register Name
0xE000E100	Port G	Port F	...	UART1	UART0	Port E	Port D	Port C	Port B	Port A	NVIC_EN0_R
0xE000E104			...			Timer 3B	Timer 3A	SS1	UART2	Port* H	NVIC_EN1_R

** Tiva-C does not have Port H.*

Figure 7.5 Some Common Interrupts

Table 7.5 lists the most popular interrupts supported in the Tiva C TM4C123GH6PM. Included in the table are the vector addresses, IRQ number, ISR names, NVIC priority registers, and NVIC Enable registers associated with the interrupts.

TABLE 7.5 **LIST OF COMMON INTERRUPTS**[9]

Some Common Interrupts Vector Address	Interrupt Number	IRQ	ISR Name in Startup.s	NVIC	Priority Bits	NVIC_ ENx_R	Enable Bit
0x00000038	14	−2	PendSV_ Handler	NVIC_SYS_ PRI3_R	23–21		
0x0000003C	15	−1	SysTick_ Handler	NVIC_SYS_ PRI3_R	31–29		
0x00000040	16	0	GPIOPortA_ Handler	NVIC_PRI0_R	7–5	NVIC_ EN0_R	0
0x00000044	17	1	GPIOPortB_ Handler	NVIC_PRI0_R	15–13	NVIC_ EN0_R	1
0x00000048	18	2	GPIOPortC_ Handler	NVIC_PRI0_R	23–21	NVIC_ EN0_R	2
0x0000004C	19	3	GPIOPortD_ Handler	NVIC_PRI0_R	31–29	NVIC_ EN0_R	3
0x00000050	20	4	GPIOPortE_ Handler	NVIC_PRI1_R	7–5	NVIC_ EN0_R	4
0x00000054	21	5	UART0_Handler	NVIC_PRI1_R	15–13	NVIC_ EN0_R	5
0x00000058	22	6	UART1_Handler	NVIC_PRI1_R	23–21	NVIC_ EN0_R	6
0x0000005C	23	7	SSI0_Handler	NVIC_PRI1_R	31–29	NVIC_ EN0_R	7
0x00000060	24	8	I2C0_Handler	NVIC_PRI2_R	7–5	NVIC_ EN0_R	8
0x00000064	25	9	PWM0Fault_ Handler	NVIC_PRI2_R	15–13	NVIC_ EN0_R	9
0x00000068	26	10	PWM0_Handler	NVIC_PRI2_R	23–21	NVIC_ EN0_R	10

9 Adapted from Valvano, Table 9.1, p. 354.

TABLE 7.5 **LIST OF COMMON INTERRUPTS (*CONTINUED*)**

Some Common Interrupts Vector Address	Interrupt Number	IRQ	ISR Name in Startup.s	NVIC	Priority Bits	NVIC_ENx_R	Enable Bit
0x0000006C	27	11	PWM1_Handler	NVIC_PRI2_R	31–29	NVIC_EN0_R	11
0x00000070	28	12	PWM2_Handler	NVIC_PRI3_R	7–5	NVIC_EN0_R	12
0x00000074	29	13	Quadrature0_Handler	NVIC_PRI3_R	15–13	NVIC_EN0_R	13
0x00000078	30	14	ADC0Seq0_Handler	NVIC_PRI3_R	23–21	NVIC_EN0_R	14
0x0000007C	31	15	ADC0Seq1_Handler	NVIC_PRI3_R	31–29	NVIC_EN0_R	15
0x00000080	32	16	ADC0Seq2_Handler	NVIC_PRI4_R	7–5	NVIC_EN0_R	16
0x00000084	33	17	ADC0Seq3_Handler	NVIC_PRI4_R	15–13	NVIC_EN0_R	17
0x00000088	34	18	WDT_Handler	NVIC_PRI4_R	23–21	NVIC_EN0_R	18
0x0000008C	35	19	Timer0A_Handler	NVIC_PRI4_R	31–29	NVIC_EN0_R	19
0x00000090	36	20	Timer0B_Handler	NVIC_PRI5_R	7–5	NVIC_EN0_R	20
0x00000094	37	21	Timer1A_Handler	NVIC_PRI5_R	15–13	NVIC_EN0_R	21
0x00000098	38	22	Timer1B_Handler	NVIC_PRI5_R	23–21	NVIC_EN0_R	22
0x0000009C	39	23	Timer2A_Handler	NVIC_PRI5_R	31–29	NVIC_EN0_R	23
0x000000A0	40	24	Timer2B_Handler	NVIC_PRI6_R	7–5	NVIC_EN0_R	24
0x000000A4	41	25	Comp0_Handler	NVIC_PRI6_R	15–13	NVIC_EN0_R	25
0x000000A8	42	26	Comp1_Handler	NVIC_PRI6_R	23–21	NVIC_EN0_R	26
0x000000AC	43	27	Comp2_Handler	NVIC_PRI6_R	31–29	NVIC_EN0_R	27
0x000000B0	44	28	SysCtl_Handler	NVIC_PRI7_R	7–5	NVIC_EN0_R	28
0x000000B4	45	29	FlashCtl_Handler	NVIC_PRI7_R	15–13	NVIC_EN0_R	29

TABLE 7.5 **LIST OF COMMON INTERRUPTS (*CONTINUED*)**

Some Common Interrupts Vector Address	Interrupt Number	IRQ	ISR Name in Startup.s	NVIC	Priority Bits	NVIC_ENx_R	Enable Bit
0x000000B8	46	30	GPIOPortF_Handler	NVIC_PRI7_R	23–21	NVIC_EN0_R	30
0x000000BC	47	31	GPIOPortG_Handler	NVIC_PRI7_R	31–29	NVIC_EN0_R	31
0x000000C0	48	32	GPIOPortH_Handler	NVIC_PRI8_R	7–5	NVIC_EN1_R	0
0x000000C4	49	33	UART2_Handler	NVIC_PRI8_R	15–13	NVIC_EN1_R	1
0x000000C8	50	34	SSI1_Handler	NVIC_PRI8_R	23–21	NVIC_EN1_R	2
0x000000CC	51	35	Timer3A_Handler	NVIC_PRI8_R	31–29	NVIC_EN1_R	3
0x000000D0	52	36	Timer3B_Handler	NVIC_PRI9_R	7–5	NVIC_EN1_R	4
0x000000D4	53	37	I2C1_Handler	NVIC_PRI9_R	15–13	NVIC_EN1_R	5
0x000000D8	54	38	Quadrature1_Handler	NVIC_PRI9_R	23–21	NVIC_EN1_R	6
0x000000DC	55	39	CAN0_Handler	NVIC_PRI9_R	31–29	NVIC_EN1_R	7
0x000000E0	56	40	CAN1_Handler	NVIC_PRI10_R	7–5	NVIC_EN1_R	8
0x000000E4	57	41	CAN2_Handler	NVIC_PRI10_R	15–13	NVIC_EN1_R	9
0x000000E8	58	42	Ethernet_Handler	NVIC_PRI10_R	23–21	NVIC_EN1_R	10
0x000000EC	59	43	Hibernate_Handler	NVIC_PRI10_R	31–29	NVIC_EN1_R	11
0x000000F0	60	44	USB0_Handler	NVIC_PRI11_R	7–5	NVIC_EN1_R	12
0x000000F4	61	45	PWM3_Handler	NVIC_PRI11_R	15–13	NVIC_EN1_R	13
0x000000F8	62	46	uDMA_Handler	NVIC_PRI11_R	23–21	NVIC_EN1_R	14
0x000000FC	63	47	uDMA_Error	NVIC_PRI11_R	31–29	NVIC_EN1_R	15

- Registers NVIC_ICER0–ICER7 are used to disable interrupt sources. Each bit of register NVIC_ICER0 clears one interrupt from IRQ0 (Interrupt Number 16) to IRQ31 (Interrupt Number 47). Similarly, each bit of register NVIC_ICER1 clears one interrupt from IRQ32 to IRQ63, and so on. For example, bit 7 of register NVIC_ICER2 clears IRQ95. These registers are also called NVIC_DIS0_R to NVIC_DIS7_R.
- Registers NVIC_ISPR0–ISPR7 are used to raise an interrupt.
- Registers NVIC_ICPR0–ICPR7 are to clear a pending interrupt.
- Registers NVIC_IABR0–IABR7 are read-only registers to show if a corresponding interrupt is active or not.
- Registers NVIC_IPR0–IPR59 are to set interrupt priority.
- When an exception/interrupt happens, assuming the corresponding interrupt has been enabled and all the related registers have been properly configured, the ARM processor changes its PC to the vector address corresponding to the interrupt in the vector table. The vector address is the pointer to the starting address of the ISRBy default, and the vector table is located at the lowest address of the memory: address 0. However, this default address can be changed by reprogramming the vector table offset register. The exception or ISR addresses are arranged by priority orders, and each of them is a 4-byte address in little-endian format. Table 7.5 shows a vector table of several ISR vector addresses. For instance, for exception/interrupt number 19 (TM4C123 GPIO Port D handler), its vector address is 19*4 = 76 (decimal) = 0x4C. Another example is the SysTick timer interrupt. Its interrupt priority is 15, so its vector address is 15*4 = 60 (decimal) = 0x3C. The vector addresses are pointers to starting addresses of the corresponding interrupt service addresses.

The vector table is usually loaded into memory from a startup file like "startup_TM4C123.s" for TI Tiva-C TM4C123 processor. Figures 7.6 and 7.7 are examples of how the vector table is set up in an example project run with the Keil IDE.

According to Figure 7.7, the first 4 bytes of the vector table are the SP (Stack Pointer). We can see in the memory browser windows of Figure 7.7 (red dot number 1) the first 4-byte word at address 0 of the memory is the address of the stack, 0x20000428, and it's also shown as register R13 (SP) in Figure 7.7 (red dot number 1). Please note that the data in the memory windows are in little-endian format. The next 4-byte word is 0x0000026D (red dot number 2 of Figure 7.7), which contains address 0x0000026C (the least significant bit of the word 0x0000026D is 1 used to denote Thumb-2 instruction), which is the starting address of the exception Reset_Handler, as shown in the Disassembly windows of the same figure (red dot number 2). Similarly, red dot number 3 of Figure 7.7 shows the starting address, 0x0000_0270, of the HardFault_Handler.

Global Interrupt Control—Register PRIMASK and BASEPRI

These registers provide global control of all interrupt and exception requests. The PRIMASK register is a 1-bit register that disables or enables all ARM maskable interrupts or exceptions. Bit 0 is the interrupt mask bit I, which enables all interrupts and exceptions when its value is 0. Otherwise, all the maskable interrupt or exception requests are not allowed. The BASEPRI register allows interrupt or exception requests with

```
_Vectors     DCD  __initial_sp            ; Top of Stack
             DCD  Reset_Handler           ; Reset Handler
             DCD  NMI_Handler             ; NMI Handler
             DCD  HardFault_Handler       ; Hard Fault Handler
             DCD  MemManage_Handler       ; MPU Fault Handler
             DCD  BusFault_Handler        ; Bus Fault Handler
             DCD  UsageFault_Handler      ; Usage Fault Handler
             DCD  0                       ; Reserved
             DCD  0                       ; Reserved
             DCD  0                       ; Reserved
             DCD  0                       ; Reserved
             DCD  SVC_Handler             ; SVCall Handler
             DCD  DebugMon_Handler        ; Debug Monitor Handler
             DCD  0                       ; Reserved
             DCD  PendSV_Handler          ; PendSV Handler
             DCD  SysTick_Handler         ; SysTick Handler
; External Interrupts Vector or Handler   ; IRQ#  Peripheral
             DCD  GPIOA_Handler           ;  0:   GPIO Port A
             DCD  GPIOB_Handler           ;  1:   GPIO Port B
             DCD  GPIOC_Handler           ;  2:   GPIO Port C
             DCD  GPIOD_Handler           ;  3:   GPIO Port D
             DCD  GPIOE_Handler           ;  4:   GPIO Port E
```

FIGURE 7.6 The Vector Definitions in the Cortex-M4 Microcontroller.

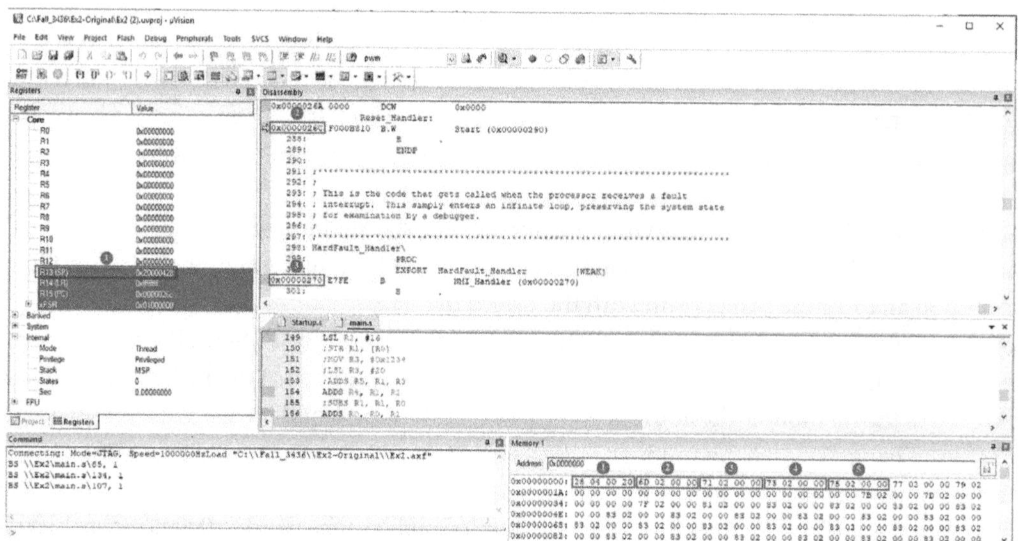

FIGURE 7.7 Keil Display of the Interrupt/Exception Vector Table.

higher priority to interrupt but prevent lower priority interrupt requests from happening. When the value of register BASEPRI is zero, the priority feature is disabled, and so all interrupts are allowed to happen. An example of the use of register BASEPRI is when its value is set to 4, all interrupt or exception requests of priority 0, 1, 2, or 3 are allowed to happen but interrupt requests of priority 4 or higher will be blocked. Note that only bits 7–5 of register BASEPRI are used to set eight different levels of priority. In addition, these two registers are only accessible by ARM assembly instructions MSR or MRS, so to access them in C codes, we need to use the in-line assembly or use the intrinsic function _enable_irq() or _disable_irq().

2.3 Tivaware and Keil CMSIS Interrupt Support

Besides directly configuring interrupt support registers, we can also use subroutines and macros in the TI Tivaware Peripheral Library or CMSIS core macros and functions. We usually use the Tivaware Library with CCS and the CMSIS Core Library with Keil IDE. For example, to enable interrupt IRQn, we can use the CMSIS core function NVIC_EnableIRQ(IRQn) or the Tivaware Peripheral Library function IntEnable(IRQn). Tables 7.6 and 7.7 list some of Tivaware and CMSIS Core Library functions to configure interrupts.

TABLE 7.6 **THE CMSIS CORE FUNCTIONS FOR INTERRUPT CONTROLS**[10]

CMS IS Core Function	Descriplion
void NVIC_EnableIRQ(IRQn_Type IRQn)	Enable an external interrupt
void NVIC_DisableIRQ(IRQn_Type IRQn)	Disable an external interrupt
void NVIC_SetPriority(IRQn_Type IRQn, uint32_t priority)	Set the priority for an interrupt
void__enable_irq(void)	Clear PRIMASK to enable all interrupts
void__disable_irq(void)	Set PRIMASK to disable all interrupts
void NVIC SetPriorityGrouping(unit32_t PriorityGroup)	Set priority grouping structure

TABLE 7.7 **THE NVIC API FUNCTIONS IN THE TIVAWARE PERIPHERAL DRIVER LIBRARY**[11]

API Function	Description
void IntEnable(uint32_t ui32Interrupt)	Enable an interrupt
void IntDisable(uint32_t ui32Interrupt)	Disable an interrupt
unit32_t IntIsEnabled(uint32_t ui32Interrupt)	Check if an interrupt has been enabled. Returning a non-/ero indicates that the interrupt is enabled
bool IntMasterEnable(uint32_t ui32Interrupt)	Enable processor to receive any interrupt. Returning a True means that all interrupts are enabled
bool IntMasterDisable(uint32_t ui32Interrupt)	Prevent processor from receiving any interrupt. Returning a True means that all interrupts are disabled
void IntPendClear(uint32_t ui32Interrupt)	Clear a specified pending interrupt
void IntPendSet(uint32_t ui32Interrupt)	Set a specified interrupt to be pending status
int32_t IntPriorityGet(uint32_t ui32Interrupt)	Ciel the priority level for a specified interrupt
void IntPrioritySet(uint32_t ui32Interrupt, uint8_t ui8Priority)	Set the priority level for a specified interrupt

10 Bai, *Practical Microcontroller Engineering*, 313.

11 Bai, 307.

3. TIVA-C Interrupts and Exceptions

For the Tiva-C (TM4CGH6PM) microcontroller, all faults and exceptions, such as hard fault, bus fault, memory management fault, SVCall, and NMI, are generally handled by fault handlers or system handlers developed by the microcontroller manufacturer—namely, Texas Instruments. Meanwhile, all maskable interrupt requests are handled by user-defined interrupt service routines (ISR). All the peripheral modules inside the Tiva-C, such as GPIO, UART, ADC, PWM, and timers, have interrupts supported by NVIC registers and other related registers. In the following section, we will discuss how to configure the GPIO interrupts. Before each GPIO interrupt request can be supported, we'll have to configure the GPIO pin(s) by using register SYSCTL_RCGCGPIO_R to enable a particular GPIO port. Then we will need to configure registers GPIO_DIR_R, GPIO_DEN_R, GPIO_AMSEL_R, and GPIO_AFSEL_R of the specific GPIO port before using local interrupt configuration non-NVIC registers, the NVIC registers, and, finally, the global interrupt registers PRIMASK and BASEPRI.

3.1. Local Interrupt Configurations of GPIO Pins

Figure 7.8 shows configuration registers for GPIO Port A interrupts. Other ports have similar registers, which have similar offset addresses and different base addresses. See chapter 6 for more examples of configuring GPIO interrupts. Here are the APB base addresses of all the ports' interrupt registers:

- GPIO_PORTA_IS_R @0x40004404
- GPIO_PORTB_IS_R @0x40005404
- GPIO_PORTC_IS_R @0x40006404

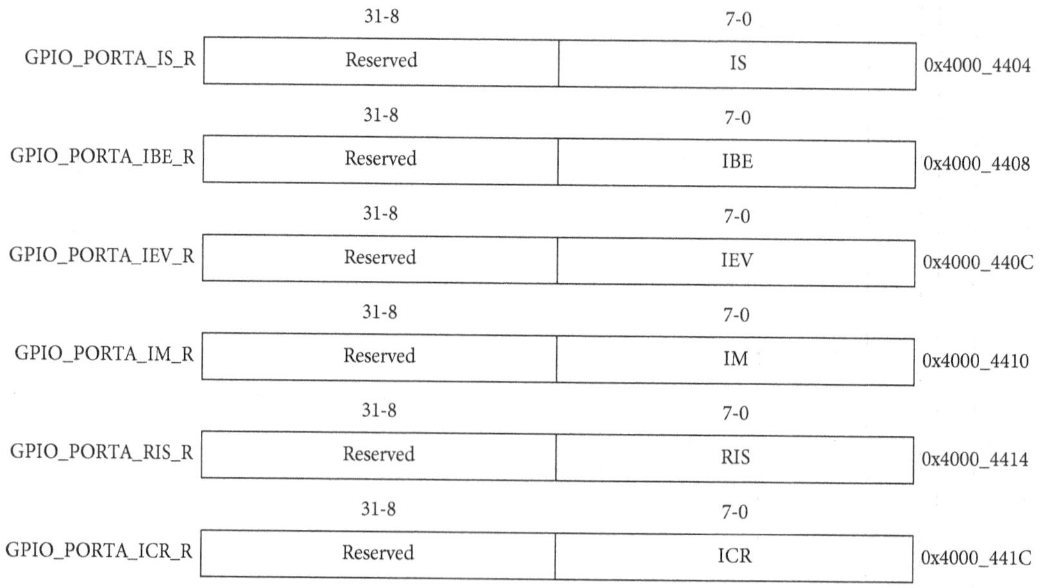

Register	31-8	7-0	Address
GPIO_PORTA_IS_R	Reserved	IS	0x4000_4404
GPIO_PORTA_IBE_R	Reserved	IBE	0x4000_4408
GPIO_PORTA_IEV_R	Reserved	IEV	0x4000_440C
GPIO_PORTA_IM_R	Reserved	IM	0x4000_4410
GPIO_PORTA_RIS_R	Reserved	RIS	0x4000_4414
GPIO_PORTA_ICR_R	Reserved	ICR	0x4000_441C

FIGURE 7.8 GPIO Port A Interrupt Registers.

- GPIO_PORTD_IS_R @0x40007404
- GPIO_PORTE_IS_R @0x40024404
- GPIO_PORTF_IS_R @0x40025404
  - Each bit of the first 8 bits of the Interrupt Sense register GPIO_PORTA_IS_R corresponds to a pin of Port A. When a bit is set, the corresponding pin is configured to detect a level. When a bit is reset, the pin is to detect edges. For example, if bit 2 is a "0," Pin 2 of Port A is edge sensitive. Otherwise, it's level sensitive.
  - Similarly, the Interrupt Both Edges register GPIO_PORTA_IBE_R also has 8 bits and each bit when set ("1") configures the corresponding pin to detect both rising and falling edges. Only one edge is detected by a pin if the corresponding bit is reset ("0"). For example, if bit 1 is set, pin 1 trigger a Port A interrupt on both edges.
  - Register GPIO_PORTA_IEV_R works together with register GPIO_PORTA_IS_R to configure a rising or a falling edge/level. For example, if bit 4 of register GPIO_PORTA_IS_R is reset ("0") and bit 4 of register GPIO_PORTA_IEV_R is set ("1"), Pin 4 of Port A will trigger a local interrupt on a rising edge. Another example, bit 3 of register GPIO_PORTA_IS_R is set ("1") and bit 3 of register GPIO_PORTA_IEV_R is reset ("0"), Pin 3 of Port A is configured to detect a low level.
  - Each bit of register GPIO_PORTA_IM_R when set is to enable a local interrupt on a pin. For example, if bit 7 is set ("1"), local interrupt on Pin 7 of Port A is enabled.
  - A bit of register GPIO_PORTA_RIS_R indicates the status of the local interrupt status on the corresponding pin. For example, if bit 6 is set, a local interrupt condition on Pin 6 of Port A has happened.
  - Each bit of register GPIO_PORTA_ICR_R when set is used to clear the local interrupt status of the corresponding pin. For example, if bit 3 is set ("1"), the local interrupt status of Pin 3 Port A is cleared. If bit 3 is not set ("0"), Pin 3's local interrupt status is not affected.

3.2. Using NVIC Registers to Configure Interrupts

To enable an interrupt source, we have to enable and set its priority in NVIC registers. Depending on versions of the TM4C123 microcontroller, TI provides up to five interrupt set-enabled registers, NVIC,_EN0,_R, NVIC_EN1_R, NVIC_EN2_R, NIC_EN3_R, NVIC,_EN4_R, to enable interrupts associated with peripherals, such as GPIO ports, UART, and timers (see Table 7.8 below) and five interrupt disabled registers, NVIC_DIS0_R-NVIC_DIS4_R, to disable interrupts. To enable an interrupt source, write one ("1") to the related bit in the appropriate NVIC_EN*n*_R (*n* = 0–4). To disable an interrupt source, write one ("1") to the related bit in the appropriate NVIC_DIS*n*_R (*n* = 0–4). Writing zeros will have no effect. For example, to enable the Port C interrupt, bit 2 of register NVIC_EN0 needs to be set to one.

In theory, there are sixty interrupt priority registers, from NVIC_PRI0 to NVIC_PRI59, to set priority levels for all the peripheral interrupts. In reality, only fourteen priority registers from NVIC_PRIO0_R to register NVIC_PRI13_R are used in this Tiva C microcontroller (TM4C123GH6PM) as shown in Table 7.9 below. Each register is a 32-bit register, but each register only uses the upper 3 bits of each byte in the register to set priority. For example, only bits 7–5 of register NVIC_PRI0_R are used to set a priority level for GPIO Port A module, as shown in Table 7.9, and bits 4–0 are not used.

TABLE 7.8 **NVIC ENABLE REGISTERS**[12]

Enable Register	32 Enable Bits									
	0	1	2	3	4	5	6-29	30	31	Address
NVIC_EN0_R	PORTA	PORTB	PORTC	PORTD	PORTE	UARTO	... ...	PORTF	PORTG	0xE000E100
NVIC_EN1_R	PORTH	UART2	SS11	Timer3A	Timer3B	12C1	... ...	UART6	UAR17	0xE000E104
NVIC_EN2_R	...	...	...	...	12C2	I2C3	... ...	WTimer0A	WTimer0B	0xE000E108
NVIC_EN3_R	WT1A	WT1B	WT2A	WT2B	WT3A	WT3B	... ...	GPIOQ2	GPIOQ3	0xE000E10C

TABLE 7.9 **NVIC PRIORITY REGISTERS**[13]

Address	31–29	23–21	15–13	7–5	Name
0xE000E400	GPIO Port D	GPIO Port C	GPIO Port B	GPIO Port A	NVIC_PRI0_R
OxE000E404	SSI0, Rx Tx	UART1, Rx Tx	UART0, Rx Tx	GPIO Port E	NVIC_PRI1_R
0xE000E408	PWM Gen 1	PWM Gen 0	PWM Fault	I2C0	NVIC_PRI2_R
0xE000E40C	ADC Seq 1	ADC Seq 0	Quad Encoder	PWM Gen 2	NVIC_PRI3_R
0xE000E410	Timer 0A	Watchdog	ADC Seq 3	ADC Seq 2	NVIC PRI4 R
0xE000E414	Timer 2A	Timer 1B	Timer 1A	Timer 0B	NVIC_PRI5_ R
0xE000E418	Comp 2	Comp 1	Comp 0	Timer 2B	NVIC_PRI6_R
0xE000E41C	GPIO Port G	GPIO Port F	Flash Control	System Control	NVIC_PRI7_R
0xE000E420	Timer 3A	SSI1, Rx Tx	UART2, Rx Tx	GPIO Port H	NVIC_PRI8_R
0xE000E424	CAN0	Quad Encoder 1	I2C1	Timer 3B	NVIC_PRI9_R
0xE000E428	Hibernate	Ethernet	CAN2	CAN1	NVIC_PRI10_R
0xE000E42C	uDMA Error	uDMA Soft Tfr	PWM Gen 3	USB0	NVIC_PRI11_R
0xE000ED20	SysTick	PendSV	--	Debug	NVIC_SYS_PRI3_R

3.3. Examples of an Interrupt Initialization and ISR

In the following example, we create interrupts on Pin 4 and Pin 0 of Port F, which are connected to Switch SW1 and Switch SW2, respectively. Any time a switch, say SW2, is pressed, the program will toggle LED green. Similarly, Switch SW1 will cause LED blue to toggle. This is just a simple demonstration of using a GPIO pin as an interrupt source, and for the sake of simplicity, the switches are not debounced. This program was compiled and executed

12 Bai, 281.

13 Bai, 279.

successfully with IDE Keil version 4 or version 5. This program needs to run with the TI startup.s program.

```
    AREA Block1, DATA, READWRITE, ALIGN=2

cnt  DCD 0x0; reserve 4 bytes of memory for variable cnt

    AREA Ex1, CODE, READONLY, ALIGN=2

;Define memory addresses for NVIC registers

NVIC_PRI7_R         EQU 0xE000E41C

NVIC_EN0_R          EQU 0xE000E100

NVIC_EN1_R          EQU 0xE000E104

;Define memory addresses for GPIO Port F Configuration regis-
ters

GPIO_PORTF_LOCK_R  EQU 0x40025520

GPIO_PORTF_CR_R    EQU 0x40025524

GPIO_PORTF_AMSEL_R EQU 0x40025528

GPIO_PORTF_PCTL_R  EQU 0x4002552C

GPIO_LOCK_KEY      EQU 0x4C4F434B

GPIO_PORTF_DATA_R  EQU 0x400253FC

GPIO_PORTF_DIR_R   EQU 0x40025400

GPIO_PORTF_AFSEL_R EQU 0x40025420

GPIO_PORTF_PUR_R   EQU 0x40025510

GPIO_PORTF_DEN_R   EQU 0x4002551C

;GPIO Port F Interrupt Configuration registers

GPIO_PORTF_IBE_R   EQU 0x40025408 ;GPIO Port F Interrupt Both
Edges

GPIO_PORTF_IEV_R   EQU 0x4002540C; Interrupt Event
```

```
GPIO_PORTF_IM_R     EQU 0x40025410 ;Interrupt Mask

GPIO_PORTF_RIS_R    EQU 0x40025414 ;Raw Interrupt Status

GPIO_PORTF_ICR_R    EQU 0x4002541C;Interrupt Clear

GPIO_PORTF_IS_R     EQU 0x40025404   ;Interrupt Sense


      EXPORT Start

      EXPORT GPIOPortF_Handler

      ENTRY

Start

      BL Port_Init ; Initialize the GPIO Port F

      BL PF_Int_Init; Configure the GPIO PortF interrupt

;Creating a loop to keep track of where the current instruction is executed when the interrupt happens

;Inspecting the values of R0-R6 relative to each other will let us know where the current instruction is.

;For example, when the interrupt happens and the system is halted by a breakpoint at the beginning of the ;interrupt handler (line 12). Here are the register values:   R0=0xA1, R1=0xA2, R2=0xA3, R3=0xA4, R4=some

;random value, R5=0x0, R6=0x0. We can guess that the system is interrupted when executing line 5 and line 6

;is the next instruction to be executed. The reason is that the system must have completed line 5 (register R3

;is updated) but it has not executed line 6 since register R4 has not been updated.

;

      MOV R0, #0xA1
```

```
LoopS

      ADD R1, R0, #1

      ADD R2, R1, #1

      ADD R3, R2, #1

      ADD R4, R3, #1

      ADD R5, R4, #1

      ADD R6, R5, #1

      ADD R0, R6, #1

      B LoopS


GPIOPortF_Handler; GPIO Port F Interrupt Service Routine

      PUSH {LR}; save the Link Register since there is nested
subroutine jump

      BL Check_PF; call subroutine Check_PF to see which
switch is pressed

      POP {LR}

      LDR R0, =GPIO_PORTF_ICR_R

      MOV R1, #0x11

      STR R1, [R0] ; clear the interrupt flags

      LDR R0, =cnt

      LDR R1, [R0]

      ADD R1, R1, #1

      STR R1, [R0] ;update cnt (the number of interrupts)

      BX LR ; return from interrupt
```

```
B_PF0 ; Toggle the Red LED

        LDR R4, = GPIO_PORTF_DATA_R

        LDR R5,  [R4]

        AND R5, R5, #0x2

        EOR R5, R5, #0x2

        STR R5, [R4]

        BX LR

B_PF4 ;Toggle the Blue LED

        LDR R4, = GPIO_PORTF_DATA_R

        LDR R5,  [R4]

        AND R5, R5, #0x4

        EOR R5, R5, #0x4

        STR R5, [R4]

        BX LR


Check_PF ; Check to see which switch, SW1 or SW2, is pressed
(for simplicity, no debouncing is done here)

        LDR R0, =GPIO_PORTF_RIS_R; get the raw interrupt status

        LDR R1, [R0]

        ANDS R2, R1, #0x01;check to see if PF0 (SW2) causes the
interrupt

        BNE B_PF0                    ;if yes, go to B_BF0 to toggle
the Red LED

        ANDS R2, R1, #0x10; check to see if PF4 (SW0) causes
the interrupt
```

```
        BNE B_PF4                   ;if yes, go to B_PF4 to toggle
the Blue LED

        BX LR


        PF_Int_Init ; Configuring GPIO Port F interrupt

        MOV R1, #1

        MSR PRIMASK, R1; Disable the global interrupt


        LDR R0, =GPIO_PORTF_IM_R; Disable the local GPIO Port F
interrupt

        MOV R1, #0x00

        STR R1, [R0]

        LDR R0, =GPIO_PORTF_IS_R

        MOV R1, #0x00               ; Edge detect

        STR R1, [R0]

        LDR R0, =GPIO_PORTF_IBE_R

        MOV R1, #0x00               ;one edge

        STR R1, [R0]

        LDR R0, =GPIO_PORTF_IEV_R

        MOV R1, #0x00               ; Falling Edge detect

        STR R1, [R0]

        LDR R0, = NVIC_PRI7_R; GPIO Port F priority

        LDR R1, =0xFF00FFFF

        LDR R2, [R0]

        AND R2, R2, R1
```

```
        LDR R1, =0x00A00000      ; priority 5
        ORR R2, R2, R1
        STR R1, [R0]
        LDR R0, = NVIC_EN0_R;Enable GPIO Port F interrupt
        LDR R1, =0x40000000
        LDR R2, [R0]
        ORR R2, R2, R1
        STR R2, [R0]
        MOV R2, #0x0
        LDR R0, =GPIO_PORTF_IM_R
        MOV R1, #0x11
        STR R1, [R0] ; Enable interrupts on Port F pin 0 and
pin 4


        MOV R1, #0
        MSR PRIMASK, R1; store 0 to PRIMASK register to enable
the global interrupt
        BX LR


        Port_Init ; Initialize GPIO Port F pin 0-4
        ; Enable Port F
        LDR R1, =SYSCTL_RCGCGPIO_R
        LDR R0, [R1]
        ORR R0, R0, #0x20
        STR R0, [R1]
```

```
        NOP

        NOP ; Wait for portF clock to stablize

        ; Port F Init, port F pin 4,0 for SW1, SW2,
respectively

        LDR R0,=GPIO_PORTF_LOCK_R ; unlock portF

        LDR R1,=0x4C4F434B

        STR R1, [R0]

        LDR R0,=GPIO_PORTF_CR_R

        MOV R1, #0xFF

        STR R1, [R0]

        LDR R0, =GPIO_PORTF_DIR_R ;input portF pin 4 and 0

        LDR R1, [R0]

        BIC R1, R1, #0x11

        ;LDR R1, [R0]

        ORR R1, R1, #0xE; output portF pin 7,3-1

        STR R1, [R0]

        LDR R0, =GPIO_PORTF_PUR_R

        LDR R1, [R0]

        ORR R1, R1, #0x11; pullup

        STR R1, [R0]

        LDR R0, =GPIO_PORTF_AMSEL_R

        LDR R1, [R0]

        BIC R1, R1, #0x1F;disable analog functionality on Port
 F pin 0-4

        STR R1, [R0]
```

```
LDR R0, =GPIO_PORTF_DEN_R

LDR R1, [R0]

ORR R1, R1, #0x1F; Enable Digital functionality on Port F pin 0-4

STR R1, [R0]

LDR R0, =GPIO_PORTF_AFSEL_R

LDR R1, [R0]

BIC R1, R1, #0x1F;disable alternate function on Port F pin 0-4


STR R1, [R0]

LDR R0, =GPIO_PORTF_PCTL_R

LDR R1, [R0]

LDR R2, =0xFFF00000;disable alternate functionality mapping on pin 0-4 of port F.

AND R1, R1, R2 ;

STR R1, [R0]

;Initialize cnt

LDR R0, =cnt

LDR R1, =0x0

STR R1, [R0]

BX LR


ALIGN

END
```

4. MSP432 Interrupt

Similar to TI Tiva-C TM4C23GHPM, to activate an MSP432 interrupt, first, we need to configure the peripheral module, such as the GPIO or UART, then enable its local interrupt registers, and, finally, the global interrupt registers PRIMASK and BASEPRI. Please note that the registers for the GPIO modules of the MSP432 are different than those of the Tiva-C TM2C123.

EXERCISES

1. Redo the example in Section 3.4 using the Tivaware Peripheral Library.

2. Redo the example in Section 3.4 using CMSIS Core Library.

3. True or False:
    - **a.** The hard fault exception can be prohibited by register BASPRI.
    - **b.** The reset exception's priority is programmable.
    - **c.** When bit 0 of the PRIMASK register is set to 0, all the maskable interrupts are enabled.
    - **d.** The Tivaware Peripheral Library and the CMSIS Core Library have the same API interface for interrupt configuration.
    - **e.** When an interrupt request is accepted, all the registers R0–R15 are saved before the PC is changed to the starting address of the ISR.
    - **f.** When an interrupt request is accepted, the LR is set to 0xFFFFFFF9.
    - **g.** A software interrupt is generated by a special processor instruction.
    - **h.** An internal interrupt happens when a peripheral device changes its hardware status.
    - **i.** When register PRIMASK is set to zero and register BASPRI is set to the value of 0x0000_000A, an interrupt request with the priority level of eight will not be blocked.
    - **j.** After the ISR of an exception completes, the system returns to where it left off.

4. Write an ISR for Port F. Use Port F Pins 4 and 0, which are connected to Switch SW2 and Switch SW1 on the Tiva-C kit, respectively, to trigger interrupts. In the ISR, check to see which switch is pressed to turn on the red or green LEDs connected to Port F Pin 1 or Pin 2, respectively. Make sure you write all the code to enable Port F, enable the interrupt by using register NVIC EN0, and so on.

5. Provide a brief description of when an interrupt request is accepted and when it returns.

6. Describe all the conditions for an interrupt to happen.

7. Why doesn't a SysTick ISR need to clear the interrupt flag to acknowledge the interrupt?

8. What is interrupt nesting?

9. Redo the example in Section 3.3 using processor MSP432 and the direct memory access method.

10. Redo the example in Section 3.3 using processor MSP432 and the Tivaware Peripheral Library.

11. Redo the example in Section 3.3 using processor MSP432 and the CMSIS Core Library.

12. Figure 7.9 is a status of a microcontroller, Tiva C, when an interrupt happens and then is halted by a breakpoint right at the beginning of the interrupt ISR. Answer the following questions:

    a. What peripheral device causes this interrupt?

Registers

Register	Value
Core	
R0	0x0000000d
R1	0x0000000e
R2	0x0000000f
R3	0x00000010
R4	0x00000011
R5	0x00000012
R6	0x0000000c
R7	0x00000000
R8	0x00000000
R9	0x00000000
R10	0x00000000
R11	0x00000000
R12	0x00000000
R13 (SP)	0x200003e8
R14 (LR)	0xfffffff9
R15 (PC)	0x000002ae
xPSR	0x0100002e
N	0
Z	0
C	0
V	0
Q	0
GE	1
T	Disabled
IT	46
ISR	
Banked	
System	
Internal	
Mode	Handler
Privilege	Privileged
Stack	MSP
States	0
Sec	0.00000000
FPU	

FIGURE 7.9 Problem 12.

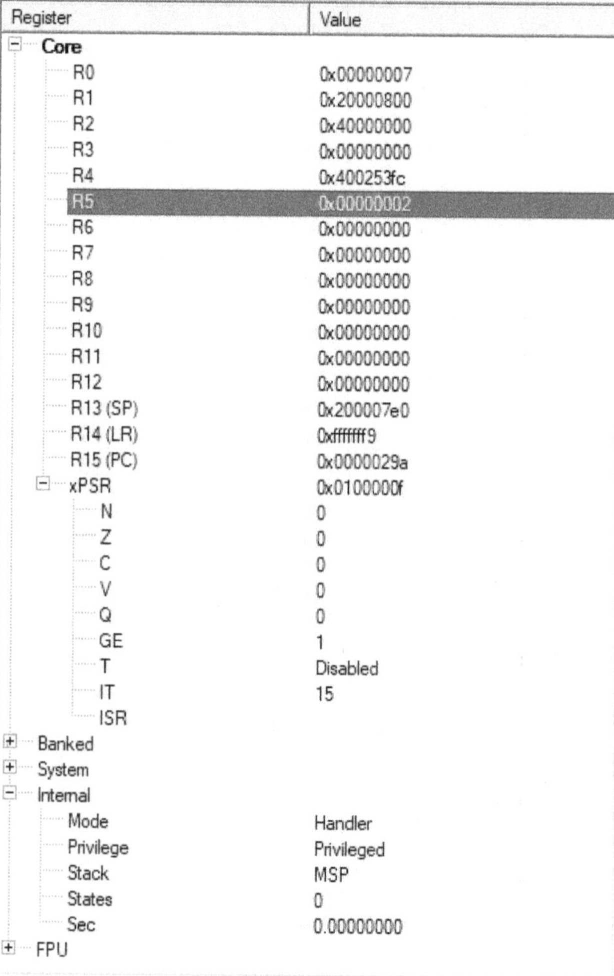

Register	Value
Core	
R0	0x00000007
R1	0x20000800
R2	0x40000000
R3	0x00000000
R4	0x400253fc
R5	0x00000002
R6	0x00000000
R7	0x00000000
R8	0x00000000
R9	0x00000000
R10	0x00000000
R11	0x00000000
R12	0x00000000
R13 (SP)	0x200007e0
R14 (LR)	0xfffffff9
R15 (PC)	0x0000029a
xPSR	0x0100000f
N	0
Z	0
C	0
V	0
Q	0
GE	1
T	Disabled
IT	15
ISR	
Banked	
System	
Internal	
Mode	Handler
Privilege	Privileged
Stack	MSP
States	0
Sec	0.00000000
FPU	

FIGURE 7.10 Problem 15.

b. The figure shows the value of the Stack Pointer to be 0x200003E8. Use this information and Figure 7.9 to fill in the following memory locations (the format is little endian and each slot represents a byte of data):

0x200003E8																
0x200003F8																

c. When the ISR completes its program and the system returns from the interrupt, what is the memory address of the instruction line that the system returns to?

13. Write an assembly program using the SysTick Timer to cause an interrupt every 1ms. Assume that the system clock is the default 16MHz.

14. Solve problem 13 using C language instead of Assembly.

15. Figure 7.10 is a status of a microcontroller, Tiva C, when an interrupt happens and then is halted by a breakpoint right at the beginning of the interrupt ISR. Answer the following questions:
    a. What peripheral device causes this interrupt?
    b. The figure shows the value of the Stack Pointer to be 0x200007E0. Use this information and Figure 7.10 to fill in the following memory locations (the format is little endian and each slot represents a byte of data):

0x200007E0																
0x200007F0																

    c. When the ISR completes its program and the system returns from the interrupt, what is the memory address of the instruction line that the system returns to?

Credits

Fig. 7.7: Arm Limited, "Keil Display of the Interrupt/Exception Vector Table," http://www.keil.com/product/. Copyright © by Arm Limited.

Table 7.6: Ying Bai, "The CMSIS core functions for interrupt control," Practical Microcontroller Engineering with ARM Technology, pp. 266. Copyright © 2015 by John Wiley & Sons, Inc.

Table 7.7: Ying Bai, "The NVIC API functions in the TivaWare peripheral driver library," Practical Microcontroller Engineering with ARM Technology, pp. 307. Copyright © 2015 by John Wiley & Sons, Inc.

Table 7.8: Ying Bai, "NVIC Enable Registers," Practical Microcontroller Engineering with ARM Technology, pp. 281. Copyright © 2015 by John Wiley & Sons, Inc.

Table 7.9: Ying Bai, "NVIC Priority Registers," Practical Microcontroller Engineering with ARM Technology, pp. 279. Copyright © 2015 by John Wiley & Sons, Inc.

Fig. 7.9: Copyright © by Texas Instruments Incorporated.

Fig. 7.10: Copyright © by Texas Instruments Incorporated.

Chapter 8

Bluetooth Low Energy

1. Introduction

The world is interconnected not only between far-flung places but also within your living room. For example, your television set communicates with your remote controllers, or your Bluetooth earbuds are connecting to your smartphone.

Bluetooth was originally designed to replace cables connected between electronic devices, but more features were added later to improve the technology to allow it to become a low-cost and low-power wireless standard for short distance data or voice communication. Its specification is currently managed by the Bluetooth Special Interest Group, whose members cover a wide range of electronic applications from computer manufacturers to consumer electronic companies.

There are several Bluetooth standards. We limited our discussion to the Bluetooth low energy (BLE), which provides the same communication range (about 10 meters) as the classic Bluetooth standard, but its device consumes significantly less energy. This standard is aimed at applications such as fitness devices, entertainment, health care, and the like. It uses frequency-hopping technology, which helps it work very well in noisy or congested areas. It can use any of the 40 frequency bands located near 2.4 GHz.

Bluetooth is called a personal network because a person with a smartphone, for example, can connect up to seven devices. For BLE devices to communicate with each other, they follow two important protocols, Generic Access Protocol (GAP) and Generic Attributes (GATT). GAP controls advertising and connections between devices. GAP allows a device to act as a broadcaster, an observer, a peripheral, or a central device. A device can act on one or many roles at the same time. A broadcaster periodically sends out advertising packets. Meanwhile, an observer designed for read only listens for advertising with data. For example, a temperature sensor can broadcast its readings periodically for anyone to listen to. A peripheral device broadcasts advertising data and waits for central devices to connect to. A peripheral device is usually a small battery-operated sensor with little processing power such as a temperature sensor or a pressure sensor, and a central device is typically a tablet or a smartphone with a lot of processing power. After the devices are connected, the advertising stops and the devices use GATT to exchange data over a BLE connection. In Bluetooth terminology, pairing involves a smartphone connecting to an embedded system, such as a fitness device. This pairing establishes a connection between a master, the smartphone, and a slave, the fitness device, or between a client and a server (we will discuss more on this model later).

According to GATT, for two Bluetooth devices to communicate, they have to support the same "profiles." GATT defines profile as a set of functions geared toward a certain application. For example, a headset profile's support functions related to headsets or a human interface device (HID) profile is used by a Nintendo Wii controller to command a Nintendo Wii system. A profile has many predefined services, and within a service, there may be many characteristics. A characteristic can be thought of like a variable in the C language, and it can be readable, writeable, or both. Each characteristic is associated with a unique 128-bit number called the universally unique identifier (UUID). A BLE device can use a 16-byte or a 16-bit UUID. A characteristic UUID is used in a request from a client to access this characteristic. A characteristic can also have one or more descriptors, which are information, such as its unit and its name. It also has a handle. Like the C language, a handle on a characteristic is a pointer to a structure in a GATT that has all the information about that characteristic. Handles cannot be sent across the Bluetooth network, but they are used by the host and controller to track characteristics. However, UUIDs, rather than handles, can be passed across the network. Even though the handle of a characteristic is unique, a characteristic may have many different UUIDs. A BLE device can have as many services and characteristics as it needs.

A Bluetooth network, which is also known as a piconet, uses the master-slave model to manage the data transfer between devices. In the Bluetooth network, a master can connect up to seven slaves, but a slave can only pair with one master. The master coordinates and controls the data transfer in the network. It can send data to the slave and request data from the slave. However, the slave can only communicate with the master and cannot talk with other slaves on the network. When a smartphone connects to an embedded system like a fitness device, it becomes the client, and the embedded system becomes the server. To get data from the server, the client issues a read request. However, if the client wants to send data to the server, it uses a write request. If the client wants the server to continue sending data to the client without being requested, it will issue a notify or (read or write) indication command to the server.

In the server-client paradigm, to read a characteristic, the client makes a read indication request to the server. Inside the request, there is a UUID associated with the desired characteristic. The server will respond with the value of the wanted characteristic by doing a read confirmation. The returned data may be one or more bytes. For a long number of bytes, the response can be broken into many messages. The size of the data is decided during the initialization of the characteristic.

Similarly, the client makes a write indication request when it wants to set the value of a characteristic. The request also contains a UUID of the characteristic to be written to. A write confirmation response is returned to the client when the data have been written.

If a client wants to keep up to date on the value of a certain characteristic in a server, it can make a notify request to the server. The request includes a UUID assigned to the characteristic to be notified. The server responds with an acknowledgment and streams data back to the client either periodically or whenever the value changes. The client can start the notification by activating a listen command on the smartphone or stopping the notification.

The master can act as a central device or other devices, such as a broadcaster. It has information that other devices may need (e.g., current temperature). The broadcaster can advertise, but it is not connectable. For instance, a thermometer can send out its temperature reading but other devices cannot connect with it. Another type of device that can scan for advertisement but is not connectable is, for example, a temperature display, which can display temperatures sent out by a broadcaster. That device is called an observer.

2. The Bluetooth Protocol Stack[1]

The Bluetooth protocol stack typically includes a host layer and a controller layer. The users' code and the operating system are located above the host layer.

The controller layers include a physical layer (PHY), a link layer (LL), and a host controller interface (HCI) layer.

The PHY supports a 1 Mbps adaptive frequency-hopping Gaussian frequency-shifting keying radio working in the 2.4 GHz ISM band. It is divided into forty channels of which thirty-seven are used for data exchange and three are used for advertising and broadcasting. The frequency-hopping technology allows Bluetooth devices to operate in this noisy frequency band without much inference.

The LL helps higher layers deal with all the low-level details, such as the timing specification of the PHYs by hiding them in this layer. It communicates with higher layers via the HCI interface.

The HCI layer allows communication between the host and the controller via a standardized interface. The Bluetooth core specification defines commands and events that can be sent across the HCI between the host and the controller.

The host layer is responsible for a logical link control and adaption protocol (L2CAP), a Generic Access Protocol (GAP), a GATT profile, a security manager (SM), and an attribute protocol (ATT). The L2CAP resource manager block manages some scheduling between channels to make sure the L2CAP channel with quality of service can always access the physical channel. It also performs a fragmentation and combination process. For example, it takes large packets from upper layers and chops them into smaller packets to fit the maximum payload size, 27 bytes, of a BLE packet. When receiving many smaller size packets, it combines them into bigger packets to be sent upstream. L2CAP is also responsible for multiplexing different protocols from upper layers into BLE format packets. For example, it routes the ATT and the SM protocol to the BLE. Both of these protocols will be covered later.

The GAP block provides basic functions, such as device discovery, connection modes, security, and authentication, as shown in Figure 8.1. Upon reset, the device is in an idle state.

1 "Core Specifications," Bluetooth, n.d., https://www.bluetooth.com/specifications/bluetooth-core-specification.

FIGURE 8.1 GAP State Diagram.

If the device is a slave or an embedded system, it will start advertising (transmitting data without being connected with any master) either to let initiators know they can request to connect to it or to send out data to listening devices without the need to be connected (for example, a weather beacon sends out weather information to anyone who wants to listen to it). On the other hand, if the device is a master or a smartphone, it's scanning for advertisement. When receiving advertising packets, it sends a scan request to the advertiser, and the advertiser answers with a scan response. The system is now in the device discovery state. The scanner knows the advertiser's information and can put out a connection request. When accepting the connection request, the advertiser becomes a slave, and the initiator now is the master. The system is in the connection state.

The GATT block provides interfaces for accessing and/or modifying service characteristics. The GATT also shows the hierarchy of services, characteristics, and attributes of the attribute server. The SM provides peer-to-peer protocols to create encryption keys and identify keys over a dedicated fixed L2CAP channel. Figure 8.2 shows the organization of the BLE stack layers where the BLE host resides in an application processor, such as the launchpad (LP) Tiva C and the BLE controller in the TI BLE 2650 device.

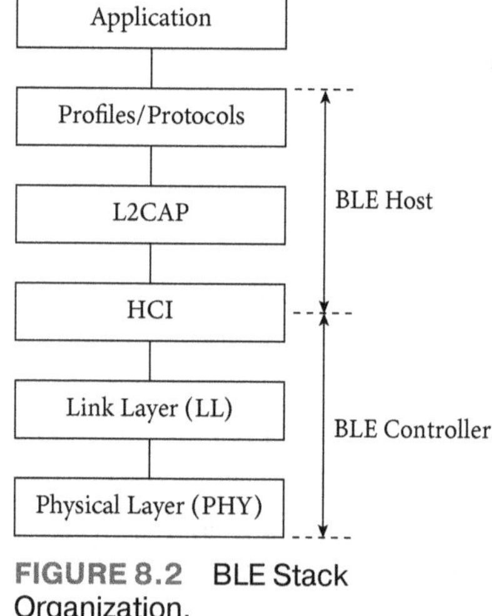

FIGURE 8.2 BLE Stack Organization.

3. The Client Server Model[2]

Data transfer in Bluetooth is based on the GATT, which is an extension of the ATT. ATT is a stateless client server protocol, where a client requests data from a server and a server sends data to clients. When a request is still pending (i.e., no response has been received), no new request can be issued. A server can connect to many clients, but a client can only connect to one server. Kevin Townsend et al. (2014)[3] described GATT as follows: "GATT defines generic data objects that can be used and reused by a variety of application profiles (known as GATT-based profiles). It maintains the same client/server architecture present in ATT, but the data is now encapsulated in services, which consist of one or more characteristics. Each characteristic can be thought of as the union of a piece of user data along with metadata (descriptive information about that value

2 Valvano, *Embedded Systems.*

3 Kevin Townsend, Carles Cufi, Akiba, and Robert Davidson, *Getting Started with Bluetooth Low Energy* (Sebastopol, CA: O'Reilly Media, 2014), 27.

such as properties, user-visible name, units and more)." We can think of a characteristic like a variable, and a service is like a folder containing many variables.

The client device can send requests to the server device to ask for a read, write, or notify. If the client wants to know the value of a characteristic, it can send a read request. The server will return the value of the requested characteristic. When the client wants to change the value of a characteristic, it can send a write request with a new value. The server responds with a write confirmation after assigning a new value to the characteristic. When the client wants to keep up to date on a certain characteristic in the server, it issues a notify request. The server streams back the value of the requested characteristic periodically or when the value of the characteristic changes. A client can only send one request at a time. A request is completed after a response is received.

4. Using TI CC2650[4,5]

The TI CC2650 is used as a slave after it's flashed with an image of the Simple Network Processor (SNP) while the TI TM4C123/MSP432 launchpad (LP) is used as the Application Processor (AP or LP) or the master to communicate with the slave SNP via a set of seven wires: (1) power, (2) ground, (3) Reset, (4) Tx, (5) Rx, (6) master ready (MRDY), and (7) slave ready (SRDY). While Reset, MRDY, and SRDY are negative logic signals (i.e., they go low when they are asserted), Tx and Rx are positive logic signals (i.e., they go high when they are asserted). This signal handshake scheme is called the Network Processor Interface (NPI),[6] which is used to send/receive data/commands between an application processor, such as the LP Tiva C, and an SNP, such as the TI C2650 device. It's also called the Unified NPI to differentiate it from the legacy NPI.

To initialize Bluetooth, the master (AP/LP) resets the slave (SNP) by asserting its output Reset for at least 10 ms while holding signal Master Ready (MRDY) high, as shown in Figure 8.3.

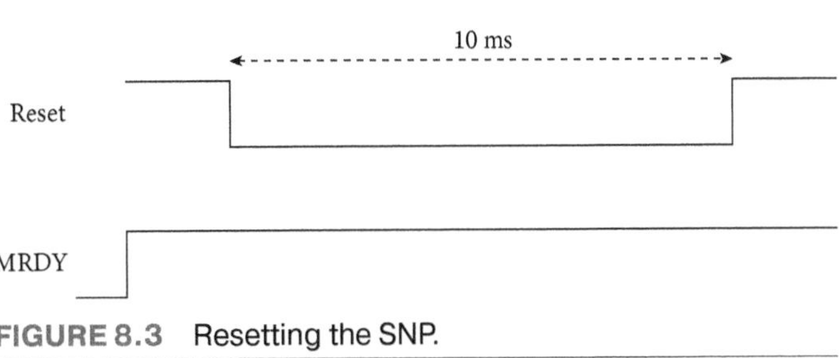

FIGURE 8.3 Resetting the SNP.

4 "SimpleLink™ *Bluetooth*® Low Energy CC2640 Wireless MCU," Texas Instruments, 2016, http://www.ti.com/lit/ml/swru476/swru476.pdf.

5 "Simple Network Processor API Guide for BLE-Stack Version 2.2.0," Texas Instruments, May 2016,. https://software-dl.ti.com/msp430/msp430_public_sw/mcu/msp430/simple_msp432_sdk_bluetooth_plugin/1.25.00.42/exports/simplelink_msp432_sdk_bluetooth_plugin_1_25_00_42/docs/CC2640SimpleNetworkProcessorAPIGuide.pdf. Accessed 6/23/2021.

6 "Network Processor Interface (NPI)," Texas Instruments, accessed June 3, 2020, http://dev.ti.com/tirex/explore/content/simplelink_cc13x2_26x2_sdk_3_10_00_53/docs/ble5stack/ble_user_guide/html/ble-stack-common/npi-index.html.

MRDY
SRDY
Rx
Tx
Reset

FIGURE 8.4 Master Sending Message/Command to Slave.

To send a message to the slave SNP, the master (AP/LP) asserts the MRDY waiting for the SRDY to go low. Once SRDY goes low, the master can begin sending messages/commands to the slave using signal Rx. After completing the message transmission, the master disasserts MRDY, telling the slave that it finishes with the message. The slave responds by disasserting SRDY, signaling the master when it receives the message successfully. During this entire transaction, signal Reset is maintained in a high state (inactive). The sequence is shown in the following Figure 8.4.

Figure 8.5 shows the case of a slave sending a message to a master. When the slave (SNP) wants to send a message to the master (AP), it begins by asserting signal SRDY. The master responds by asserting signal MRDY, agreeing to receive a message from the slave. The slave then transmits its message on signal Tx and disasserts signal SRDY once it finishes the message transmission. The master signals that it receives the message successfully by disasserting signal MRDY.

The format of a message is shown in Figure 8.6, where each box is a UART frame of a byte of data. A UART frame is composed of 1 start bit, 8 data bits, and 1 stop bit. Each message begins with a Start of Frame (SOF), which is 0xFE in hex or 254 in decimal. The next two boxes are reserved for the length of the payload data. Length is in little-endian format. After the two command boxes, the payload boxes carry the parameters of the commands. The payload can be empty if the command has no parameters. The message ends with a Frame Check Sequence (FCS), which is the "exclusive-or" of all the data, excluding the SOF and the FCS (Figure 8.6).

FIGURE 8.5 Slave Sending Message to Master.

SOF	Byte 0	Byte 1	Byte 2	Byte 3	Byte 4–Byte (L + 3)	FCS
Start of Frame 0xFE	Payload Length L	0	Cmd0	Cmd1	Pay Load (L Bytes)	Frame Check Sequence

FIGURE 8.6 Format of an NPI Message.

Typically, after module CC2650 is reset, the LP starts programming the 2650 by adding services and characteristics to it before adding advertising commands to make the SNP begin advertising.

4.1. Add Service and Add Service Response

To add services, the LP sends the SNP command "Add Service," "35, 81" as follows:

```
LP->SNP FE, 03, 00, 35, 81, 01, F0, FF, B9
```

All the numbers in the commands/messages are in hexadecimal and little-endian format (i.e., the less significant number goes before the more significant number). For example, "10, F0" means 0xF010.

Where FE is SOF (Start of Frame), "03, 00" is the length of the payload, which is 3 bytes since the format is little endian. Command C0, C1 is "35, 81," which is the SNP Add Service command. The next byte, "01" is a parameter of the Add Service command, and it means this is a primary service. If a secondary service is desired, a "02" should be sent instead. The next two bytes, "FFF0," represent the UUID of the service. B9 is the FCS.

After receiving the command Add Service from the LP, the SNP responds with an Add Service Response message, as in the following:

```
SNP->LP FE, 01, 00, 75, 81, 00, F5
```

Where "FE" is SOF, "01, 00" is the 1-byte length of the payload. Commands C0, C1 are "75, 81," which represent the Add Service Response command. Byte "00" is the parameter of this command, and it means "success." F5 is the FCS.

4.2. Add Characteristic and Add Characteristic Response

After adding a service, the LP can send an SNP Add Characteristic Value Declaration command to the SNP. This command adds two attributes required by the Bluetooth specification: characteristic value and characteristic declaration. The following is an example of the SNP Add Characteristic Valuation Declaration command sent from the LP to the SNP:

```
LP->SNP FE, 08, 00, 35, 82, 03, 0A, 00, 00, 00, 02, F1, FF, BA
```

The first byte is SOF, and the second and third bytes are the length of the payload, which is 8-bytes long in this example. The fourth and fifth bytes are command C0, C1, which are "35, 82," which are the opcodes for the SNP Add Characteristic Value Declaration commands. The sixth byte, "03," is the Value Permission. In this case, it means GATT read and write permission. The next two bytes, "0A, 00," are the Value Properties, and here they mean GATT Read and GATT Write Properties. The ninth and tenth bytes, "00, 02," are the Value Max Length, which represent 200 in hexadecimal or 512 bytes (since the parameters of the SNP commands are in little-endian format). The next two bytes, "F1, FF" or 0xFFF1, are the value of the UUID of this characteristic. The last byte "BA" is the FCS.

Like before, after receiving the Add Characteristic Value command, the SNP responds with an Add Characteristic Value Declaration Response command:

```
SNP->LP FE, 03, 00, 75, 82, 00, 1E, 00, EA
```

After the first byte of SOF and the 2-byte payload length of 1, the next 2 bytes, "75, 82," are the Add Characteristic Value Declaration Response command. The sixth byte, "00," is the status parameter of the command, and it means success. If this byte has a value different than zero, it means the Add Characteristic command fails, and this byte now represents the SNP error codes. The next two bytes, "1E,00," are the attribute handle of the characteristic value. The last byte of the command sequence, "EA," is the FCS.

4.3. Add Characteristic Descriptors and Add Characteristic Descriptor Response

The Add Characteristic Descriptors Declaration command is sent from the LP to the SNP to add one or more attributes to a characteristic, such as a user description string, client characteristic configuration descriptor (CCCD), presentation format, server characteristic configuration, or aggregate format. The following is an example of using this command:

```
LP->SNP FE, 0B, 00, 35, 83, 80, 01, 05, 00, 05, 00, 44, 61,
74, 61, 00, 0C
```

After the first byte of SOF(FE) is the 2-byte data length of eleven (0xB). Following the Add Characteristic Descriptors Declaration commands, "35, 83," the 1-byte header "80" specifies that a user Description String attribute is added. The next byte, "01," indicates a GATT read permission attribute. The next two bytes, "05, 00," are the Max Length field of the characteristic. Another two bytes, "05,00," signal an initial length of the string. The next four bytes—"44, 61, 74, 61"—are the ASCII equivalent of the string "data." The next byte, "00," is the null character marking the end of a string. The last byte of "0C" is the FCS of this command.

Like the previous cases, after receiving this command, the SNP sends back an Add Characteristic Descriptors Declaration Response to signal the LP that it received the command successfully or not.

```
SNP->LP FE, 04, 00, 75, 83, 80, 00, 1F, 00, 6D
```

The seventh byte is a successful response, "00," that adds a user descriptor attribute, "80." The eighth to the ninth bytes, "1F, 00," are the handle of the attribute added. After adding all characters, LP needs to ask the SNP to register this service as follows:

```
LP-> SNP FE, 00, 00, 35, 84, B1
```

And if the registration is successful, the SNP sends back the following message:

```
SNP-> LP FE, 05, 00, 75, 84, 00, 1C, 00, 29, 00, C1
```

where the 5 data bytes are 00 (successful), "1C, 00" = first attribute of the registered service and "29, 00" = the last attribute of the registered service.

4.4. Advertising

After defining the services and characteristics, the LP sends four more commands to the SNP to set up and start advertising: Set Device Name, Set Advertising1, Set Advertising2, and Start Advertising.

Set Device Name

To set the device name in the server, the LP sends the SNP Set GATT Parameter command as follows:

```
LP->SNP FE, 12, 0, 35, 8C, 01, 00, 00, ….DE
```

The fourth and fifth bytes, "35, 8C," are the Set GATT Parameter command. The sixth byte, "01," is the Service ID, which indicates a Generic Access Service. The next two bytes, "00, 00," are the Parameter ID, which means Device Name. All the data bytes up to the FCS, "DE," are the ASCII-equivalent bytes of the device name.

Set Advertising Data and Response

Before advertising, the SNP needs to be programmed with a set advertising data command. In a typical example, the LP will issue two advertising data commands to the SNP: one to set up the nonconnectable advertisement data and one to the connectable advertising data. An example of the first command is as follows:

```
LP->SNP FE,0B,00,55,43,01,02,01,06,06,FF,0D,00,03,00,00,EE
```

After the first byte, SOF and the payload data length of 11, "0B,00," the fourth and fifth bytes, are the command Set Advertising Data, "55, 43". The sixth byte is the parameter Non-connectable Advertisement Data, "01." The 7th to the 16th bytes are related to the identity of the company, device id, and so on. The last byte, "EE," is the FCS.

A Set Advertising Data Response cycle is returned to the LP to signal whether the command Set Advertising is executed successfully or not.

```
NP->LP FE,01,00,55,43,00,17
```

An example of a second command to set up connectable advertisement data is shown in the following:

```
LP->SNP FE,1B,00,55,43,00,10,09,53,68,61,70,65,20,74,68,65,
20,57,6F,72,6C,64,05,12,50,00,20,03,02,0A,00,0C

LP->SNP FE,0C,00,55,43,00,01,09,05,12,50,00,20,03,02,0A,00,7E
```

After the first byte of SOF, "FE," and the 2-byte payload data length of 12 (0x000C), "0C, 00," are the Set Advertising Data, "55, 43." The sixth byte, "00," represents the command parameter Scan Response Data.

Start Advertising and Response

To begin advertising, the LP issues the Start Advertising command, "55, 42," to the SNP. The following is an example of a Start Advertising Command:

```
LP->SNP FE,0E,00,55,42,00,00,00,64,00,00,00,00,01,00,00,0
0,C5, 02,BB
```

The first byte after the command is "00," which represents the parameter Connectable Undirected Advertisements. The seventh and eighth bytes, "00, 00," are the time-out parameters, and in this case, this means advertise indefinitely. The ninth and tenth bytes (in little-endian format), "64, 00," are the advertising interval in units of 625 microseconds. Please see Section 9.3.1 in the documentation (of reference 5 cited earlier) within the footnote for more details on the other command parameters. Similar to other commands, the SNP sends back the start advertising command response to notify the LP of the success or failure of the execution of the command.

Read Request

When a client wants to read the value of a characteristic that has been added earlier, the SNP will issue a characteristic read indication command to the LP. The LP then will have 30 seconds to send a characteristic read confirmation command, "55, 87," to the SNP with the characteristic value. If the LP does not respond within 30 seconds, an ATT time-out will happen, and the connection will be lost. No communication will occur until the connection is reestablished.

When a client wants to write new data to a characteristic added earlier, the SNP will send a characteristic write indication command, "55, 88," to the LP, and the LP will have 30 seconds to respond regarding whether it allows the write by sending a characteristic write confirmation command to the SNP. Similarly, to the read case noted earlier, a time-out and a communication loss will happen if the LP does not respond within 30 seconds.

The best way to study a technology is to actually implement it. The TI hardware mentioned earlier provides a good platform to learn about Bluetooth BLE, and Project Zero, which we are presenting in the following section, is a good lab for you to get familiar with it. ESP32 is another microcontroller that has both Bluetooth BLE and Wi-Fi integrated. It also supports C, as well as MicroPython languages, and it's another good platform to implement Bluetooth technology applications.

5. Example Project[7]

5.1. Project Zero (TI CC2650)

"Project Zero" from TI is an example of using Bluetooth to communicate with a smartphone.

The lab setup is an LP MSP432P0401R connected to a CC2650 platform, which was previously programmed to have an SNP image (the procedure to flash BoosterPack 2650 is described at the end of the lab). The LP MSP432P0401R (LP/AP) communicates with the BoosterPack CC2650, which acts as a Simple Network Processor SNP through a UART or SPI serial connection. After being programmed with an SNP image, the BoosterPack CC2650 (SNP) can be driven through a simple API (SAP) to provide BLE wireless connectivity to

7 TI Project Zero,.TI does not provide direct access to this Project Zero any more. To access this project, you need to install SimpleLink Acdemy version v1.11 at http://software-dl.ti.com/lprf/simplelink_academy/overview.html#v1-08-june-21st-2016. Accessed 6/24/21.

any BLE master, such as a smartphone. This allows the LP/AP to offload all the BLE protocol processing to the SNP, thus freeing the LP to handle other tasks.

The SNP supports three different threads: BLE Connection/Advertising Management Thread, Button Management Thread, and SNP Update Thread.

The BLE connection/advertising management thread is responsible for broadcasting messages to surrounding devices. It also manages all interaction with the SAP drivers and supports callbacks from the SAP layer. The user codes of the LP start the BLE initialization by calling function ProjectZero_createTask, which in turn calls ProjectZero_init to initialize the SNP and the BLE. It also sets up and runs the main state machine for Project Zero through a forever loop. All the functions mentioned earlier reside in file project_zero.c.

The Button Management Thread manages the button services, whose support code is contained in file button_service.c. The main program starts the process by calling function buttonTask_createTask, which was put in file project_zero.c. The function initializes an RTOS queue to hold data about the status of the button when the LP and SNP communicate via function ProjectZero_buttonTaskFxn, which is executed in a thread called buttonthread. File button_service.c contains functions to support button services, such as ButtonService_addService; to add the button services, such as ButtonService_registerAppCBs; to register callback functions, such as ButtonService_setParameter; to set parameters, such as ButtonService_getParameter; and to get parameters of a button service.

The SNP update thread manages the updating of the SNP device with a firmware image from the LP's flash memory. The main program starts the update thread by calling the function updateSNP_createTask (main_tirtos.c), which initializes all the parameters before creating the thread snpTask running function ProjectZero_updateSNP_taskFxn. The flash ROM update starts when semaphore updateSNPSemHandle is posted.

5.2. ESP32 (with Built-in BLE Module)

ESP32 is a cheap microcontroller that has built-in Wi-Fi and BLE capabilities. It has a C++ library that makes BLE programming much easier with C++ classes built to hide BLE's complex details and expose high level interfaces for programs to use.[8] Some of the popular classes are, for example, BLEServer (which models a server), BLEService, BLECharacteristic, BLEDescriptor, and BLEAdvertising, so to create a BLE server program, we only have to write a few lines of code as in the BLE Server program 8.1 (a slightly modified version of a BLE Server program from the Arduino IDE Library). Its pseudo code is as follows:

1. Initialize the BLE environment: BLEDevice::Init("BLEServer");
2. Create the server: BLEServer *pServer = BLEDevice::createServer();

8 https://github.com/nkolban/esp32-snippets/blob/master/Documentation/BLE%20C%2B%2B%20Guide.pdf. Accessed 4/8/2021.

3. Create the characteristic: BLECharacteristic *pCharacteristic = pService->createCharacteristic(

```
CHARACTERISTIC_UUID,

BLECharacteristic::PROPERTY_READ |

BLECharacteristic::PROPERTY_WRITE

);
```

4. Set the value of the Characteristic: pCharacteristic->setValue("Hello World");
5. Set the Advertising: BLEAdvertising *pAdvertising = BLEDevice::getAdvertising(); and add more parameters for the Advertising.
6. Start Advertising: BLEDevice::startAdvertising();

   You can use the LightBlue Explorer, a free Iphone app (downloadable from the Apple Store), to connect to the BLE server and to read/write the characteristic of the server. Program 8.1 is written for the microcontroller ESP32 to run in the Arduino IDE.

```
/*

Based on Neil Kolban example for IDF: https://github.com/
nkolban/esp32-snippets/blob/master/cpp_utils/tests/BLE%20
Tests/SampleServer.cpp

Ported to Arduino ESP32 by Evandro Copercini

updates by chegewara

*/


#include <BLEDevice.h>

#include <BLEUtils.h>

#include <BLEServer.h>


// See the following for generating UUIDs:

// https://www.uuidgenerator.net/
```

```
#define SERVICE_UUID        "4fafc201-1fb5-459e-8fcc-
c5c9c331914b"

#define CHARACTERISTIC_UUID
"beb5483e-36e1-4688-b7f5-ea07361b26a8"


void setup() {

Serial.begin(115200);

Serial.println("Starting BLE work!");


BLEDevice::init("BLE Server");

BLEServer *pServer = BLEDevice::createServer();

BLEService *pService = pServer->createService(SERVICE_UUID);

BLECharacteristic *pCharacteristic =
pService->createCharacteristic(

            CHARACTERISTIC_UUID,

BLECharacteristic::PROPERTY_READ |

BLECharacteristic::PROPERTY_WRITE

            );


pCharacteristic->setValue("Hello World");

Serial.println("Hello World");

pService->start();

// BLEAdvertising *pAdvertising = pServer->getAdvertising();
// this still is working for backward compatibility

BLEAdvertising *pAdvertising = BLEDevice::getAdvertising();

pAdvertising->addServiceUUID(SERVICE_UUID);
```

```
pAdvertising->setScanResponse(true);

pAdvertising->setMinPreferred(0x06);  // functions that help
with iPhone connections issue

pAdvertising->setMinPreferred(0x12);

BLEDevice::startAdvertising();

Serial.println("Characteristic defined! Now you can read it in
your phone!");

}


void loop() {

// put your main code here, to run repeatedly:

delay(2000);

}
```

Program 8.1: BLE Server

Program 8.2 is another example of a BLE server with a characteristic having a Notify property. It will keep updating the client on its characteristic's new values (Figure 8.7) when the option "listen for notification" is toggled on.

Figure 8.8 echoes the information received by the server for a different writeable characteristic. For example, when the client writes a new value of 0x66676869 (Figure 8.8), the server terminal displays characters "fghi" since their ASCII codes are 0x66676869.

```
/*

Video: https://www.youtube.com/watch?v=oCMOYS71NIU

Based on Neil Kolban example for IDF: https://github.com/nkolban/esp32-snippets/
blob/master/cpp_utils/tests/BLE%20Tests/SampleNotify.cpp

Ported to Arduino ESP32 by Evandro Copercini


Create a BLE server that, once we receive a connection, will send periodic notifications.

The service advertises itself as: 6E400001-B5A3-F393-E0A9-E50E24DCCA9E

Has a characteristic of: 6E400002-B5A3-F393-E0A9-E50E24DCCA9E - used for receiv-
ing data with "WRITE"
```

Has a characteristic of: 6E400003-B5A3-F393-E0A9-E50E24DCCA9E - used to send data with "NOTIFY"

The design of creating the BLE server is:

1. Create a BLE Server,
2. Create a BLE Service,
3. Create a BLE Characteristic on the Service,
4. Create a BLE Descriptor on the characteristic,
5. Start the service.
6. Start advertising.

In this example, rxValue is the data received (only accessible inside that function).
And txValue is the data to be sent, in this example just a byte incremented every second.

```
*/

#include <BLEDevice.h>

#include <BLEServer.h>

#include <BLEUtils.h>

#include <BLE2902.h>


BLEServer *pServer = NULL;

BLECharacteristic * pTxCharacteristic;

bool deviceConnected = false;

bool oldDeviceConnected = false;

uint8_t txValue = 0;
```

// See the following for generating UUIDs:
// https://www.uuidgenerator.net/

```
#define SERVICE_UUID            "6E400001-B5A3-F393-E0A9-
E50E24DCCA9E" // UART service UUID

#define CHARACTERISTIC_UUID_RX
"6E400002-B5A3-F393-E0A9-E50E24DCCA9E"

#define CHARACTERISTIC_UUID_TX
"6E400003-B5A3-F393-E0A9-E50E24DCCA9E"


class MyServerCallbacks: public BLEServerCallbacks {

void onConnect(BLEServer* pServer) {

deviceConnected = true;

};


void onDisconnect(BLEServer* pServer) {

deviceConnected = false;

}

};


class MyCallbacks: public BLECharacteristicCallbacks {

void onWrite(BLECharacteristic *pCharacteristic) {

std::string rxValue = pCharacteristic->getValue();


if (rxValue.length() > 0) {

Serial.println("*********");

Serial.print("Received Value: ");

for (int i = 0; i < rxValue.length(); i++)
```

```
Serial.print(rxValue[i]);


Serial.println();

Serial.println("*********");

}

}

};

void setup() {

Serial.begin(115200);


// Create the BLE Device

BLEDevice::init("UART Service");


// Create the BLE Server

pServer = BLEDevice::createServer();

pServer->setCallbacks(new MyServerCallbacks());


// Create the BLE Service

BLEService *pService = pServer->createService(SERVICE_UUID);


// Create a BLE Characteristic

pTxCharacteristic = pService->createCharacteristic(

            CHARACTERISTIC_UUID_TX,

            BLECharacteristic::PROPERTY_NOTIFY
```

```
                    );

    pTxCharacteristic->addDescriptor(new BLE2902());

    BLECharacteristic * pRxCharacteristic =
    pService->createCharacteristic(
                    CHARACTERISTIC_UUID_RX,
                    BLECharacteristic::PROPERTY_WRITE
                    );

    pRxCharacteristic->setCallbacks(new MyCallbacks());

    // Start the service
    pService->start();

    // Start advertising
    pServer->getAdvertising()->start();
    Serial.println("Waiting a client connection to notify...");
    }

    void loop() {

    if (deviceConnected) {
            pTxCharacteristic->setValue(&txValue, 1);
            pTxCharacteristic->notify();
```

```
txValue++;

 delay(10); // bluetooth stack will go into congestion, if
too many packets are sent

}



 // disconnecting

 if (!deviceConnected && oldDeviceConnected) {

       delay(500); // give the bluetooth stack the chance to
get things ready

       pServer->startAdvertising(); // restart advertising

       Serial.printl-
n("start advertising");

       oldDeviceConnected =
deviceConnected;

}

// connecting

if (deviceConnected && !oldDeviceCon-
nected) {

       // do stuff here on connecting

       oldDeviceConnected =
deviceConnected;

}
```

Program 8.2: BLE Server with Notify Characteristic

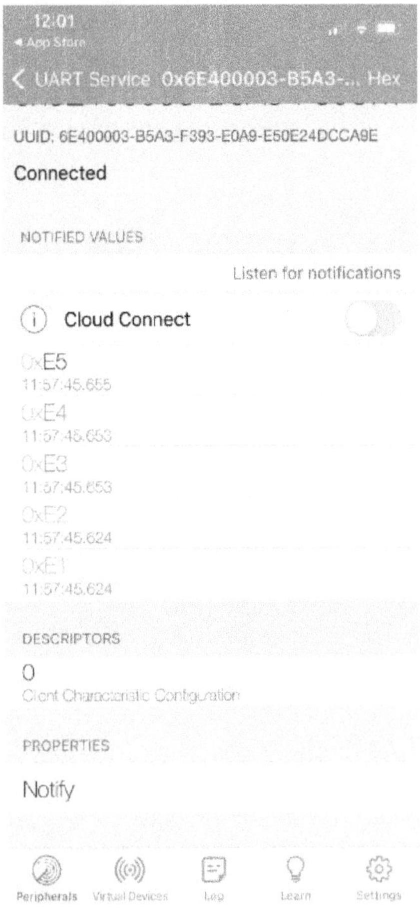

FIGURE 8.7 Notify Characteristic.

EXERCISES

1. Using Project Zero, add another service with several characteristics.

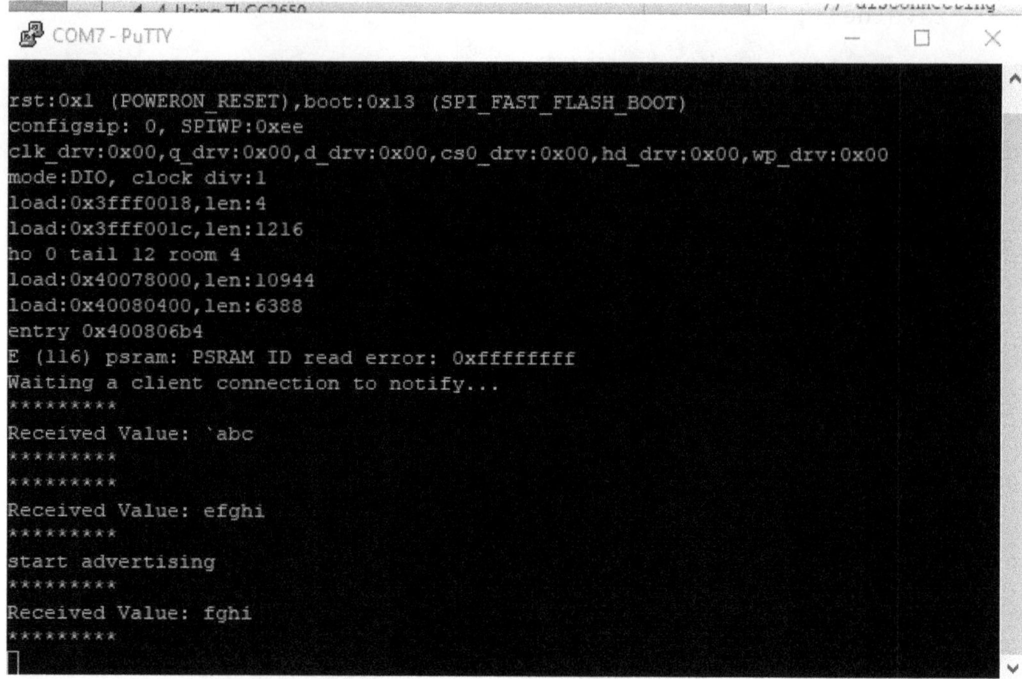

FIGURE 8.8 Putty terminal showing interaction between the Server and the Client.

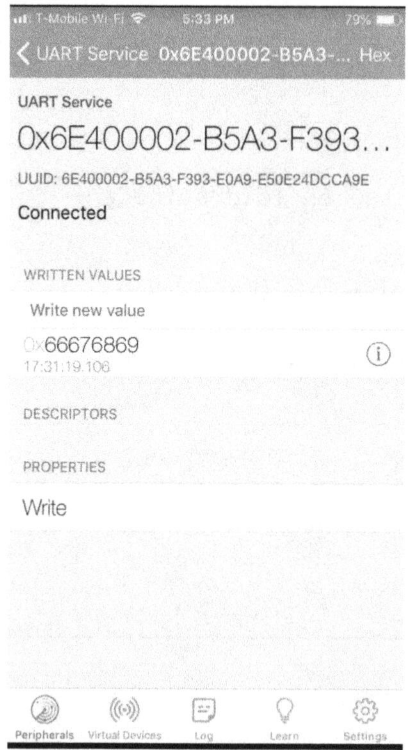

FIGURE 8.9 The client's (Iphone) interaction with the Server.

2. Design a nonconnectable beacon that keeps repeating a message, such as "Bluetooth Is a Cool Technology." Use the Tiva C and the CC2650 as the server/advertiser and a smartphone as a scanner/client.

3. Use Bluetooth to create a home automation system, for example, to display temperature and to turn on the fan if the temperature is too high.

4. Use Bluetooth to create a system of interconnected smoke detectors. When one alarm trips, all the alarms will sound. The alarms communicate with one another via Bluetooth.

5. Use Bluetooth to design a beacon to beam information about the operation hours of a building or other information about the building, such as whose offices are inside the building or when visitors get close to the front door of a building.

6. Use Bluetooth to transmit information like humidity levels, pH degrees, or temperatures of an agriculture system.

7. Use Bluetooth to transmit information to a smartphone from environment sensors monitoring things like bacteria (e.g., coronavirus), poison levels, or gas concentration level.

8. Design a toy car that's remotely controlled by Bluetooth.

9. Use Bluetooth to design a light that can be turned on or off by a smartphone.

10. Design a sequential scheduler where the lights will have an equal amount of time when there are multiple cars or no cars detected by the sensor. If the sensor sees a singular vehicle, then it will interrupt and allow that vehicle to pass and then return to the regular sequence. If multiple cars are detected on some but not all sides, then those vehicles will pass in a sequential order, while the side with no vehicle waits and then the system will return to the regular sequential order. We will be using LEDs as the traffic lights and a sensor compatible with the Tiva C. The scheduler can override and stop all the traffic lights with a smartphone using BLE to simulate the case when there's an emergency vehicle or when an electric train is coming to the intersection.

11. Use BLE to control movements of a motor.

12. Use BLE to transmit music from a computer to a speaker.

Credits

Fig. 8.7: Copyright © by Punch Through.

Fig. 8.8: Copyright © by Punch Through.

Fig. 8.9: Copyright © by Punch Through.

Chapter 9

Wi-Fi

1. Introduction

A product called WaveLAN created by NCR, a cash register manufacturer, debuted in 1990. It provided wireless connection between terminals to replace Ethernet cables and that led to the establishment of the first 802.11 standard. In 1999, after Steve Jobs (Apple) added wireless communication to the Mac books, wireless became a given feature in laptop computers. Wi-Fi stands for wireless fidelity, and it is based on the IEEE 802.11 standard, whose official name is wireless LAN medium access control (MAC) and PHY specification.

Using radio technology, Wi-Fi lets computers wirelessly connect to one another and connect to the internet and/or to the wired network. There are many variations of the standard, and some of them are not compatible with one another. Table 9.1 shows the specification variants with their frequency bands, speeds, and compatibilities.

TABLE 9.1 **802.11 FAMILY**

IEEE 802.11 Variant	Frequency Bands	Theoretical Speed	Compatible With
802.11a	5 GHz	54 Mbps	802.11n @5 MHz
802.11b	2.4 GHz	11 Mbps	802.11g (slower), 802.11n @2.4 MHz
802.11g	2.4 GHz	54 Mbps	802.11b (slower), 802.11n @2.4MHz
802.11n	2.4 and 5 GHz	600 Mbps	802.11a @ 5 MHz, 802.11b @2.4 MHz, 802.11n
802.11ac	Below 6 GHz	6 Gbps	

(continued)

TABLE 9.1 **802.11 FAMILY (*CONTINUED*)**

IEEE 802.11 Variant	Frequency Bands	Theoretical Speed	Compatible With
802.11ad	Up to 60 GHz	7 Gbps	
802.11af	TV white space (below 1 GHz)		
802.11a	Depends on country and allocation		
802.11ax (Wi-Fi 6)[1]	2.4 GHz, 5 GHz	10 Gbps	
802.11ay	45+ GHz	20+ Gbps	

The price difference in devices supporting 802.11a and 802.11ag is decreasing very rapidly, while prices of devices that support only 802.11b are falling precipitously. The latest Wi-Fi standard, Wi-Fi 6 or 802.11ax, offers more speed with lower latency and can support more device density than previous versions of the 802.11 specification. It's based on 5G, which is the name of the next-generation cellular technology that will replace the current 4G technology. The new technology, 5G, will bring about dramatic bandwidth improvement compared to 4G. The maximum speed of 5G is 10 Gbps, and its average speed is 1 Gbps, while the top speed of 4G is only 50 Mbps. So, for example, for a 4 GB HD movie, it would take consumers a couple of hours to download using a 4G network. With a 5G network, to download that same movie would only take seconds,[2] Wi-Fi 6 will compete with the 5G cellular network for internet connection. However, Wi-Fi 6 will still be the technology of choice for indoor networks, while the cellular 5G network will be the solution for outdoor networks. In some cases, they will be used together as complementary networks.

2. Wi-Fi Technology

Radio technology is used to connect computers and smartphones to Wi-Fi networks, and there are many limitations to radio wave propagation that we need to be aware of.

---

1 Cisco, "5 Things to Know About Wi-Fi 6 and 5G," April 2020, https://www.cisco.com/c/m/en_us/solutions/enterprise-networks/802-11ax-solution/nb-06-5-things-WiFi6-5G-infograph-cte-en.html.

2 IoT for All, "5G Is Poised to Revolutionize Industries Beyond Telecommunications," December 7, 2019, https://www.iotforall.com/5g-revolutionizing-industries-beyond-telecommunications/.

2.1. Radio Technology

Radio signals transmitted by antennas and received by Wi-Fi receivers allow wireless devices to communicate with one another. The ranges between antennas and receivers are typically about 300–500 feet outdoors and 100–150 feet indoors. Except for a few variants of the 802.11 specification, Wi-Fi devices mainly use 2.4 GHz band, which is also referred to as the industrial, scientific, medicine frequency band. It is subject to noise from cellular phones, microwave ovens, Bluetooth devices, and the like, since they are operating in the neighborhood with one another, so spread-spectrum technology is used to minimize interference.

Wi-Fi devices are half-duplex since they cannot hear while they are sending, and so they cannot detect a collision if they are sending and receiving at the same time. Depending on the version of the 802.11 specification, the radio signal is encoded and modulated using one of the following schemes: binary phase-shift keying, which transmits 1 bit per symbol, the 256 Quaternary QAM, which can carry 8 bits per symbol, etc. The received signal-to-noise ratio (SNR) must be high enough for the receiver to be able to decode the received symbols correctly. The SNR and the channel bandwidth also determine the capacity of a communication channel (C) according to the following Shannon-Hartley channel capacity theorem:

$$C = W.\log_2(1 + SNR),$$

where W is the channel bandwidth.

The scheme to allow a communication channel to be shared among users by assigning different carrier frequencies to different users is called a frequency division multiple access. Similarly, a time division multiple access assigns different time slots to different users or the code division multiple access scheme assigns different receivers with different mathematical codes.

The bit error rate, which is the fraction of erroneously decoded bits, is the ultimate measure of quality in digital transmission. Its typical values are between 10^{-3} to 10^{-9} bps.

2.2. Basic Components

Any wireless device joining a Wi-Fi network is called a wireless station (STA). A STA can be a laptop, a smartphone, a desktop, or a tablet. A basic building block of a Wi-Fi network is composed of two or more wirelessly connected STAs, and they create a basic service set (BSS), which is controlled by a single coordination function (CF). The CF determines when an STA receives and when it transmits. Depending on the radio coverage, not all STAs in a BSS can communicate directly to each other.

2.3. Operating Modes

Devices operating within the 802.11a/b/g specification can be configured in one of four operating modes.

Infrastructure Mode (or Master or Access Point (AP) Mode)

A Basic Service Set working in the infrastructure mode must have at least one wireless access point, which is basically an STA with some more functionality. An 802.11-compliant wireless

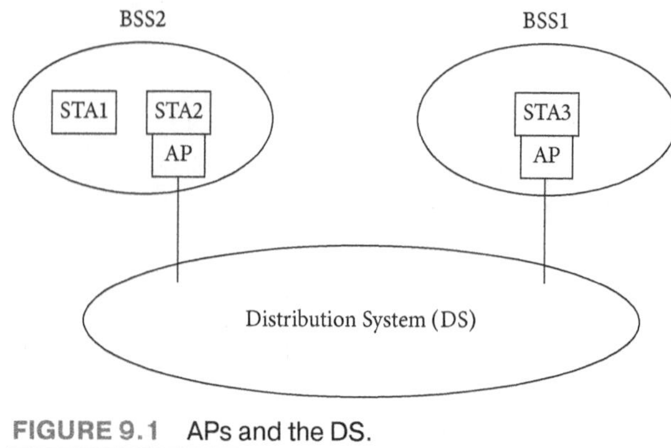

FIGURE 9.1 APs and the DS.

router usually contains AP functionality. The AP allows clients of the wireless network to access wired networks. Any wireless device that wants to join a BSS has to be associated with an AP, which lets its associated STAs access a distribution system (DS). As shown in Figure 9.1, the DS facilitates communication among the APs. The APs are typically connected to routers/switches with built-in modems to connect to the internet. Even though the physical implementation of the DS is not defined in the 802.11 specification, the DS medium usually is composed of coaxial cables or fiber optic cables.

Since the DS medium is logically different from the wireless medium (WM), the address of the AP on the DS medium is also different from its address on the WM. For example, the different addresses of the AP router are shown in Figure 9.2. The router in Figure 9.2 is connected to two APs (access points), each of which is connected to a different subnet. The left side of the router is connected to the subnet 192.168.1.0/24 and the right side to subnet 192.169.3.0/24, where the symbol /24 means that the leftmost 24 bits indicate the address of the subnet. For example, subnet 192.168.1 is one subnet (left) and 192.168.3 is the other subnet (right).

This infrastructure mode is also called client mode. A device in this mode joins a network managed by a master (AP) by sending its credential, and if accepted, it will be associated with that AP. Devices operating in this mode do not communicate with one another. They can only communicate with the associated master. Each AP is assigned a service set identifier (SSID) and a media access control (MAC) address. A MAC address is a unique address assigned to a network interface controller to allow it to communicate with other devices within a network segment. When you want to choose a Wi-Fi network to connect to, your wireless device (iPhone, laptop, etc.) usually shows a list of SSIDs (APs) to choose from. Periodically, APs send out beacon frames, which include their MAC address and their SSID. Your wireless device picks one of the APs by sending

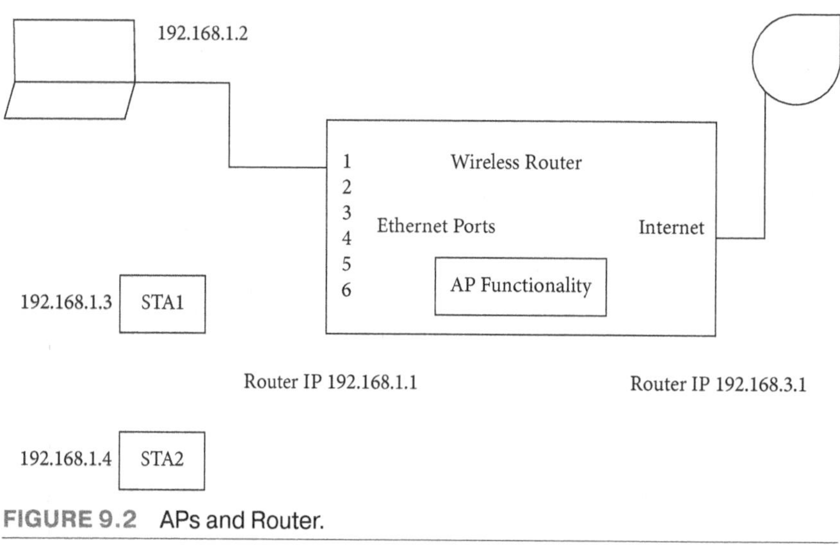

FIGURE 9.2 APs and Router.

an association request to the selected AP, which in turn sends an association response to your wireless device to allow your device to be associated with this AP if it does not require authentication. Otherwise, your wireless device needs to authenticate itself via username and password before it can be associated with the AP.

Ad Hoc Mode

One of the simplest types of Wi-Fi networks is an independent BSS, where STAs communicate with one another directly using ad hoc mode. No AP is needed in this mode. This is a peer-to-peer model.

A BSS operating in ad hoc mode is isolated from other Wi-Fi networks or other wired LANs. However, this ad hoc mode can still be very useful and can be used anywhere. For example, in a combat zone or in a rural area without any network infrastructure, this ad hoc network allows people to connect and communicate. Another example is in a meeting, an ad hoc network can be set up to let people share files or cooperatively work together on anything they want.

Monitor Mode

This mode is used for debug or monitor purposes and for devices in normal communication mode. A device in this mode does not transmit any data.

Extended Service Set (ESS)

An ESS is a network that is formed with a common DS and two or more BSSs. An ESS can be a complex network with arbitrary size. Figure 9.3 shows an example of an ESS network.

Note that the DS is not part of the ESS. To enable mobility in a wireless network, the DS keeps track of where STAs are located so that data can be delivered to the AP associated with the destination STA. Moreover, the network name, SSID, must be the same for all the APs in the ESS.

Hotspot

A hotspot is an area that has a wireless network that allows users to access the internet. A hotspot, which is connected to the broadband internet, has one or more APs. An AP can usually support up to 30 users, and its range of function is about 100–150 feet indoors and up to 300 feet outdoors.

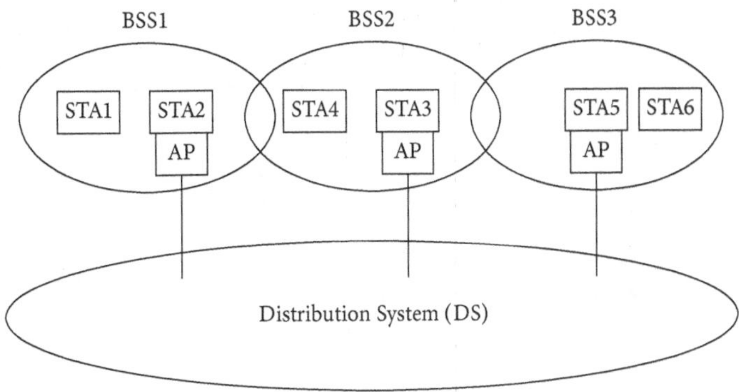

FIGURE 9.3 ESS.

2.4. Five-Layer Transmission Control Protocol/Internet Protocol (TCP/IP) Model

Even though it's not an international standard like the open system interconnect (OSI) model, which has seven layers, the TCP/IP model is widely used on the internet, and it has only five layers.

Layer 1 (PHY) specifies the physical medium where the communication takes place. It could be the radio waves for Wi-Fi or the cables for the Ethernet. Layer 2 (data link layer [DLL]) defines the protocol for devices to communicate. For example, the 802.11 uses the carrier sense multiple access/collision avoidance (CSMA/CA) protocol to prevent collision between packets. To follow the CSMA protocol, a station that wants to transmit a message first listens to the network. If it's not busy, the station is allowed to send its message. Otherwise, it will pause and wait to transmit the message at a later time. The network layer is layer 3. It's also known as the Internet Protocol layer or simply the internet layer. This is the place where the routing of packets happens. Packets can go from the local network and are routed to another network. Any node on the internet can be reached by its globally unique IP address. Layer 4 is the transport layer, which provides a way to access a particular service on the destination node. For example, Transmission Control Protocol (TCP), User Datagram Protocol (UDP), and Stream Control Transmission Protocol (SCTP) are the protocols available at this layer. UDP is usually used for video or audio streaming, and it is "connectionless" (i.e., it does not check to make sure the packets arrive or not). On the other hand, the TCP protocol checks to make sure all the packets arrive at the destination. The top layer, layer 5, is the application layer where the application software takes place.

Figure 9.4 illustrates the TCP/IP model. The TCP model can be thought of as a person delivering a letter to a city office building.[3] The person first has to walk (PHY), pay attention to the road traffic (DLL), turn at the correct intersections to arrive at the correct address (the network layer), go to the correct floor and the correct room number in the building (the transport layer), and then give the letter to the receptionist (the application layer).

The 802.11 specification defines the two layers in the five-layer TCP model in Figure 9.4. These two layers, the PHY and the DLL (Data Link Layer), are exactly the same two layers defined by the Ethernet specification (802.3). The DLL is actually made up of two layers, the media access (MAC) and the logical link control (LLC) layer.

Layer 5	Application Layer	
Layer 4	Transport Layer	
Layer 3	Network Layer	
Layer 2	Data Link Layer	Logical Link Control (LLC) Media Access Control (MAC)
Layer 1	Physical Layer	

FIGURE 9.4 TCP/IP Model.

The physical layer (PHY) defines such things as modulation methods, encoding schemes, and radio signal transmission. For example, 802.11b once used the deprecated frequency-hopping spread spectrum but currently uses the direct sequence spread spectrum. The PHY operates in specific frequency bands, as shown in Table 9.1.

The MAC layer is a sublayer of the DLL. As mentioned earlier, the 802.11 specification uses the CSMA/CA protocol at this layer. The 802.11 MAC requires the Wi-Fi network to use a MAC address with a format similar to that of the Ethernet

3 WnDW.net, *Wireless Networking in the Developing World*, 3rd ed. (Scotts Valley, CA: CreateSpace, 2013), 92.

MAC address. The MAC address assigned by the manufacturer of the network card is a 48-bit address, and it looks like this: 40:6C:8F:52:59:41. The first 24 bits of the MAC address are unique to a manufacturer. For example, in the previous example of the MAC address, Apple is the manufacturer with the assigned address of 40:6C:8F. Every device that is connected to a Wi-Fi or Ethernet network has a unique MAC address created by the device's manufacturer. A MAC address is used in switches to route packets from device to device within a network, and it never crosses internet gateways or router boundaries. It's only used in layer 1 and 2 (PHY and DLL) and never used directly on the internet. Instead, the IP addresses, which we discuss next, are used on the internet.

2.5. The IP

The IP operates on layer 3 and layer 4 of the TCP/IP model. Version 6 (IPv6) is the current version of the IP, and the previous version is version 4 (IPv4). Currently, about half of the internet connections use IPv6, and it's expected that by 2020, most of them will use IPv6. It's estimated that dual-stack networks, which can run both versions, will be common until about 2020. IPv4 and IPv6 are very similar, except for the length of the addresses. The IPv6 address is a 128-bit number, whereas the IPv4 address is 32 bits long.

IPv6 Addressing

The Ipv6 address is a 128-bit number that is often written in chunks of four hexadecimal numbers separated by colons. Here is an IPv6 address example: 2001:0cd8:5678:0000:0000:0000:0000:0003. It can also be written as 2001:0cd8:5678::3, where :: represents the chunks of 0s. The following are some special addresses:

- ::1 (0000:0000:0000:0000:0000: 0000:0000:0001) is the loopback address.
- :: (all zero) is an undetermined address.

The IPv6 address is usually split into two 64-bit parts, prefix and interface identifier. IPv6 nodes on the same link or network normally have the same prefix address.

IPv4 Addressing

The IPv4 address is a 32-bit number that is often written in chunks of 8-bit decimal numbers separated by periods. An example of an IPv4 address is 9.1.18.1 or 192.168.1.1. The following are some special IPv4 addresses:

- 127.0.0.1 is the IPv4 loopback address.
- 0.0.0.0 is an undetermined address.

Global IP Addresses

IP addresses must be unique and cannot be used at the same time at different nodes on the internet, so they must be allocated by some global authority. This authority is the Internet

Assigned Number Authority (IANA). It divides the IP address space into some large subnets, which are delegated to the five regional internet registries (RIRs). Each of these RIRs allocates smaller blocks of addresses to internet service providers (ISPs) in its region. The ISP in turn assigns smaller blocks of addresses to its clients. This process of address assignment enables each node on the internet to have a unique address so that there is no ambiguity about where a packet is routed to.

Static IP Addresses

When the ISP assigns one or a block of static IP addresses, the addresses will never change. These addresses are usually mapped to known servers, such as email service servers or web servers.

Dynamic IP Addresses

When a home computer is connected to the internet or a laptop connects to a hotspot, it's typically assigned a dynamic address by the ISP. The ISP wants to use the dynamic address assignment to allow it to have fewer IP addresses than its total number of customers because the ISP only needs to provide IP addresses to active clients, and not all clients are active at the same time. Using the dynamic host configuration protocol (DHCP) or the point-to-point protocol, a node can be assigned a randomly dynamic IP address from a pool of addresses kept by the ISP or by a certain policy. The DCHP server assigns an IP address to a node for only some periods of time (called the lease time). The node must renew the DHCP lease before it expires, or it will lose its access to the internet. The newly assigned IP address may be the same one or one of those addresses from a pool. Even though DHCP works for both IPv4 and IPv6, IPv6 has another more commonly used mechanism to assign addresses called stateless address autoconfiguration (SLAAC).

2.6. IEEE 802.11 Services

The following services are required by the 802.11 specification. However, their implementation is not defined by the specification:

Station Services

To be compliant with the IEEE 802.11 specification, all STAs must provide the following station services.

1. *Authentication:* This authentication process is used to identify an STA before it's allowed to join the network. The 802.11 specification defines the following two authentication services:
   a. *Open system authentication:* This is the default authentication method, and there are no keys involved. The station that wants to authenticate with another station sends a frame with the identity information of the sending station. The receiving

station sends back a frame to tell the sending station whether it recognizes the identity of the authenticating station.

b. *Shared key authentication:* Stations authenticate using shared information of a secret key that they obtain independently from the wireless network.

2. *Deauthentication:* This service is used to void an existing authentication.
3. *Privacy:* To protect the content of a message, an STA must be able to encrypt its data frames so that nobody except the intended recipient can read it. Wired equivalency privacy (WEP) or Wi-Fi protected access (WPA) are some algorithms used to encrypt messages. More details will be discussed in later sections.
4. *MAC Service Data Unit (MSDU) delivery:* The MSDU data frame must be delivered to the correct recipient. MSDU is a data frame from the network layer that's handed to the Logical Link Control (LLC) sub-layer inside the Data Link Layer.

Distribution System Services (DSS)

An STA that also has the access point (AP) function must implement the following distribution system services in addition to the four station services mentioned earlier:

1. *Association:* An STA must be associated with an access point (AP) before it can send or receive information through a distribution system (DS). Each STA can only be mapped to one AP, but each AP can associate with many STAs.
2. *Reassociation:* This service changes the association of a station from one AP to another AP.
3. *Disassociation:* An existing association may be terminated by a station or by an AP.
4. *Distribution:* This service manages the delivery of MSDUs within a distribution system.
5. *Integration:* This service handles the delivery of MSDUs between the wireless DS and a wired LAN on the other side of a portal.

State Variables

There are two state variables for each STA: one for authentication and one for association. Therefore, a station is either authenticated or unauthenticated. Once authenticated, the station can be either associated or unassociated. The state existing between a source and a destination station determines which frames can be exchanged between them. A station can be in one of the following three states:

- *State 1:* Unauthenticated and unassociated
- *State 2:* Authenticated and unassociated
- *State 3:* Authenticated and associated

3. Wi-Fi Security

To obtain secure communication in a wireless network is a complicated issue to tackle compared to a wired network. A wireless device must have ways to prove its identity, as well as that of the connected device with which it wants to communicate. Since there are no cable connections between the two devices, there is no physical evidence that they are connected to the devices they want to connect to.

To ensure that a wireless network is secure, it must satisfy three criteria: (1) mutual authentication, (2) private communication, and (3) data integrity.

The goal of mutual authentication is to assure the identities of both the AP and the client. The AP must know for certain who the client is to determine whether to allow it to join the network or not. On the other hand, the AP also needs to authenticate itself to prevent a rogue AP from masquerading as a legitimate AP to steal sensitive information from unsuspecting clients or to cause denial-of-service attacks. The objective of privacy is to protect information being sent wirelessly through open space and available for everyone to read. One way to solve this problem is to use strong encryption algorithms. Finally, the goal of data integrity is to make sure the data arrives at the destination intact.

3.1. WEP (Wired Equivalency Privacy) Encryption

WEP was the first encryption algorithm introduced from the original 802.11 specification to make the wireless communication intended to be as secure as a wired connection. A secret key, usually a passphrase, is input into the AP. Any STA that wants to associate with the AP must know this secret key. After translating the passphrase into a 40-bit key, it's combined with a 24-bit initialization vector to create a 64-bit encryption key. With this key, the RC4 algorithm is used to transform the key into a keystream to encrypt sending messages. However, the WEP protocol turned out a very easily broken one because there are many limitations on this method:

- *No mutual authentication:* Only the client can authenticate, and this can lead to rogue AP since we cannot authenticate AP.
- *No user-level authentication:* Since a static WEP key is stored on a device, security can be compromised if the device is stolen or used without permission.
- *WEP is used for both encryption and authentication:* WEP encryption is a static-shared key that is preconfigured on all APs and clients, and therefore changing the key is a very time-consuming task. Thus it's very likely that the key will be left unchanged or rarely modified. Originally, the WEP key was specified to be a 40-bit number, but it has now been changed to a 104-bit number. Regardless, the WEP key has been found to be easily hacked in a short time.

3.2. WPA and WPA2

WPA and WPA2 were introduced in the 802.11i specification to provide new solutions for replacing the flawed WEP. WPA is based on the third draft of 802.11i, and WPA2 is based on the final ratified version. Open authentication is required to use WPA or WPA2. Two modes of operation, personal and enterprise, are defined in the 802.11i specification, as shown in Table 9.2.

For authentication, WPA uses the pre-shared key (PSK) for personal mode or the extensible authentication protocol for enterprise mode. WPA2 strengthens the encryption by changing the RC4 algorithm with the advanced encryption standard (AES). The temporal key integrity protocol (TKIP) is used in WPA and WPA2 to manage keys dynamically instead of using a static key, as in WEP. Once a session is authenticated, a 128-bit temporary key for that session is created, and then it's combined with the station's MAC address, TKIP sequence counter, and a 48-bit initialization vector to create an encryption key. Therefore, each station will use a different key to encrypt sending messages, and TKIP manages the update and distribution of these keys across the network. Depending on the configuration, a key can be used once per packet or up to once every ten thousand packets. Thus the WLAN security is significantly improved with WPA or WPA2 by using a dynamic key that can choose between 280 trillion keys, compared to using just one static key in WEP. However, the TKIP method used in WPA still makes it vulnerable to malicious attacks.[4] WPA2 with AES encryption instead of TKIP has proved to be secure so far.

TABLE 9.2 **802.11I OPERATION MODES**

	Personal Mode	Enterprise Mode
WPA	Authentication: PSK Encryption: TKIP/MIC	Authentication: 802.1X/EAP Encryption: TKIP/MIC
WPA2	Authentication: PSK Encryption: AES-CCMP	Authentication: 802.1X/EAP Encryption: AES-CCMP

4. Wireshark

One of the best tools to debug and/or to learn about networks (or wireless networks) is a free application called Wireshark.[5] It is the most popular network protocol analyzer and it is widely used in industrial and academic environments. It allows users to capture live packets of many protocols such as Ethernet, 802.11 wireless, and so on for debugging or offline analysis. We are going to use Wireshark to inspect a wireless trace to analyze different kinds of wireless frames.

4 Martin Beck and Erik Tews, "Practical Attacks against WEP and WPA," Aircrack-ng, November 8, 2008, https://dl.aircrack-ng.org/breakingwepandwpa.pdf.

5 Wireshark, https:/www.wireshark.org

In general, Figure 9.5 shows the MAC frame format when the Type is not equal to 1 (control frames) or the SubType field is not equal to 6 (Control Frame Extension)[6].

	B0 B1	B2 B3	B4 B7	B8	B9	B10	B11	B12	B13	B14	B15
	Protocol Version	Type	Subtype	To DS	From DS	More Fragments	Retry	Power Management	More Data	Protected Frame	+HTC/ Order
Bits:	2	2	4	1	1	1	1	1	1	1	1

FIGURE 9.5 Frame Control field when Type is not equal to 1 or SubType not equal to 6.

The value of the Protocol Version is 0. Depending on the value of the 2-bit Type field, a frame can be one of the four different kinds of frames: a management frame (Type = zero), a control frame (Type = 1), a data frame (Type = 2), or an extension frame (Type = 3).

A MAC frame can have up to four address fields but most of the time has only three. There are five types of address used in these fields.

- Transmitter Address (TA): Address of the transmitter, which can be a STA or an AP.
- Destination Address (DA): Address of the final recipient.
- Source Address (SA): Address of the original source of the frame.
- Receiver Address (RA): Address of the receiving AP.
- BSSID Identifier (BSSID): Address of the AP of the infrastructure BSS.

Bit 8 (To DS) and Bit 9 (From DS) determine the MAC Frame Address fields of a Frame as shown in Figure 9.6.

To DS	From DS	Addr 1	Addr 2	Addr 3	Addr 4
0	0	DA	SA	BSSID	n/a
0	1	DA	BSSID	SA	n/a
1	0	BSSID	SA	DA	n/a
1	1	RA	TA	DA	SA

FIGURE 9.6 MAC Frame Address Fields.

When both To DS and From DS bits are zero, this Frame is going from one STA to another STA residing inside the same independent basic service set (IBSS) or a Data Frame going from one non-AP STA to another non-AP STA in the same BSS.

When the values of To DS is 0 and From DS is 1, the Frame is exiting the DS.

When the value of To DS is 1 and the value of From DS is 0, it indicates that this frame is sent to the distribution system (DS).

6 IEEE Std 802.11-2016, 638.

When the values of both To DS and From DS are 1, this Frame is transmitted by a mesh STA.

4.1. Data Frame

When the value of the Type field is equal to 2, the Frame is a Data Frame but when the value of the SubType field is different from zero, it indicates some modification of the basic Data Frame (SubType = 0). For instance, when the SubType value is equal from 8 to 12, the Data Frame is a QoS (Quality of Service) Data Frame. For a list of types and subtypes of MAC frames, check Table 9.1 of the IEEE 802.11 standard.[7] Inspection of a Data frame in Figure 9.7 shows that since To DS bit is 1 and From DS bit is 0, using information from Figure 9.6, it indicates the address of the BSSID is 00:16:b6:e3:e9:8f, the Source Address is 00:17:f2:98:f0:6f, and the Destination Address is 00:16:b6:e3:e9:8f. This Data Frame is sent to the Distribution System via the AP's Port Access Entity. We can also confirm that this is a basic Data Frame since its Type's value is 2 and its SubType is 0.

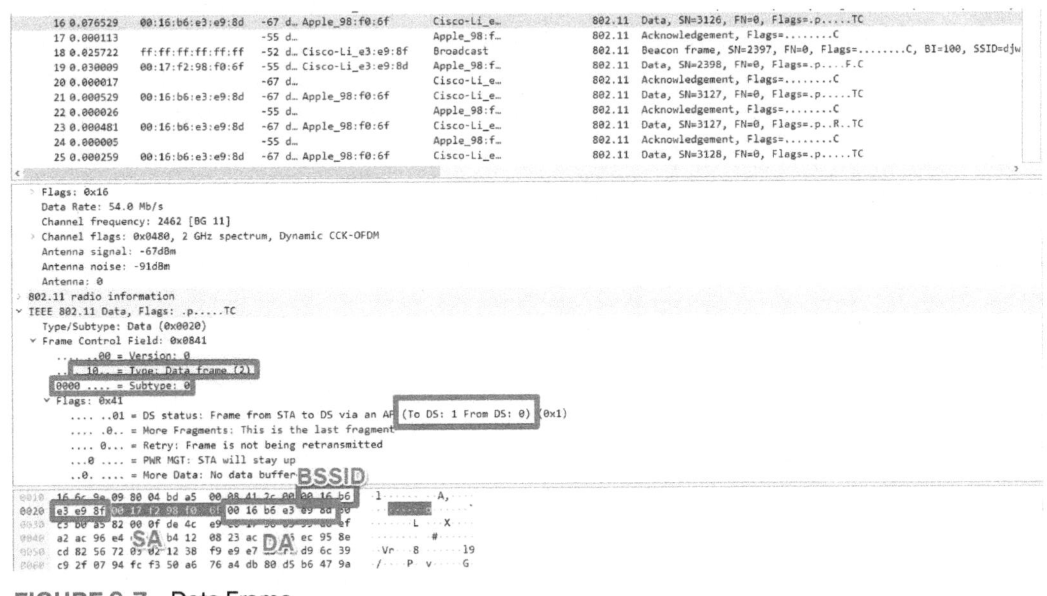

FIGURE 9.7 Data Frame.

4.2. Association Request and Response Frames

In order to receive and transmit wireless messages, a wireless device (STA) has to associate with an Access Point (AP). Before it can be associated with an AP, the STA sends an Association Request message (Frame 470) to the desired AP. In Figure 9.8 and Figure 9.9, captured

7 IEEE Std 802.11-2016, 639–645.

from a Wireshark trace,[8] one can see that the STA, an Apple device named Apple_ac:6c:26 at address 00:16:b6:e3:e9:8f, is sending an Association Request to the AP named Cisco-Li_e3:e9:8f located at address 00:16:b6:e3:e9:8f, which is also the address of the BSSID.

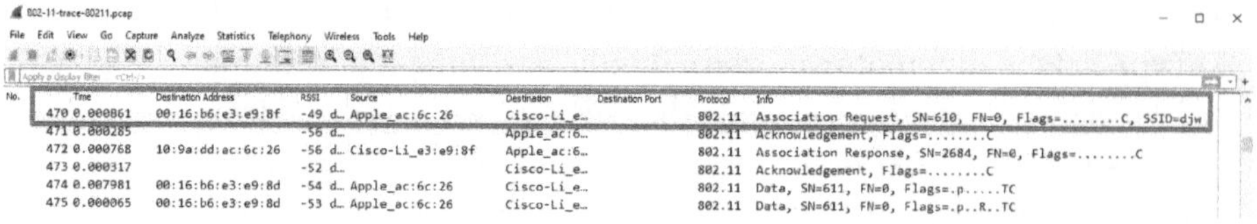

FIGURE 9.8 Association Request Frame.

Inspecting Figure 9.9, we could find more details about Frame 470. For example, the Frame Control Field shows that this frame is a Management frame (Type = 0) and it is an Association Request frame (Subtype = 0). The Tagged parameters indicates the SSID of the AP with which the wireless device requests to be associated is named "djw" and it supports many data rates ranging from 1Mbits/sec to 54 Mbits/sec. It also supports Extended Rates of 6, 9, 12, and 48 Mbits/sec. Wireshark also shows that the name of the vendor of this wireless adapter used inside the wireless device is "Broadcom" (Figure 9.9). By clicking on the Radiotap header or the 802.11 radio information lines from the middle panel of the Wireshark windows, we can get more information about this frame, like the wireless radio signal level, the noise level, the signal to noise ratio, or the wireless channel being used.

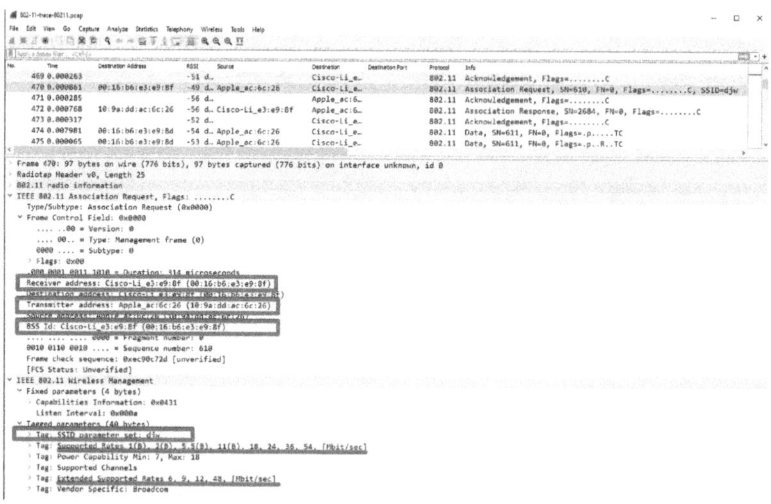

FIGURE 9.9 Receiver and Transmitter Addresses in Association Request Frame.

8 Wireshark, https://kevincurran.org/com320/labs/wireshark/trace-80211.pcap. Accessed 3/11/2021.

As shown in Figure 9.10, Frame 471 is the Acknowledgment frame the AP Cisco-Li_e3:e9:8f sends back to the wireless device Apple_ac:6c:26 to acknowledge that it has received the Association Request frame correctly.

```
802-11-trace-80211.pcap
File Edit View Go Capture Analyze Statistics Telephony Wireless Tools Help
Apply a display filter ... <Ctrl-/>
No. Time       Destination Address  RSSI  Source             Destination  Destination Port  Protocol  Info
469 0.000263                        -51 d...                   Cisco-Li_e...                  802.11    Acknowledgement, Flags=........C
470 0.000861   00:16:b6:e3:e9:8f    -49 d... Apple_ac:6c:26    Cisco-Li_e...                  802.11    Association Request, SN=610, FN=0, Flags=........C, SSID=djw
471 0.000285                        -56 d...                   Apple_ac:6...                  802.11    Acknowledgement, Flags=........C
472 0.000768   10:9a:dd:ac:6c:26    -56 d... Cisco-Li_e3:e9:8f Apple_ac:6...                  802.11    Association Response, SN=2684, FN=0, Flags=........C
473 0.000317                        -52 d...                   Cisco-Li_e...                  802.11    Acknowledgement, Flags=........C
474 0.007981   00:16:b6:e3:e9:8d    -54 d... Apple_ac:6c:26    Cisco-Li_e...                  802.11    Data, SN=611, FN=0, Flags=.p.....TC

> Frame 471: 39 bytes on wire (312 bits), 39 bytes captured (312 bits) on interface unknown, id 0
> Radiotap Header v0, Length 25
> 802.11 radio information
v IEEE 802.11 Acknowledgement, Flags: ........C
    Type/Subtype: Acknowledgement (0x001d)
  v Frame Control Field: 0xd400
      .... ..00 = Version: 0
      .... 01.. = Type: Control frame (1)
      1101 .... = Subtype: 13
    > Flags: 0x00
    .000 0000 0000 0000 = Duration: 0 microseconds
    Receiver address: Apple_ac:6c:26 (10:9a:dd:ac:6c:26)
    Frame check sequence: 0x32091e79 [unverified]
    [FCS Status: Unverified]
```

FIGURE 9.10 The Acknowledgment Frame.

The AP examines the wireless parameters of the wireless device's Association Request and compares them to its own parameters. If they are matched, the AP sends an Association Response frame (Figure 9.11) back to the wireless devices with a status code of 0 (successful) and an Association ID (0x0005 in Figure 9.11) allowing the wireless device to start receiving or sending wireless messages via this AP. However, if there is a mismatch and the AP decides that the difference is not serious (not a blocking factor to the association), it allows the wireless device access and sends its own parameters in the Association Response back to the wireless device.

```
802-11-trace-80211.pcap
File Edit View Go Capture Analyze Statistics Telephony Wireless Tools Help
Apply a display filter ... <Ctrl-/>
No. Time       Destination Address  RSSI  Source             Destination  Destination Port  Protocol  Info
469 0.000263                        -51 d...                   Cisco-Li_e...                  802.11    Acknowledgement, Flags=........C
470 0.000861   00:16:b6:e3:e9:8f    -49 d... Apple_ac:6c:26    Cisco-Li_e...                  802.11    Association Request, SN=610, FN=0, Flags=........C, SSID=djw
471 0.000285                        -56 d...                   Apple_ac:6...                  802.11    Acknowledgement, Flags=........C
472 0.000768   10:9a:dd:ac:6c:26    -56 d... Cisco-Li_e3:e9:8f Apple_ac:6...                  802.11    Association Response, SN=2684, FN=0, Flags=........C
473 0.000317                        -52 d...                   Cisco-Li_e...                  802.11    Acknowledgement, Flags=........C
474 0.007981   00:16:b6:e3:e9:8d    -54 d... Apple_ac:6c:26    Cisco-Li_e...                  802.11    Data, SN=611, FN=0, Flags=.p.....TC
475 0.000065   00:16:b6:e3:e9:8d    -53 d... Apple_ac:6c:26    Cisco-Li_e...                  802.11    Data, SN=611, FN=0, Flags=.p..R..TC

> Frame 472: 83 bytes on wire (664 bits), 83 bytes captured (664 bits) on interface unknown, id 0
> Radiotap Header v0, Length 25
> 802.11 radio information
v IEEE 802.11 Association Response, Flags: ........C
    Type/Subtype: Association Response (0x0001)
  v Frame Control Field: 0x1000
      .... ..00 = Version: 0
      .... 00.. = Type: Management frame (0)
      0001 .... = Subtype: 1
    > Flags: 0x00
    .000 0001 0011 1010 = Duration: 314 microseconds
    Receiver address: Apple_ac:6c:26 (10:9a:dd:ac:6c:26)
    Destination address: Apple_ac:6c:26 (10:9a:dd:ac:6c:26)
    Transmitter address: Cisco-Li_e3:e9:8f (00:16:b6:e3:e9:8f)
    Source address: Cisco-Li_e3:e9:8f (00:16:b6:e3:e9:8f)
    BSS Id: Cisco-Li_e3:e9:8f (00:16:b6:e3:e9:8f)
    .... .... .... 0000 = Fragment number: 0
    1010 0111 1100 .... = Sequence number: 2684
    Frame check sequence: 0xb33e68d2 [unverified]
    [FCS Status: Unverified]
v IEEE 802.11 Wireless Management
  v Fixed parameters (6 bytes)
    > Capabilities Information: 0x0411
      Status code: Successful (0x0000)
      ..00 0000 0000 0101 = Association ID: 0x0005
  v Tagged parameters (24 bytes)
    > Tag: Supported Rates 1(B), 2(B), 5.5(B), 11(B), 18, 24, 36, 54, [Mbit/sec]
    > Tag: Extended Supported Rates 6, 9, 12, 48, [Mbit/sec]
    > Tag: Vendor Specific: Broadcom
```

FIGURE 9.11 Association Response Frame.

4.3. Beacon Frames

To connect to a wireless network, a device can scan for a particular network (active scan) or it can wait for beacon frames from potential AP's (passive scan). Active scan gets immediate response from an AP, but passive scan typically takes longer since an AP usually sends out beacon frames every 100 ms. Inspecting a Beacon frame in Figure 9.12, this is a Management frame (Type = 0) and is a Beacon frame (SubType = 8). Since both To DS and From DS bits are zero, this frame is not leaving the DS and following information from Figure 9.6, and the Destination Address (DA) is FF:FF:FF:FF:FF:FF, which is the broadcast address. Next to the DA is the SA, which is 00:16:b6:e3:e9:8f (AP) and the BSSID is the same as the SA.

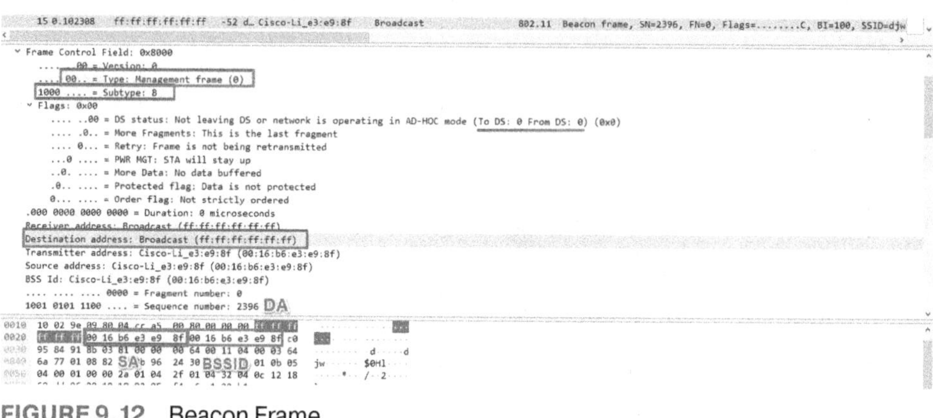

FIGURE 9.12 Beacon Frame.

4.4. Probe Request and Response Frames

To scan actively for a network, a wireless device can send a probe request to the broadcast address ff:ff:ff:ff:ff:ff. It can also specify the SSID it wants to connect to, only the AP corresponds to the SSID will respond in this case. The station can also set the SSID to zero and this is called a Null Probe Request or Wildcard SSID, which will cause all the AP within range to respond.

Figure 9.13 shows a Probe Request frame (Type = 0 and SubType = 4). Since both To DS and From DS bits are zero, the frame has the address format of DA, SA, and BSSID, so

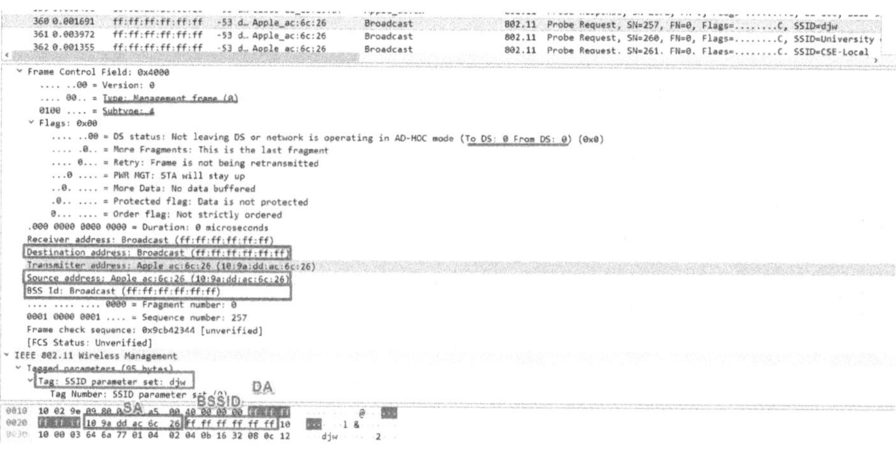

FIGURE 9.13 Probe Request.

SA =10:9a:dd:ac:6c:26 and DA and the BSSID are ff:ff:ff:ff:ff:ff. Once the probe request is sent, the wireless device starts a ProbeTimer countdown. After the timer times out, the device begins processing answers coming back. If no answer is found, the device sends another probe request to a different AP.

For a list of all parameters carried inside a Probe Request, please check Table 8.26 of the IEEE 802.11 specification.[9] The AP simply checks to make sure the station meets the minimum requirement of the BSS before sending back a Probe Response. A Probe Response frame looks very similar to a Beacon Frame except for a few things such as it does not contain QoS capability information, nor any information requested by the device and the like. Figure 9.14 shows information about a Probe Response frame that is a response to the Probe Request frame of Figure 9.13. The values of Type (0) and SubType (5) of this frame indicates it's a Probe Response frame.[10] The Destination Address of this Probe Response frame is device Apple_ac located at address 10:9a:dd:ac:6c:26, which is the address of the wireless device sending out the Probe Request frame of Figure 9.13. You also see that the SSID of the Probe Request frame in Figure 9.13 and that of the Probe Response frame of Figure 9.14 are the same. The AP that sends out this Probe Response frame is located at address 00:16:b6:e3:e9:8f.

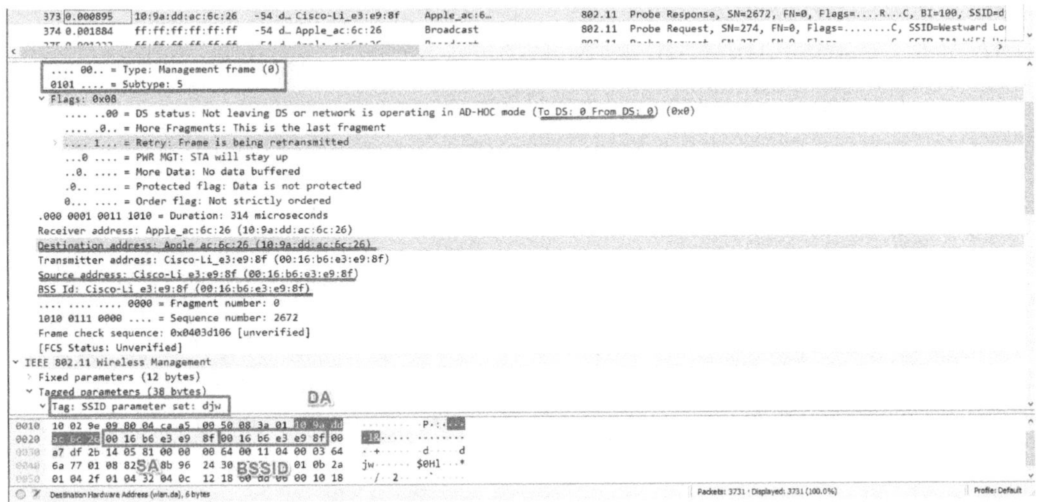

FIGURE 9.14 Probe Response Frame.

After receiving the Probe Response frame, the wireless device sends an Acknowledgment frame to the AP that sends the Probe Response frame as shown in Figure 9.15. Note that there is no source address in this frame. The reason is the AP already knows what wireless device sends the Acknowledgment frame since it is the one that sends the Probe Response to the wireless device earlier.

9 IEEE Std 802.11-2016, 696–698.

10 IEEE Std 802.11-2016, Table 9.1, 639.

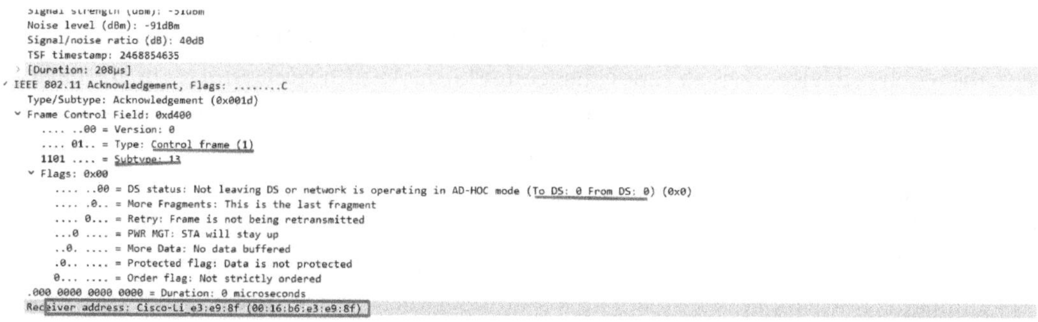

```
Signal strength (dBm): -51dBm
Noise level (dBm): -91dBm
Signal/noise ratio (dB): 40dB
TSF timestamp: 2468854635
> [Duration: 208µs]
IEEE 802.11 Acknowledgement, Flags: ........C
  Type/Subtype: Acknowledgement (0x001d)
  Frame Control Field: 0xd400
    .... ..00 = Version: 0
    .... 01.. = Type: Control frame (1)
    1101 .... = Subtype: 13
    Flags: 0x00
      .... ..00 = DS status: Not leaving DS or network is operating in AD-HOC mode (To DS: 0 From DS: 0) (0x0)
      .... .0.. = More Fragments: This is the last fragment
      .... 0... = Retry: Frame is not being retransmitted
      ...0 .... = PWR MGT: STA will stay up
      ..0. .... = More Data: No data buffered
      .0.. .... = Protected flag: Data is not protected
      0... .... = Order flag: Not strictly ordered
  .000 0000 0000 0000 = Duration: 0 microseconds
  Receiver address: Cisco-Li_e3:e9:8f (00:16:b6:e3:e9:8f)
```

FIGURE 9.15 Acknowledgment Frame.

5. Connecting to Wireless Networks

One of the ways to connect to wireless networks is by using the Tiva C together with the TI CC3100 Wi-Fi SimpleLink module. Another cheaper solution is to use the microcontroller ESP32, which has a built-in Wi-Fi module and a BLE (Bluetooth Low Energy) module. In the following examples, we will use the ESP32 to scan for Wi-Fi networks, connect to a local Wi-Fi network, or use as a network sniffer.

5.1. Scanning Wi-Fi Networks

Using Arduino IDE, the following code scans and prints out the names of all the scanned networks.[11]

```
/*

*  This sketch demonstrates how to scan WiFi networks.

*  The API is almost the same as with the WiFi
Shield library,

*  the most obvious difference being the different file you
need to include:

*/

#include "WiFi.h"


void setup()
```

11 Arduino, https://www.arduino.cc/en/Guide/ArduinoWiFiShield#scan-for-available-networks. Accessed 3/17/21.

```
{

Serial.begin(115200); //Set yp a serial connection at baud
rate of 115200


// Set WiFi to station mode and disconnect from an AP if it
was previously connected

WiFi.mode(WIFI_STA);

WiFi.disconnect();

delay(100);


Serial.println("Setup done");

}


void loop()

{

Serial.println("scan start"); //Scanning for wireless network


// WiFi.scanNetworks will return the number of networks found

int n = WiFi.scanNetworks();

Serial.println("scan done");

if (n == 0) {

      Serial.println("no networks found");

} else {

      Serial.print(n);

      Serial.println(" networks found");
```

```
        for (int i = 0; i < n; ++i) {
        // Print SSID and RSSI for each network found
        Serial.print(i + 1);
        Serial.print(": ");
        Serial.print(WiFi.SSID(i));
        Serial.print(" (");
        Serial.print(WiFi.RSSI(i));
        Serial.print(")");
        Serial.println((WiFi.encryptionType(i) == WIFI_AUTH_
OPEN)?" ":"*");
        delay(10);
        }
        }
Serial.println("");

// Wait a bit before scanning again
delay(5000);
}
```

Program 9.1: WiFiScan

5.2. Joining a Wireless Network

The following program can be used to join a wireless network.

```
//Replace "yourNetwork" with your network name and the
network key with your real password before //running the
program12.
```

12 Arduino, https://www.arduino.cc/en/Guide/ArduinoWiFiShield#wep-network-example. Accessed 3/17/21.

```
#include <WiFi.h>


char ssid[] = "yourNetwork";     //  your network SSID (name)

char key[] = "ABBADEAF01";     // your network key

int keyIndex = 0;             //your network key Index number

int status = WL_IDLE_STATUS;     // the Wifi radio's status


void setup() {

       // initialize serial:

       Serial.begin(9600);

       // attempt to connect using WEP encryption:

       Serial.println("Attempting to connect to
WEP network...");

       status = WiFi.begin(ssid, keyIndex, key);

       // if you're not connected, stop here:

       if ( status != WL_CONNECTED) {

              Serial.println("Couldn't get a wifi connection");

              while(true);

       }

       // if you are connected, print out info about
the connection:

       else {

              Serial.println("Connected to network");

       }

}
```

```
void loop() {
        // do nothing
}
```

Program 9.2: Joining a WEP Wi-Fi Network

We can also record activities on wireless networks by using an ESP product like the ESP-WROVER-KIT_VB as a wireless sniffer and then use Wireshark to analyze the data.

6. Conclusion

Wi-Fi is a convenient way to connect to the internet without the need for cables or wires, and it's getting faster and cheaper. With the 5G network, the theoretical speed of 10–50 Gbps will enable numerous unforeseeable wireless applications. So, the future of Wi-Fi is very bright indeed.

EXERCISES

1. Describe the five layers of the TCP/IP protocol.
2. What is WEP? Why is it not widely used?
3. Describe the WPA and WPA2 algorithms.
4. What is a MAC address, and how is it used?
5. How are dynamic IP addresses assigned in IPv4?
6. Describe the differences between IPv6 and IPv4 protocols.
7. Using the trace at https://kevincurran.org/com320/labs/wireshark/trace-80211.pcap, answer the following questions:
    a. Locate a set of Authentication Requests and Authentication Responses. Identify addresses of the transmitter, the receiver, and the AP.
    b. Locate a Beacon frame. Identify the address of the AP.
    c. Locate a set of Probe Request and Probe Response frames. Identify addresses of all the involved STA and AP.
    d. Locate a Data frame and identify the addresses of the transmitter, receiver, and BSSID involved in the transaction.

8. Use the Shannon-Hartley theorem to calculate the channel capacity of a network with a bandwidth of 4 KHz and SNR of 38 dB.

9. Design a system to read the temperature inside a greenhouse, and use Wi-Fi to post it to a server.

10. Design a system to water a plant using the following steps:
    a. Check the humidity of the soil.
    b. If it is dry, check the weather using Wi-Fi to see if rain is in the forecast. If it is predicted that the rain is coming within three hours, do not water the plant. Otherwise, water it.

    Hints: You can use the TI Tiva C or the MSP432, the TI CC3100/CC3200 wireless MCU, the humidity sensor Sparkfun RHT03, a relay to turn water on or off, and a RTOS like TI RTOS or FreeRTOS to create this project.

11. Use an ESP-WROVER-KIT_VB to sniff wireless frames in your wireless network and then use Wireshark to identify the activities.

12. Write a program to connect to your local wireless network and then connect to openweathermap.org to obtain the local weather forecast. You need to register for a free account with openweathermap.org to obtain a key to login to obtain weather information. You can use a cheap ESP32 or a Tiva C together with a wireless module CC3100 from TI.

Credits

Projects

To truly understand the Tiva C microcontroller, besides doing the labs, you need to work on projects. The following are some suggested projects for you to take up.

Project 1—Traffic Light Controller

Purpose: Design a state machine to control the traffic lights using distance sensors to detect traffic and input buttons to let pedestrians request to cross (Figure 10.1). To simplify the project, the traffic light controller's requirements are simplified as follows:

- The traffic lights for north-south direction are the same ones for the south-north direction and the same is true for the east-west direction.
- There are no left turn signals.

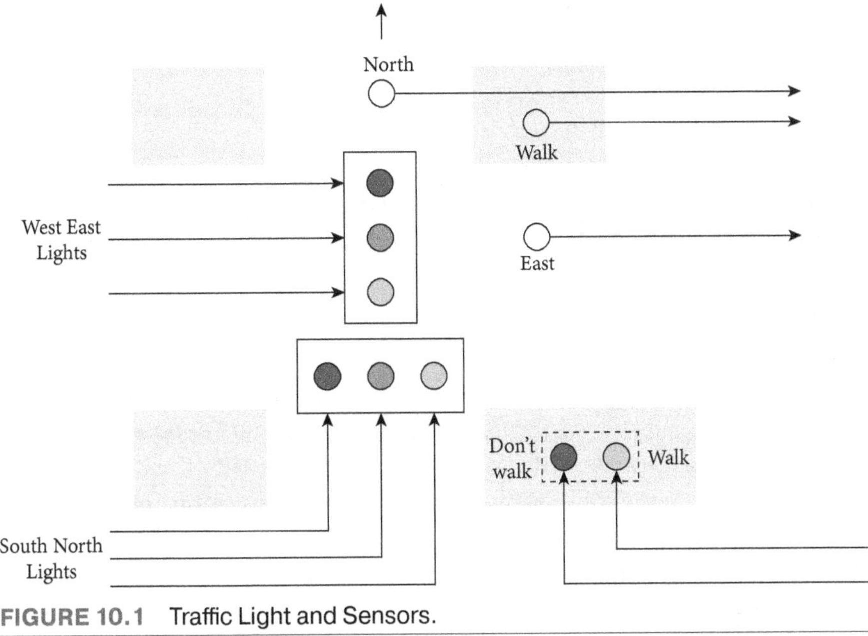

FIGURE 10.1 Traffic Light and Sensors.

- Anytime the button "Walk" is pressed, the green lights turn to yellow and then red while other red lights remain red. After that, the "Walk" light turns green allowing pedestrians to walk. A short while later, the "Don't Walk" light turns on. After a short period, both of them become red, and the traffic lights operate normally again.
- If the north-south traffic light is on and cars in the east-west direction are detected, the traffic light for the north-south direction will turn yellow for a short time before becoming red. A short time later, the traffic light for the east-west direction will turn green.
- The same thing applies to traffic in the east-west direction.
- *Hints:* Design a state machine with three inputs and eight outputs. The inputs are as follows:
  - The sensor for north-south traffic
  - The sensor for east-west traffic
  - The button for the "Walk" request
  - The outputs for the traffic lights
  - The outputs for the "Don't Walk" and "Walk" lights

Challenges: Extend the traffic controller design to make it a real traffic light controller with more realistic requirements. For example, add "Walk" request buttons at all four corners of the intersection, "Turn Left" traffic lights, traffic sensors at the four corners of the intersection, or an "Emergency" button to simulate the condition for all the traffic to stop when there is an emergency vehicle (e.g., ambulance, police, or coming to the intersection).

Project 2—An Autonomous Robot

Purpose: Build a robot to run on a track autonomously. It should be able to meet the following requirements:

- It can turn around if it runs to a dead end.
- It can turn right if it gets to an intersection.
- It can stop at a designated stop line.
- It can navigate a track autonomously by staying at a fixed distance from the track wall.
- It can start transmitting its distance from the wall to a PC via the Bluetooth link once it crosses a designated line.
- It can measure its own travel time from the start line until the stop line.

Implementation: The parts list for this robot is in Appendix A. It's better to program this robot using a RTOS like the TI RTOS or FreeRTOS, but it can also be done with the bare-metal approach. The state machine describing the behavior of the robot using the TI RTOS to implement is listed in Appendix B. The robot has two distance sensors: one in front and one near the right side. The robot uses the side distance sensor to find the distance from the wall, and that information is used to control the motors that try to maintain a constant distance from the wall. If the measurement from the side distance sensor is too large, it implies that the robot is at an intersection. In that case, it will turn right. If the measurement from the front distance sensor is too small (smaller than some low limit), that means the robot needs to do a U-turn since it is approaching a wall. To do a U-turn, it can idle one motor and keep the other motor at a normal speed until the front sensor returns a large measurement value. When encountering a stop line, the robot can turn off all of its PWM signals, which are used to drive the motors, and force all the other sensors to go to idle.

Project 3—A Smart Plant-Watering System

Purpose: Design an embedded system to monitor the humidity of the soil of a plant and provide water if it is too dry and if there is no imminent rain in the forecast (Figure 10.2).

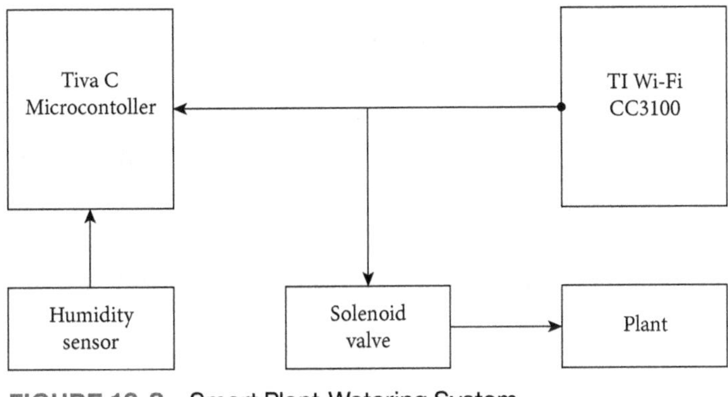

FIGURE 10.2 Smart Plant-Watering System.

Implementation: Use a GPIO port of a microcontroller like the Tiva C or the MSP432 to interface with a low-cost humidity sensor, such as the Sparkfun RHT03, and, depending on the weather forecast, to control a solenoid valve to turn water on or off. The TI Wi-Fi CC3100 is used to access a weather station to check on the rain forecast, and it can be used to post some data on the web, such as the time the water is turned on and for how long.

Project 4—Weather Station

Purpose: Design a weather station to monitor temperature, humidity, and other data, such as the amount of rainfall, the pH of the soil, or the velocity of the wind, and then display the data on the web.

Implementation: Use a microcontroller like the Tiva C or the MSP432 to interface with the temperature sensor, the humidity sensor, or the pH sensor, to collect data and then use the TI Wi-Fi CC3100 to connect to a website, such as the free BeeBottle.com or IoTguru.com to display/update data. You can also use a cheap ESP32 microcontroller (having a built-in Wi-Fi) with its own web server to build this project.[1]

1 Emmanuel Odunlade, "ESP32 Webserver Tutorial," Electronics-lab.com, n.d., https://www.electronics-lab.com/project/esp32-webserver-tutorial/.

Project 5—Temperature Monitor Station

Purpose: Create a monitor system to keep track of the temperature in a lab or a house and send a text when the temperature exceeds a certain limit. This can be used as a safety check.

Implementation: You can use a Tiva C or a MSP432 microcontroller to interface with a temperature sensor. Put your code in a loop to check the temperature and compare it with a temperature limit. If it exceeds the limit, send a text to a phone number. Otherwise, continue the loop. You can also use the interrupt approach instead of the polling to implement it.

Project 6—An Environment Monitor System

Purpose: Design an Internet of Things (IoT) system to monitor environmental parameters, such as carbon dioxide or carbon monoxide, and then send the data to the cloud for analysis.

Implementation: You can use a microcontroller like the Tiva C or the MSP432 to interface with the carbon dioxide sensor, carbon monoxide sensor, or humidity sensor and then use TI Wi-Fi CC3200 to connect to a Wi-Fi hotspot to send the data. You can also experiment with using the MultiTech Conduit IoT kit to connect to a low-bandwidth, long-distance LPWAN network to transfer data.

Project 7—Solar Panel Tracker

Purpose: A solar panel tracker is used to make sure that the sunlight always strikes a flat solar panel at 90° to obtain the maximum solar energy.

Implementation: You can design a tracker for a solar panel by using a microcontroller to control stepper motors to keep the solar panel perpendicular to the sunlight. You can either calculate the sun position at any particular time during the day and then move the solar panel to the appropriate position, or you can use sensors to guide the solar panel to an optimal position. You need stepper motors to either tilt the panel or move it forward, backward, or sideways to adjust to the sun's position.

You can extend this project further by adding batteries to store the sun's energy and an inverter to convert from DC to AC to power household devices, such as light, fan, radio, or TV.

Project 8—Exploring the Wi-Fi 802.11 Protocol

Using Wireshark

Purpose: The best way to learn about the 802.11 Wi-Fi protocol is to look at all the frames of data exchanged between wireless devices.

Implementation: Using the monitoring tool Wireshark,[2] we can capture and examine data frames being transferred over the air between devices. Wireshark is a free network protocol analyzer, and there are many resources available to help you use the tool. Many examples of network traffic are available for you to learn or experiment with the tool.[3] In the following, I'll look at an example of a wireless trace[4] and extract information from the data frames.

After downloading and installing Wireshark, open the wireless trace from the zip file of the link. We can see many 802.11 beacon frames at the beginning of the trace. The beacon frames are management frames broadcasted by the AP to advertise its existence. For example, examining Frame 1 shows that this frame is a management frame type 0 with an address of 00:16:b6:e3:e9:8f. Under the "Tagged Parameters" section or the "Info" part of the frame in Figure 10.3, we find that its SSID is "djw." Under the "Radiotap Header" section, the data rate is about 1 Mb/s, and the channel frequency of Channel 11 is 2462MHz. Other details from the section "802.11 Radio Information" show an SNR of about 40 dB, a pretty good number.

Frame 16 is a data frame (type 2) sent from an STA Apple_98:f0:6f (00:17:f2:98:f0:6f) to the AP Cisco-Li_e3:e9:8f (00:16:b6:e3:e9:8f) (found under "IEEE 802.11 Data, Flags"). The data rate is 54 Mb/s, and the SNR ratio can be calculated by subtracting the antenna noise from the antenna signal (−67 + 91 = 24 dB).

You can also find other kinds of 802.11 management frames, such as the deauthentication frame (frame 1735) when the STA deassociates it from the AP or the authentication frames (frames 1740–1742) when the STA wants to associate itself with the AP.

802-11-trace-80211.pcap

File Edit View Go Capture Analyze Statistics Telephony Wireless Tools Help

Apply a display filter ... <Ctrl-/>

No.	Time	TX Rate	Destination Address	RSSI	Source	Destination	Protocol	Info
1	0.000000	1.0	ff:ff:ff:ff:ff:ff	-51 dBm	Cisco-Li_e3:e9:8f	Broadcast	802.11	Beacon frame, SN=2382, FN=0, Flags=........C, BI=100, SSID=djw
2	0.102427	1.0	ff:ff:ff:ff:ff:ff	-51 dBm	Cisco-Li_e3:e9:8f	Broadcast	802.11	Beacon frame, SN=2383, FN=0, Flags=........C, BI=100, SSID=djw
3	0.102452	1.0	ff:ff:ff:ff:ff:ff	-51 dBm	Cisco-Li_e3:e9:8f	Broadcast	802.11	Beacon frame, SN=2384, FN=0, Flags=........C, BI=100, SSID=djw
4	0.102387	1.0	ff:ff:ff:ff:ff:ff	-51 dBm	Cisco-Li_e3:e9:8f	Broadcast	802.11	Beacon frame, SN=2385, FN=0, Flags=........C, BI=100, SSID=djw
5	0.102350	1.0	ff:ff:ff:ff:ff:ff	-51 dBm	Cisco-Li_e3:e9:8f	Broadcast	802.11	Beacon frame, SN=2386, FN=0, Flags=........C, BI=100, SSID=djw
6	0.102400	1.0	ff:ff:ff:ff:ff:ff	-52 dBm	Cisco-Li_e3:e9:8f	Broadcast	802.11	Beacon frame, SN=2387, FN=0, Flags=........C, BI=100, SSID=djw
7	0.102445	1.0	ff:ff:ff:ff:ff:ff	-51 dBm	Cisco-Li_e3:e9:8f	Broadcast	802.11	Beacon frame, SN=2388, FN=0, Flags=........C, BI=100, SSID=djw
8	0.102518	1.0	ff:ff:ff:ff:ff:ff	-52 dBm	Cisco-Li_e3:e9:8f	Broadcast	802.11	Beacon frame, SN=2389, FN=0, Flags=........C, BI=100, SSID=djw
9	0.102357	1.0	ff:ff:ff:ff:ff:ff	-52 dBm	Cisco-Li_e3:e9:8f	Broadcast	802.11	Beacon frame, SN=2390, FN=0, Flags=........C, BI=100, SSID=djw
10	0.102446	1.0	ff:ff:ff:ff:ff:ff	-52 dBm	Cisco-Li_e3:e9:8f	Broadcast	802.11	Beacon frame, SN=2391, FN=0, Flags=........C, BI=100, SSID=djw
11	0.102246	1.0	ff:ff:ff:ff:ff:ff	-52 dBm	Cisco-Li_e3:e9:8f	Broadcast	802.11	Beacon frame, SN=2392, FN=0, Flags=........C, BI=100, SSID=djw
12	0.102533	1.0	ff:ff:ff:ff:ff:ff	-52 dBm	Cisco-Li_e3:e9:8f	Broadcast	802.11	Beacon frame, SN=2393, FN=0, Flags=........C, BI=100, SSID=djw
13	0.102362	1.0	ff:ff:ff:ff:ff:ff	-52 dBm	Cisco-Li_e3:e9:8f	Broadcast	802.11	Beacon frame, SN=2394, FN=0, Flags=........C, BI=100, SSID=djw
14	0.102435	1.0	ff:ff:ff:ff:ff:ff	-52 dBm	Cisco-Li_e3:e9:8f	Broadcast	802.11	Beacon frame, SN=2395, FN=0, Flags=........C, BI=100, SSID=djw
15	0.102308	1.0	ff:ff:ff:ff:ff:ff	-52 dBm	Cisco-Li_e3:e9:8f	Broadcast	802.11	Beacon frame, SN=2396, FN=0, Flags=........C, BI=100, SSID=djw

```
    [Preamble: 96µs]
    [Start: 2441646343µs]
    [End: 2441647111µs]
v IEEE 802.11 Beacon frame, Flags: ........C
   Type/Subtype: Beacon frame (0x0008)
  v Frame Control Field: 0x8000
     .... ..00 = Version: 0
     .... 00.. = Type: Management frame (0)
     1000 .... = Subtype: 8
   v Flags: 0x00
      .... ..00 = DS status: Not leaving DS or network is operating in AD-HOC mode (To DS: 0 From DS: 0) (0x0)
      .... .0.. = More Fragments: This is the last fragment
      .... 0... = Retry: Frame is not being retransmitted
      ...0 .... = PWR MGT: STA will stay up
```

FIGURE 10.3 Wireshark Monitor.

2 "About Wireshark," Wireshark, accessed December 31, 2019, https://www.wireshark.org.

3 "Traffic Analysis Exercises," Malware-Traffic=Analysis.net, accessed December 31, 2019, https://www.malware-traffic-analysis.net/training-exercises.html.

4 http://gaia.cs.umass.edu/wireshark-labs/wireshark-traces.zip. Accessed 2/02/2020.

A Simple IoT System

We can build a simple IoT system to collect weather information like humidity and temperature readings and display them on a website. One way to do it is by using a temperature sensor like Sensirion AG SCC30-DB with an I2C interface to connect to a microcontroller with built-in wireless module like the ESP32 to implement this idea. ESP32 also has two I2C modules to interface with I2C devices.

Voice-Controlled Lighting Using Wi-Fi

You can use a voice command/message to trigger the IFTTT (If This Then That) applet from Google Home Assistant to send a digital message to the Blynk Server, which is an open-source Java server responsible for forwarding messages between mobile applications and some microcontrollers like ESP32. The messages will then be converted to logic signals to turn on/off a light bulb via a relay. More information about the Blynk server and IFTTT is available here.[5,6]

Open Garage Door Notification

Assuming the distance sensor is located a short distance from the garage, you can use it to measure the distance between the sensor and the garage. If the distance is too far, the garage door is open. Otherwise, it's close. You can use this fact to set a value high or low on a virtual pin, which in turn is connected to a Blynk widget. The Blynk widget updates the status of the pin on your smartphone at a programmable reading frequency. You'll need a distance sensor like `Sharp GP2Y0A41SK0F`[7] and a microcontroller with built-in Wi-Fi capability like an ESP32 and a smartphone like an Iphone with a Blynk widget.

Exploring Bluetooth Using Pybluez

Purpose: One of the best ways to learn about a new subject is to do a project on it. In this project, you will have a chance to communicate with a Bluetooth device and learn many kinds of responses.

Implementation: You can use Python with the pybluez[8] library to interface with a Bluetooth device. However, you may not be able to use the Bluetooth BLE protocol with pybluez and Windows 10. The following example is a simple piece of code using pybluez to scan for Bluetooth devices.

---

5 Blynk, https://community.blynk.cc/t/blynk-ifttt-details-guide-how-to-connect-both/5772. Accessed 4/13/2021.

6 Rose de Fremery, "How to Use IFTTT with Google Home," Lifewire, https://www.lifewire.com/how-to-use-ifttt-with-google-home-4172627. Accessed 4/13/21.

7 "Sharp GP2Y0A41SK0F Analog Distance Sensor 4-30cm," Pololu, https://www.pololu.com/product/2464. Accessed 4/15/2021.

8 "Pybluez Releases," GitHub, https://github.com/pybluez/pybluez/releases, accessed December 31, 2019.

```
import bluetooth
nb_devices = bluetooth.discover_devices(duration=8,lookup_names=True,flush_
cache=True,
lookup_class=False)
print(\"found %d devices\" %len(nb_devices))
for addr, name in nb_devices:
print(\" %s -  %s\", (addr, name))
```

Smart Lighting Controlled by Low-Energy Bluetooth

Use a smartphone to turn on or off a light bulb by using BLE Bluetooth. You need a microcontroller and a BLE module like an Arduino Uno microcontroller with an Adafruit nRF8001 Bluefruit board or a microcontroller with a built-in BLE module like ESP32, a relay to turn on/off the power to the light bulb. You can use Arduino IDE, which has a C++library supporting BLE functions to run your program.

A BLE Beacon to Broadcast Sale Advertisement When Customers Are Approaching the Sale Stall

When customers approaching the sale stall, triggered by the distance sensor, the ESP32's BLE module will start advertising for nearby smartphones to pick up the sale promotion messages. You can use an ESP32 with a built-in BLE module and a distance sensor like an ultrasonic Diymore[9] to implement this project. You can also use FreeRTOS and the Arduino IDE to develop programs for this project.

Door Opener Controlled by a Smartphone via BLE

Use a smartphone to send a message to a BLE device like an ESP32 to control the operation of a motor to open or close a door. You can use a Blynk app on your phone to send a message to your ESP32 board to control a pin to turn on or off a motor. Blynk provides more information on creating a Blynk project.[10]

Credits

Fig. 10.3: Copyright © by Wireshark.

---

9 Amazon.com: diymore DC 5V Waterproof Ultrasonic Distance Sensor Measuring Ranging Transducer Module with 2.5M Cable for Arduino: Industrial & Scientific

10 Blynk, https://docs.blynk.cc/. Accessed 4/15/2021.

Part List for the Robot Project

Parts	Quantities for One Robot	Unit Price	Subtotal	
Chassis and Main Electronics:				
5" Round Plastic Robot Chassis RRC04A (Base Layer)	1	7.15	$7.15	http://www.pololu.com/catalog/product/1500
Prototype Matrix Paper PCB Universal Board Prototyping Kit	1	$6.25	$6.25	https://www.ebay.com/itm/10pcs-7-x-9-cm-DIY-Prototype-Matrix-Paper-PCB-Universal-Board-prototyping-kit-B-/221711896460?epid=1748692470&hash=item339f0f0f8c:g:ybkAAOSwBLIU~sdvLink
1.25" Stand-Offs 1 (Package of Four)	2	1.79	$3.58	https://www.pololu.com/product/1951
100:1 Micro Metal Gearmotor with Extended Shaft	2	14.41	$28.82	http://www.pololu.com/catalog/product/2204
2-Pin Socket Header for Motor Power	2	0.23	$0.46	https://www.pololu.com/product/1012

(*continued*)

Parts	Quantities for One Robot	Unit Price	Subtotal	
Pololu Ball Caster with 3/4" Plastic Ball	2	3.59	$7.18	http://www.pololu.com/catalog/product/954
Extended Micrometal Gearmotor Brackets (Pair)	1	4.99	$4.99	http://www.pololu.com/catalog/product/1089
DRV8835 Dual Motor Driver Carrier	1	3.89	$3.89	https://www.pololu.com/product/2135
14-Pin DIP Socket for Motor Driver	1	0.3	$0.30	https://solarbotics.com/product/dc-14_pin/
40 x 7 mm Wheels (Pair)	1	3.75	$3.75	https://www.pololu.com/product/1453
Battery Holder 6 AA Back-to-Back	1	1.58	$1.58	https://www.pololu.com/product/1156
Male 1 × 40 Pin Headers for Launchpad	2	0.6	$1.20	https://www.pololu.com/product/965
Pololu 5V Step-Up/Step-Down Voltage Regulator S7V7F5	1	4.25	$4.25	http://www.pololu.com/product/2119
Pololu 6V, 500mA Step-Down Voltage Regulator D24V5F6	1	4.25	$4.25	http://www.pololu.com/product/2844
Rocker Switch: 3-Pin, SPDT, 10A	1	0.64	$0.64	https://www.pololu.com/product/1406
Tiva C	1			http://www.ti.com/ww/en/launchpad/launchpads-connected-ek-tm4c123gxl.html#tabs
Serial Wireless Communication:				

(*continued*)

Parts	Quantities for One Robot	Unit Price	Subtotal	
BlueSMIRF Bluetooth Module RN-42	1	27.95	$27.95	https://www.sparkfun.com/products/12577
6-pin Socket Headers for BlueSMIRF Module	1	0.44	$0.44	https://www.pololu.com/product/1016
Digital Light Sensor:				
QTR-1RC Reflectance Sensor (Digital Output)	2	3.75	$7.50	http://www.pololu.com/catalog/product/2459
.75" Standoffs 1 (Package of Four)	1	1.43	$1.43	https://www.pololu.com/product/1949
Analog Distance Sensors:				
3-Pin Female JST PH-Style Cable	2	1.12	$2.24	https://www.pololu.com/product/117
Sharp GP2Y0A41SK0F Analog Distance Sensor 4–30 cm	2	11.23	$22.46	https://www.pololu.com/product/2464
Bracket Pair for Sharp GP2Y0A41 Sensors - Perpendicular	1	2.99	$2.99	https://www.pololu.com/product/2677
Total Cost of a Robot			$143.30	

Appendix B

State Machine for the Autonomous Robot Project[1]

Driving through Maze—Drive.c

Drive task. The general idea is as follows:

Pend on DriveSema (posted by DriveClockFn every 50 ms) Follow wall (ReadWall_IR(), PID, set motors)

- If there is no wall on right, perform intersection right turn.
- If the wall is there, compute the error in the distance to the wall (error = measured distance
    - desired distance) and save the error in a global variable, overwriting the previous value.
- Now use the error in the PID control computation.
- Convert control to PWM for each motor and write to PWM if the wall is in front. Perform a U-turn.

If Crossline #1, start DataClockFn. If Crossline #2, stop DataClockFn.
If Stopline, stop bot, stop DriveClockFn.
If global StopFlag, stop bot, stop DriveClockFn back to Pend on DriveSema.

Drive Task States and Transitions

- START: Starting up.
    - Increase speed during each iteration. The next state occurs when the count is xxx.
    - Next state is FOLLOW1
- FOLLOW1: Following wall (PID, checking sensors) to Crossline #1.
    - Read right wall distance
        - If the right wall not detected, the next state is INTERSECTION
        - Otherwise, implement PID and motor control

1 Dr. John Glover, class notes to author

    - If Crossline #1 is detected (encoder/timer count for consecutive blacks), complete the following:
        - Start DataClockFn
        - Next state is FOLLOW2.
    - If the stopline is detected (encoder/timer count for consecutive blacks), the next state is STOP.
    - If the front wall is close, the next state is UTURN.
- FOLLOW2: Following wall (PID, checking sensors) to Crossline #2.
    - Store error value in the buffer
    - If Crossline #2 detected (encoder/timer count for consecutive blacks), complete the following:
        - Stop DataClockFn
        - Next state is FOLLOW3
    - If the stopline is detected (encoder/timer count for consecutive blacks), complete the following:
        - Stop DriveClockFn
        - Next state is STOP
    - If the front wall is close, the next state is UTURN.
    - If the right wall is not detected, the next state is INTERSECTION.
- FOLLOW3: Follow the wall (PID, checking sensors) to the stopline.
    - If the stopline is detected (encoder/timer count for consecutive blacks), then the next state is STOP.
    - If the front wall is close, then the next state is UTURN.
    - If the right wall is not detected, then the next state is INTERSECTION.
- INTERSECTION: Turning right in the intersection (using encoder/timer counts).
    - Go forward a little
    - Rotate right
    - Go forward a little
    - Next state is the previous FOLLOW state
- UTURN: U-turn rotation.
    - Make a complete U-turn rotation (using encoder/timer counts)
    - Next state is the previous FOLLOW state
- STOP: Stopping the robot.
    - Decrease speed during each iteration. The next state occurs when the count is xxx
    - Next state is OFF
- OFF: End the contest.

ReadLightW function (*results, LightSema)

(save arguments in static variables allocated here)

Set pins to output enable timer#1

Pend on LightSema

- In HWI#1, set pins to input, enable timer#2
- In HWI#2, read pins, store *results, post LightSema
- Return with pin result in *results

ReadWall_IR function (*distance)

- Read IR distance sensor(s) using ADC (noninterrupt, just wait on flag)

ReadFrontWall_US_W function (*distance) (using IR distance sensor in front)

Acquiring Data—Data.c

Statically allocate variables for communication between AcquireData and TxData, including the ping-pong buffers.

AcquireData task:

Pend on DataSema (posted by DataClockFn every 100 ms). Get most recent right wall error from global variable.

Convert to hexASCII and store into ping-pong buffer (task has two buffers, both have command prepended). As you are storing into the buffer, insert a space after the command and between each data value. Add a null byte after the last data value.

If the buffer is full, complete the following:

- Copy the full buffer pointer to Full Buffer Ptr
- Swap to the empty buffer for continued acquisition
- Post TxDataSema and back to Pend on DataSema

TxData task:
Pend on TxDataSema
Call **storeTxBufferPtr_W** (char* bufferPtr) to give the pointer to the new Full Buffer Ptr to the TX Response task. This function may wait on the TX_RWLock.
Back to Pend on TxDataSema

Receive Commands—RxCommands.c

Local command buffer and other variables are statically allocated here.

RxCmd task:
Use readFrame(char *localCmdBuffer) function to read in the frame via the UART. The readFrame() function should be stripped of the leading colon and ending checksum and CR/LF

(Carriage Return and Linefeed) as they are read in and processed. In other words, there is no sense in storing those characters in the buffer. What is returned in localCmdBuffer is just a null-terminated string of characters consisting of the two-character command, followed optionally by argument characters. There is the noninterrupt approach (to get started) and the interrupt approach (final).

Call readFrame(char* localCmdBuffer) to read in frame, char by char, no interrupts. As each character is read, the state machine processes the frame.

When the frame is complete, return from readFrame() OR.

Call readFrame(char * localCmdBuffer) to read in frame via UART interrupts: enable UART Rx interrupts.

Pend on UARTDoneSema

- In HWI Hardware Interrupt (HWI), read character and stash it in static variable, post SWI.
- In SWI, state machine processes the frame.
    - If not finished with the frame, just return from SWI
    - If finished, disable interrupts, post UARTDoneSema Return from readFrame()

Proceeding after readFrame() returns with pointer to received command buffer:

Call **storeReceivedCommand_W**(char* localCmdBuffer) to give the new command buffer to the command interpreter task. This function may wait on the CmdBuffer_RWLock.

Post NewCmdSema, repeat.

Transmit Response—TxResponse.c

Statically allocated TX Buffer Pointer.

TxResponse task:

Pend on TxResponseSema

Call writeFrame(char *bufferPointer) to transmit the data found at the TX Buffer Pointer. The data is a null-terminated response string (two-character command/ID followed optionally by more response characters). The writeFrame() function's state machine inserts the colon, checksum, and CR/LF as it writes characters to the UART.

Post TX_RWLock, indicate the readiness for the next response frame back to pend on TxResponseSema.

storeTxBufferPtr_W function (char* bufferPtr) Pend on TX_RWLock

- Copy bufferPtr to TX Buffer Ptr

- Post TxResponseSema

COMMAND INTERPRETER—CmdInt.c
The global command buffer is statically allocated in this file.

CmdInt task:

Pend on NewCmdSema
Extract command (getCmd fn) from global command buffer search table and call the appropriate cmd fn.
The return value is pointer to Cmd Response buffer (null-terminated ASCII) copy Cmd Response buffer to the local response.
Call **storeTxBufferPtr_W** (char* bufferPtr) to give the pointer to the new response buffer to the TX Response task. This function may wait on the TX_RWLock.
Post CmdBuffer_RWLock back to Pend on NewCmdSema
storeReceivedCommand_W function (char* localCmdBuffer) Pend on CmdBuffer_RWLock
Copy the command buffer contents pointed to by the argument to the global command buffer as a null-terminated string.
Commands to implement:
Allowed if not already driving:

- Read IR sensors
- Read Light sensor
- Motor movements (fwd, rotate, etc.)

Start driving allowed if already driving:

- Stop driving
- Start/stop data acquisition

RCC Register RCC[1,2]

Bit	Name	R/W	Default	Description	Comments
31:28	Reserved	RO	0		
27	ACG	RW	0	Auto clock gating used in sleep or deep sleep mode	
26:23	SYSDIV	RW	0xF	Divisor used to generate a system clock from the PLL (BYPASS = 0) or the oscillator source (BYPASS = 1)	
22	USESYSDIV	RW	0	0: System clock is used undivided 1: System clock comes from the clock divider SYSTEMDIV2 is used instead of this bit field when bit USERCC2 in register RCC2 is set	
21	Reserved				
22	USEPWMDIV			0: System clock is the PWM clock 1: PWM clock divider output is the PWM clock	

(continued)

1 Texas Instruments, *Tiva*[TM] *TM4C123GH6PM*, 254–257.

2 Texas Instruments provided file tm4c123gh6pm.h.

Bit	Name	R/W	Default	Description	Comments
19:17	PWMDIV	RW	0x07	The encoding numbers for binary counter divider to generate PWM clock	
16:14	Reserved		0x0		
13	Power Down	RW	1	0: PLL is operating 1: PLL is powered down	
10:6	XTAL	RW	0B	Crystal value for the MOSC ... 0x09 5MHz ... 0x10 10MHz ... 0x15 16MHz ...	
5:4	OSCSRC	RW	0x01	Oscillator source 0x0 MOSC 0x01 PIOSC 0x02 PIOSC/4 0x03 LFOSC	
3:1	Reserved				
0	MOSCDIS	RW	1	Main Oscillator Disable	

RCC Register RCC2[3]

Bit	Name	R/W	Default	Description	Comments
31	USERCC2	RW	0	0: RCC register fields are used. The RCC2 register fields are ignored 1: RCC2 register fields override similar ones of the RCC register fields	

(*continued*)

3 Texas Instruments, *Tiva™ TM4C123GH6PM*, 260–262.

Bit	Name	R/W	Default	Description	Comments
30	DIV400	RW	0	0: Use the SYSDIV2 bits to divide the PLL 200 MHz output to create the system clock 1: Create a 7-bit divisor by appending the bit SYSDIV2LSB to the SYSDIV2 bits and use the combined number to divide the 400MHz PLL output to create the system clock	
29	Reserved	RO			
28:23	SYSDIV2	RW	0xF	Divisor used to generate system clock from the PLL (BYPASS = 0) or the oscillator source (BYPASS = 1)	
22	SYSDIV2LSB	RW	0	0: System clock is used undivided 1: System clock comes from the clock divider SYSTEMDIV2 is used instead of this bit field when bit USERCC2 in reg RCC2 is set	
21:15	Reserved	RO	0		
14	USBPWRDN		1	0: The USB PLL works normally 1: The USB PLL is powered down	
13	PWRDN2	RW	1	0: The PLL works normally 1: The PLL is powered down	
12	Reserved	RO	0x0		
13	Power Down	RW	1	0: PLL is operating 1: The PLL is powered down	
10:7	Reserved	RO	0x0		

(*continued*)

Bit	Name	R/W	Default	Description	Comments
6:4	OSCSRC2	RW	0x01	Oscillator Source 2 0x0: MOSC 0x1: PIOSC 0x2: PIOSC/4 0x3: LFOSC 0x4-0x6: Reserved 0x7 32.768-kHz external oscillator	
3:0	Reserved	RO	0x0		

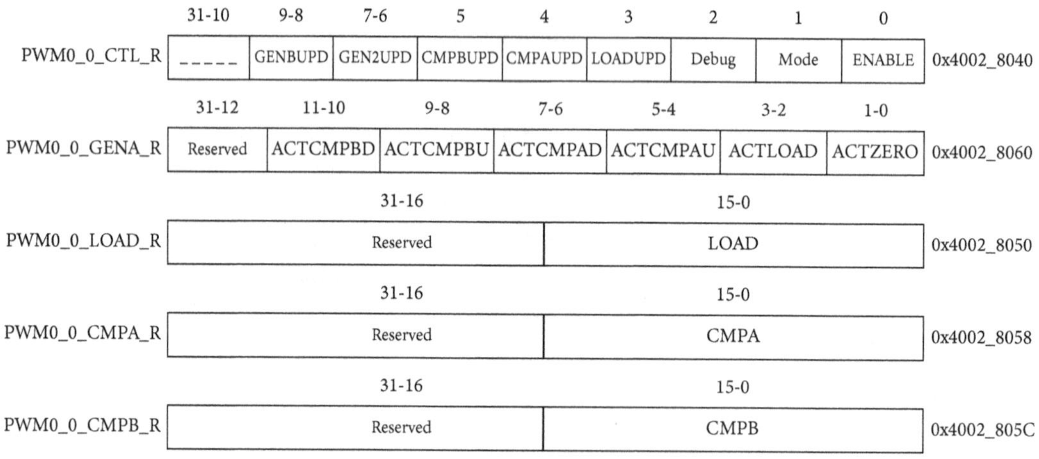

Register	31-10	9-8	7-6	5	4	3	2	1	0	Address
PWM0_0_CTL_R	_____	GENBUPD	GEN2UPD	CMPBUPD	CMPAUPD	LOADUPD	Debug	Mode	ENABLE	0x4002_8040

Register	31-12	11-10	9-8	7-6	5-4	3-2	1-0	Address
PWM0_0_GENA_R	Reserved	ACTCMPBD	ACTCMPBU	ACTCMPAD	ACTCMPAU	ACTLOAD	ACTZERO	0x4002_8060

Register	31-16	15-0	Address
PWM0_0_LOAD_R	Reserved	LOAD	0x4002_8050
PWM0_0_CMPA_R	Reserved	CMPA	0x4002_8058
PWM0_0_CMPB_R	Reserved	CMPB	0x4002_805C

Image A.1

```
//*****************************************************************
******
//
// The following are definitions for the bit fields in the PWM_O_0_CTL register.
//
//*****************************************************************
******
#define PWM_0_CTL_LATCH          0x00040000  // Latch Fault Input
#define PWM_0_CTL_MINFLTPER      0x00020000  // Minimum Fault Period
#define PWM_0_CTL_FLTSRC         0x00010000  // Fault Condition Source
#define PWM_0_CTL_DBFALLUPD_M    0x0000C000  // PWMnDBFALL Update Mode
#define PWM_0_CTL_DBFALLUPD_I    0x00000000  // Immediate
#define PWM_0_CTL_DBFALLUPD_LS   0x00008000  // Locally Synchronized
```

```
#define PWM_0_CTL_DBFALLUPD_GS  0x0000C000  // Globally Synchronized
#define PWM_0_CTL_DBRISEUPD_M   0x00003000  // PWMnDBRISE Update Mode
#define PWM_0_CTL_DBRISEUPD_I   0x00000000  // Immediate
#define PWM_0_CTL_DBRISEUPD_LS  0x00002000  // Locally Synchronized
#define PWM_0_CTL_DBRISEUPD_GS  0x00003000  // Globally Synchronized
#define PWM_0_CTL_DBCTLUPD_M    0x00000C00  // PWMnDBCTL Update Mode
#define PWM_0_CTL_DBCTLUPD_I    0x00000000  // Immediate
#define PWM_0_CTL_DBCTLUPD_LS   0x00000800  // Locally Synchronized
#define PWM_0_CTL_DBCTLUPD_GS   0x00000C00  // Globally Synchronized
#define PWM_0_CTL_GENBUPD_M     0x00000300  // PWMnGENB Update Mode
#define PWM_0_CTL_GENBUPD_I     0x00000000  // Immediate
#define PWM_0_CTL_GENBUPD_LS    0x00000200  // Locally Synchronized
#define PWM_0_CTL_GENBUPD_GS    0x00000300  // Globally Synchronized
#define PWM_0_CTL_GENAUPD_M     0x000000C0  // PWMnGENA Update Mode
#define PWM_0_CTL_GENAUPD_I     0x00000000  // Immediate
#define PWM_0_CTL_GENAUPD_LS    0x00000080  // Locally Synchronized
#define PWM_0_CTL_GENAUPD_GS    0x000000C0  // Globally Synchronized
#define PWM_0_CTL_CMPBUPD      0x00000020  // Comparator B Update Mode
#define PWM_0_CTL_CMPAUPD      0x00000010  // Comparator A Update Mode
#define PWM_0_CTL_LOADUPD      0x00000008  // Load Register Update Mode
#define PWM_0_CTL_DEBUG         0x00000004  // Debug Mode
#define PWM_0_CTL_MODE          0x00000002  // Counter Mode
#define PWM_0_CTL_ENABLE        0x00000001  // PWM Block Enable

//*************************************************************
******
//
// The following are definitions for the bit fields in the PWM_O_0_GENA register.
//
//*************************************************************
******
#define PWM_0_GENA_ACTCMPBD_M   0x00000C00  // Action for Comparator
B Down
#define PWM_0_GENA_ACTCMPBD_NONE  0x00000000  // Do nothing
#define PWM_0_GENA_ACTCMPBD_INV 0x00000400  // Invert pwmA
#define PWM_0_GENA_ACTCMPBD_ZERO 0x00000800  // Drive pwmA Low
#define PWM_0_GENA_ACTCMPBD_ONE 0x00000C00  // Drive pwmA High
#define PWM_0_GENA_ACTCMPBU_M   0x00000300  // Action for Comparator
B Up
#define PWM_0_GENA_ACTCMPBU_NONE  0x00000000  // Do nothing
#define PWM_0_GENA_ACTCMPBU_INV 0x00000100  // Invert pwmA
```

```
#define PWM_0_GENA_ACTCMPBU_ZERO 0x00000200  // Drive pwmA Low
#define PWM_0_GENA_ACTCMPBU_ONE 0x00000300  // Drive pwmA High
#define PWM_0_GENA_ACTCMPAD_M   0x000000C0  // Action for Comparator
A Down
#define PWM_0_GENA_ACTCMPAD_NONE 0x00000000  // Do nothing
#define PWM_0_GENA_ACTCMPAD_INV 0x00000040  // Invert pwmA
#define PWM_0_GENA_ACTCMPAD_ZERO 0x00000080  // Drive pwmA Low
#define PWM_0_GENA_ACTCMPAD_ONE 0x000000C0  // Drive pwmA High
#define PWM_0_GENA_ACTCMPAU_M   0x00000030  // Action for Comparator
A Up
#define PWM_0_GENA_ACTCMPAU_NONE 0x00000000  // Do nothing
#define PWM_0_GENA_ACTCMPAU_INV 0x00000010  // Invert pwmA
#define PWM_0_GENA_ACTCMPAU_ZERO  0x00000020  // Drive pwmA Low
#define PWM_0_GENA_ACTCMPAU_ONE 0x00000030  // Drive pwmA High
#define PWM_0_GENA_ACTLOAD_M    0x0000000C  // Action for Counter=LOAD
#define PWM_0_GENA_ACTLOAD_NONE 0x00000000  // Do nothing
#define PWM_0_GENA_ACTLOAD_INV  0x00000004  // Invert pwmA
#define PWM_0_GENA_ACTLOAD_ZERO 0x00000008  // Drive pwmA Low
#define PWM_0_GENA_ACTLOAD_ONE  0x0000000C  // Drive pwmA High
#define PWM_0_GENA_ACTZERO_M    0x00000003  // Action for Counter=0
#define PWM_0_GENA_ACTZERO_NONE 0x00000000  // Do nothing
#define PWM_0_GENA_ACTZERO_INV  0x00000001  // Invert pwmA
#define PWM_0_GENA_ACTZERO_ZERO 0x00000002  // Drive pwmA Low
#define PWM_0_GENA_ACTZERO_ONE  0x00000003  // Drive pwmA High
```

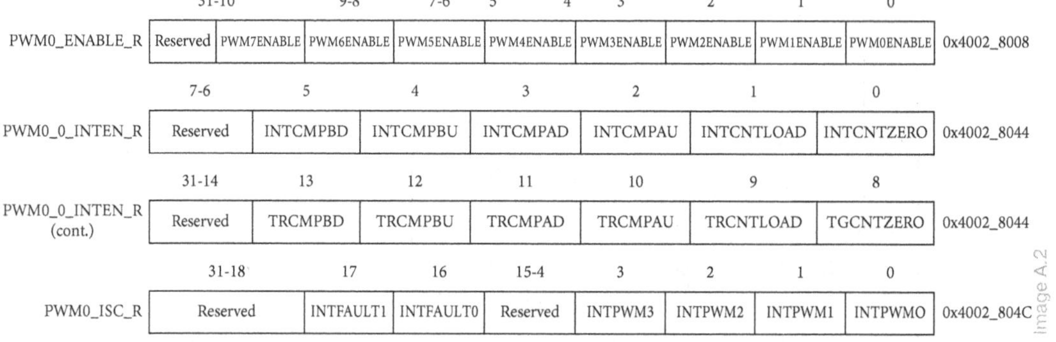

Image A.2

```
//*************************************************************
*************
//
// The following are definitions for the bit fields in the PWM_O_0_INTEN register.
//
//*************************************************************
*************
#define PWM_0_INTEN_TRCMPBD    0x00002000 // Trigger for Counter=PWMnCMPB
                                          // Down
#define PWM_0_INTEN_TRCMPBU     0x00001000  // Trigger for Counter=P-
WMnCMPB Up
#define PWM_0_INTEN_TRCMPAD    0x00000800 // Trigger for Counter=PWMnCMPA
                                          // Down
#define PWM_0_INTEN_TRCMPAU     0x00000400  // Trigger for Counter=P-
WMnCMPA Up
#define PWM_0_INTEN_TRCNTLOAD  0x00000200 // Trigger for Counter=PWMnLOAD
#define PWM_0_INTEN_TRCNTZERO  0x00000100  // Trigger for Counter=0
#define  PWM_0_INTEN_INTCMPBD     0x00000020   //  Interrupt  for
Counter=PWMnCMPB
                                          // Down
#define  PWM_0_INTEN_INTCMPBU     0x00000010   //  Interrupt  for
Counter=PWMnCMPB
                                          // Up
#define  PWM_0_INTEN_INTCMPAD     0x00000008   //  Interrupt  for
Counter=PWMnCMPA
                                          // Down
#define  PWM_0_INTEN_INTCMPAU     0x00000004   //  Interrupt  for
Counter=PWMnCMPA
                                          // Up
#define  PWM_0_INTEN_INTCNTLOAD  0x00000002   //  Interrupt  for
Counter=PWMnLOAD
#define PWM_0_INTEN_INTCNTZERO 0x00000001  // Interrupt for Counter=0
```

	31-10	9-8	7-6	5	4	3	2	1	0	
PWM0_ENABLE_R	Reserved	PWM7ENABLE	PWM6ENABLE	PWM5ENABLE	PWM4ENABLE	PWM3ENABLE	PWM2ENABLE	PWM1ENABLE	PWM0ENABLE	0x4002_8008

	7-6	5	4	3	2	1	0	
PWM0_0_INTEN_R	Reserved	INTCMPBD	INTCMPBU	INTCMPAD	INTCMPAU	INTCNTLOAD	INTCNTZERO	0x4002_8044

	31-14	13	12	11	10	9	8	
PWM0_0_INTEN_R (cont.)	Reserved	TRCMPBD	TRCMPBU	TRCMPAD	TRCMPAU	TRCNTLOAD	TGCNTZERO	0x4002_8044

	31-18	17	16	15-4	3	2	1	0	
PWM0_ISC_R	Reserved	INTFAULT1	INTFAULT0	Reserved	INTPWM3	INTPWM2	INTPWM1	INTPWMO	0x4002_804C

Image A.3

```
//*****************************************************************
******
//
// The following are definitions for the bit fields in the PWM_O_ENABLE register.
//
//*****************************************************************
******
#define PWM_ENABLE_PWM7EN       0x00000080  // MnPWM7 Output Enable
#define PWM_ENABLE_PWM6EN       0x00000040  // MnPWM6 Output Enable
#define PWM_ENABLE_PWM5EN       0x00000020  // MnPWM5 Output Enable
#define PWM_ENABLE_PWM4EN       0x00000010  // MnPWM4 Output Enable
#define PWM_ENABLE_PWM3EN       0x00000008  // MnPWM3 Output Enable
#define PWM_ENABLE_PWM2EN       0x00000004  // MnPWM2 Output Enable
#define PWM_ENABLE_PWM1EN       0x00000002  // MnPWM1 Output Enable
#define PWM_ENABLE_PWM0EN       0x00000001  // MnPWM0 Output Enable
//*****************************************************************
******
//
// The following are definitions for the bit fields in the PWM_O_INTEN register.
//
//*****************************************************************
******
#define PWM_INTEN_INTFAULT1     0x00020000  // Interrupt Fault 1
#define PWM_INTEN_INTFAULT0     0x00010000  // Interrupt Fault 0
#define PWM_INTEN_INTPWM3       0x00000008  // PWM3 Interrupt Enable
#define PWM_INTEN_INTPWM2       0x00000004  // PWM2 Interrupt Enable
#define PWM_INTEN_INTPWM1       0x00000002  // PWM1 Interrupt Enable
#define PWM_INTEN_INTPWM0       0x00000001  // PWM0 Interrupt Enable

//*****************************************************************
*************
//
// The following are definitions for the bit fields in the PWM_O_ISC register.
//
//*****************************************************************
*************
#define PWM_ISC_INTFAULT1     0x00020000  // FAULT1 Interrupt Asserted
#define PWM_ISC_INTFAULT0     0x00010000  // FAULT0 Interrupt Asserted
#define PWM_ISC_INTPWM3         0x00000008  // PWM3 Interrupt Status
#define PWM_ISC_INTPWM2         0x00000004  // PWM2 Interrupt Status
#define PWM_ISC_INTPWM1         0x00000002  // PWM1 Interrupt Status
#define PWM_ISC_INTPWM0         0x00000001  // PWM0 Interrupt Status
```

GPIO Pins

```
LDR R0, =SYSCTL_RCGCGPIO_R

LDR R1, [R0]

ORR R1, R1, #0x20

STR R1, [R0]

NOP

NOP

LDR R0,=GPIO_PORTF_LOCK_R ; unlock portF

LDR R1,=0x4C4F434B ; special number to unlock

STR R1, [R0]

LDR R0,=GPIO_PORTF_CR_R

MOV R1, #0xFF

STR R1, [R0]

LDR R0, =GPIO_PORTF_DIR_R;

LDR R1, [R0]

BIC R1, R1, #0x11

ORR R1, R1, #0xE; output portF pin 3-1

STR R1, [R0]
```

```
LDR R0, =GPIO_PORTF_PUR_R
LDR R1, [R0]
ORR R1, R1, #0x11; pullup
STR R1, [R0]
LDR R0, =GPIO_PORTF_AMSEL_R
LDR R1, [R0]
BIC R1, R1, #0x1F
STR R1, [R0]
LDR R0, =GPIO_PORTF_DEN_R
LDR R1, [R0]
ORR R1, R1, #0x1F
STR R1, [R0]
LDR R0, =GPIO_PORTF_AFSEL_R
LDR R1, [R0]
BIC R1, R1, #0x1F
STR R1, [R0]
LDR R0, =GPIO_PORTF_PCTL_R
LDR R1, [R0]
LDR R2, =0xFFF00000
AND R1, R1, R2 ;
STR R1, [R0]
```

Program A.1: Configuring GPIO Pins

Mapping Pins to Alternate Functions

;Map Port A Pin 0 and Pin1 to UART0 Rx and UART0 Tx pins, respectively.

```
LDR R0, =SYSCTL_RCGCGPIO_R

LDR R1, [R0]

ORR R1, R1, #0x01

STR R1, [R0]

NOP

NOP
```

Make Port A Pin 0 to be input and Pin 1 to be output.

```
LDR R0, =GPIO_PORTA_DIR_R;

LDR R1, [R0]

BIC R1, R1, #0x1

ORR R1, R1, #0x2

STR R1, [R0]
```

Make sure Pins 1–0 are not analog pins; they are digital pins.

```
LDR R0, =GPIO_PORTA_AMSEL_R

LDR R1, [R0]

BIC R1, R1, #0x3

STR R1, [R0]

LDR R0, =GPIO_PORTF_DEN_R

LDR R1, [R0]

ORR R1, R1, #0x3

STR R1, [R0]
```

Make sure Pins 1–0 are mapped to UART0 alternate functions.

```
LDR R0, =GPIO_PORTA_AFSEL_R

LDR R1, [R0]

ORR R1, R1, #0x3

STR R1, [R0]

LDR R0, =GPIO_PORTF_PCTL_R

LDR R1, [R0]

LDR R2, =0xFFFFFF00

AND R1, R1, R2

ORR R1, R1, 0x00000011

STR R1, [R0]
```

Program A.2: Mapping GPIO Pins to Alternate Function

GPIO Interrupts

The following code sets up interrupts for Port F Pin 0 and Pin 4. These pins are connected to switches SW2 and SW1, respectively. Anytime a switch is pressed, an interrupt happens and the ISR (Interrupt Service Routine) is executed checking to see which switch is pressed and then toggles either the Red or Blue LED of the Tiva C launchpad.

```
        AREA Block1, DATA, READWRITE, ALIGN=2

cnt  DCD 0x0102

        AREA Ex1, CODE, READONLY, ALIGN=2
```

1. Include macro definitions of addresses of NVIC and port F registers

```
NVIC_ST_CTRL_R       EQU 0xE000E010

NVIC_ST_RELOAD_R     EQU 0xE000E014

NVIC_ST_CURRENT_R    EQU 0xE000E018

NVIC_SYS_PRI3_R      EQU 0xE000ED20   ; Sys. Handlers 12 to 15
Priority
```

```
NVIC_PRI17_R       EQU 0xE000E444

NVIC_PRI7_R        EQU 0xE000E41C

NVIC_EN0_R         EQU 0xE000E100

NVIC_EN1_R         EQU 0xE000E104


GPIO_PORTF_LOCK_R  EQU 0x40025520

GPIO_PORTF_CR_R    EQU 0x40025524

GPIO_PORTF_AMSEL_R EQU 0x40025528

GPIO_PORTF_PCTL_R  EQU 0x4002552C

GPIO_LOCK_KEY      EQU 0x4C4F434B

GPIO_PORTF_DATA_R  EQU 0x400253FC

GPIO_PORTF_DIR_R   EQU 0x40025400

GPIO_PORTF_AFSEL_R EQU 0x40025420

GPIO_PORTF_PUR_R   EQU 0x40025510

GPIO_PORTF_DEN_R   EQU 0x4002551C

GPIO_PORTF_IBE_R   EQU 0x40025408

GPIO_PORTF_IEV_R   EQU 0x4002540C

GPIO_PORTF_IM_R    EQU 0x40025410

GPIO_PORTF_RIS_R   EQU 0x40025414

GPIO_PORTF_ICR_R   EQU 0x4002541C

GPIO_PORTF_IS_R    EQU 0x40025404

DELAY              EQU 8000000 ; delay 0.5sec
(=8000,000*1/16MHz)


SYSCTL_RCGCGPIO_R  EQU 0x400FE608
```

```
        EXPORT Start

        EXPORT SysTick_Handler

        EXPORT      GPIOPortF_Handler

        ENTRY

Main program

Start

              BL Port_Init

        BL PF_Int_Init

LoopS

         WFI

         B LoopS

Initialization routines for port F

PF_Int_Init

        MOV R2, #0x1

        MSR PRIMASK, R2;    store 1 to PRIMASK register to dis-
able the global interrupt

        LDR R0, =GPIO_PORTF_IS_R ; loading port F Interrupt
Sense register

        MOV R1, #0x00            ; select Edge detect

        STR R1, [R0]

        LDR R0, =GPIO_PORTF_IBE_R; loading port F Both Edges
Interrupt register

        MOV R1, #0x00            ; choose 1 Edge

        STR R1, [R0]

        LDR R0, =GPIO_PORTF_IEV_R; loading port F Interrupt
Event register
```

```
MOV R1, #0x00              ; choose Falling Edge detect

STR R1, [R0]

LDR R0, = NVIC_PRI7_R             ; loading NVIC priority
register 7 controlling priority of

LDR R1, =0xFF0FFFFF                  ; SysCtl, FlahCtl
and port F interrupts

; clearing out bits 20-23

LDR R2, [R0]

      AND R2, R2, R1

LDR R1, =0x00A00000              ; set port F interrupt
priority to 5 (bits 23-21)

ORR R2, R2, R1

STR R1, [R0]

LDR R0, = NVIC_EN0_R     ; enable port F interrupt (bit
30 of register NVIC_EN0_R)

LDR R1, =0x40000000

LDR R2, [R0]

ORR R2, R2, R1

STR R2, [R0]

LDR R0, =GPIO_PORTF_IM_R ; Enable port F interrupt (pin
0 and pin 4)

MOV R1, #0x11

STR R1, [R0]

MOV R2, #0x0

MSR PRIMASK, R2;    store 0 to PRIMASK register to
enable the global interrupt

BX LR
```

```
; Port F interrupt Service Routine

      GPIOPortF_Handler

      PUSH {LR}                ; save Link Register before
jumping to a subroutine

      BL Check_PF             ; jump to subroutine Check_PF to
see which switch (1 or 0)

       POP {LR}                 ;that has been pressed.

; Clearing old interrupts

       LDR R0, =GPIO_PORTF_ICR_R ;loading interrupt status
clear register

       MOV R1, #0x11

       STR R1, [R0]

;updating cnt, the number of getting to this ISR

       LDR R0, =cnt

       LDR R1, [R0]

       ADD R1, R1, #1

       STR R1, [R0]

       BX LR


;Checking interrupts of port F switches

Check_PF

LDR R0, =GPIO_PORTF_RIS_R ;loading port F Raw Interrupt
Status register

       LDR R1, [R0]

       ANDS R2, R1, #0x01 ;checking port F pin 0 (SW1)

       BNE B_PF0
```

```
        ANDS R2, R1, #0x10 ;checking port F pin 4 (SW0)

        BNE B_PF4

        BX LR

B_PF0

; Toggling the red LED

        LDR R4, = GPIO_PORTF_DATA_R

        LDR R5,  [R4]

        AND R5, R5, #0x2

        EOR R5, R5, #0x2

        STR R5, [R4]

        BX LR

B_PF4

; Toggling the blue LED

        LDR R4, = GPIO_PORTF_DATA_R

        LDR R5,  [R4]

        AND R5, R5, #0x4

        EOR R5, R5, #0x4

        STR R5, [R4]

        BX LR
```

Program A.3: Set up Interrupts for Port F Pin0 and Pin 4

Configuration of the System Clock

```
//Program PLL.c

#include <stdint.h>

#include “PLL.h”
```

```
#include "tm4c123gh6pm.h"

#define SYSCTL_RCC_XTAL_M        0x000007C0  // Crystal Value

#define SYSCTL_RCC_XTAL_8MHZ     0x00000380  // 8 MHz

#define SYSCTL_RCC_XTAL_16MHZ    0x00000540  // 16 MHz

#define SYSCTL_RCC2_USERCC2      0x80000000  // Use RCC2

#define SYSCTL_RCC2_DIV400       0x40000000  // Divide PLL as
400MHz vs. 200MHz

#define SYSCTL_RCC2_SYSDIV2_M    0x1F800000  // System Clock
Divisor 2

#define SYSCTL_RCC2_SYSDIV2LSB   0x00400000  // Additional LSB
for SYSDIV2\

#define SYSCTL_RCC2_PWRDN2   0x00002000  // Power-Down PLL 2

#define SYSCTL_RCC2_BYPASS2   0x00000800  // PLL Bypass 2
(bit 11)

#define SYSCTL_RCC2_OSCSRC2_M    0x00000070  // Oscillator
Source 2

#define SYSCTL_RCC2_OSCSRC2_MO   0x00000000  // MOSC

#define SYSCTL_RCC2_OSCSRC2_IO   0x00000010  // PIOSC

#define SYSCTL_RCC2_SYSDIV2_S    23

#define FREQ_80MHZ  (4<<22)

SYSCTL_RCC2_R |= SYSCTL_RCC2_BYPASS2; //Bit

SYSCTL_RCC2_R |= SYSCTL_RCC2_USERCC2; //Bit 31 (Figure 6.3)

SYSCTL_RCC_R &= ~SYSCTL_RCC_XTAL_M;       // Clear the Crys-
tal Field

SYSCTL_RCC_R += SYSCTL_RCC_XTAL_16MHZ; // Pick 16 MHz Crystal
(bit[10:6]=0x15)

 // Clear the oscillator source bit field  (bits 6-4)
```

```
            SYSCTL_RCC2_R &= ~SYSCTL_RCC2_OSCSRC2_M;// clear
oscillator source field

            //Updating the oscillator bit field to pick the
MOSC as the clock source

SYSCTL_RCC2_R += SYSCTL_RCC2_OSCSRC2_MO;


//Use the 400 MHz PLL.

SYSCTL_RCC2_R |= SYSCTL_RCC2_DIV400;


//Choose 80 MHz as the system clock by clearing the divider
field before updating its value to //four (system clock fre-
quency = PLL clock frequency/(divider value +1) = 400 MHz/5 =
80 //MHz)

// Clear system clock divider2 bit field and the divider2 LSB

SYSCTL_RCC2_R = (SYSCTL_RCC2_R &  ~(SYSCTL_RCC2_SYSDIV2_M+SY-
SCTL_RCC2_SYSDIV2LSB );

//Update the divider2 and the divider2 LSB bit field

SYSCTL_ RCC2_R |=  FREQ_80MHZ;

//Activate the PLL by clearing the PWRDN2 bit.

SYSCTL_RCC2_R &= ~SYSCTL_RCC2_PWRDN2;

//Wait until the PLL is locked by checking its status.

while((SYSCTL_RIS_R & SYSCTL_RIS_PLLLRIS)==0){};

//After the PLL has been locked, remove the BYPASS2 bit.

 SYSCTL_RCC2_R &= ~SYSCTL_RCC2_BYPASS2; //Bit 11
```

The system clock is now set up and running at 80 MHz, which is the maximum system clock frequency of the Tiva C microcontroller.

Program A.4: Configuration of the PLL for an 80-MHz System Clock

Set Up Timer 2A for Event-Counting Capture

```
void Timer2_Init(void)

{

    //initialize PORT F

    volatile unsigned long  delay;

    SYSCTL_RCGC2_R |= 0x00000020;      // 1) F clock

    delay = SYSCTL_RCGC2_R;            // delay to allow
clock to stabilize

    GPIO_PORTF_LOCK_R = 0x4C4F434B;  // 2) unlock GPIO Port F

        GPIO_PORTF_CR_R = 0x1F;

    GPIO_PORTF_AMSEL_R &= 0x00;        // 2) disable analog
function

    GPIO_PORTF_DIR_R &= ~0x011;          // 4.2) PF0/4 input

    GPIO_PORTF_DIR_R |= ~0x00E;          // 4.2) PF0/4 input

        GPIO_PORTF_PUR_R |=  0x11;

    GPIO_PORTF_AFSEL_R &= ~0x0E;     // disable alt funct on
PF3-1

    GPIO_PORTF_AFSEL_R |= 0x010;        // 5) alternate func-
tion = Timer Event Capture PF4 T2CCP0

    GPIO_PORTF_DEN_R |= 0xFF;          // 7) enable digital
pins PF4-PF1

    GPIO_PORTF_PCTL_R = (GPIO_PORTF_PCTL_R & 0xFFF0FFFF) |
0x00070000;


    //timer clock

    SYSCTL_RCGCTIMER_R |=0x04; //Timer 2

    delay = SYSCTL_RCGCTIMER_R;
```

```
//Disable Timer 2A to prevent any changes from causing Timer
2A to react.

TIMER2_CTL_R &= ~0x01;

//Select a 16-bit timer for a 16/32-bit timer or a 32-bit
timer for a 32/64-bit mode.

TIMER2_CFG_R  |= 0x00000004;

//Set Timer 2A to count up (TACDIR = 1), edge count mode
(TACMR = 0), and capture mode (TAMR = 3).

TIMER2_TAMR_R |= 0x0013; //Edge Count, Capture mode, count up

//Set Timer 2A to count the negative-edged event (TAEVENT =
0x01), which freezes counting //when the processor is halted
in debug mode (TASTALL = 1).

TIMER2_CTL_R |= 0x06; //TAEVENT=1 negative edge, TASTALL=1

//In up-count mode, the timer TIMER 2A counts up to the
values of TIMER2_TAMATCHR_R //and TTIMER2_TAPMR_R registers.
The values of TIMER2_TAPR_R and //TIMER2_TAILR_R registers
must be greater than TTIMER2_TAMATCHR_R and //TIMER2_TAPMR_R
registers for the up counting to take place.

TIMER2_TAMATCHR_R = 0x8;

TIMER2_TAILR_R = 0x10;

//Enable the capture event interrupt, which happens when the
values of TIMER2_TAPR_R and //TIMER2_TAR_R register equal to
those of TTIMER2_TAPMR_R and //TIMER2_TAMATCHR_R registers.

TIMER2_IMR_R  |= 0x02; //CAMIM Capture Mode Event Interrupt

//Clear all remaining interrupts.

TIMER2_ICR_R  |= 0x02; //CBEIM Capture Mode Event Interrupt

//Set priority and enable TIMER 2A and the global interrupts.

NVIC_PRI5_R =  (NVIC_PRI5_R&0x0FFFFFFF)|0x40000000;//Tim-
er1B=priority 2
```

```
NVIC_EN0_R = 0x1 << 23;  //Timer 2A iRQ 23, Interrupt number
39

//Enable TIMER 2A.

TIMER2_CTL_R  |= 0x01; //Enable Timer 2A

EnableInterrupts();


}

void Timer2A_Handler(void) {

        int i;

    TIMER2_ICR_R  |= 0x02; //CAEIM Capture Mode Event Inter-
rupt clear

    current = TIMER2_TAR_R;

    cnt = TIMER2_TAV_R;

    TIMER2_TAV_R = 0x0;

}

int main(void){

  Timer2_Init();

  while(1){

  }

}
```

Program A.5: Configure Timer 2A for Event-Counting Capture

Set Up Timer 1B to Generate a Square Wave Running at a Frequency of 128Hz

Need to include files startup.s and tm4c123gh6pm.h with the following file ProgA.6. We can change the frequency by changing the value of parameter DELAY below. This program runs with a default system frequency of 16MHz.

```
// Prog6-6ProgTimer1B-Ints. Producing a square wave output at
PB7 running at a frequency of 128Hz

// Flashing the Red LED at a frequency of about 14Hz


#include "tm4c123gh6pm.h"

#include <stdint.h>


void DisableInterrupts(void); // Disable interrupts

void EnableInterrupts(void);  // Enable interrupts

void GPIO_Init(void);

void Timer1B_Init(uint16_t delay);

//Producing a square wave output on portB pin 7 (PB7) with a
frequency of 128Hz.

//Creating a delay of (16000000/256) system clocks to obtain
a frequency of 256Hz.

//By toggling PB7 every Timer 1B interrupts, we create a
128Hz at PB7

#define DELAY (16000000/256)

//debug code

int main(void){

  DisableInterrupts();

  GPIO_Init();

  Timer1B_Init(DELAY);

  EnableInterrupts();
```

```
  while(1){

  }

}

void GPIO_Init(void) {

  uint8_t tp1;

  SYSCTL_RCGCGPIO_R |= 0x22;  // activate port F, port B

  //Delay for a few clock cycles

  tp1 = SYSCTL_PRGPIO_R;

  tp1 = SYSCTL_PRGPIO_R;

  GPIO_PORTF_LOCK_R = 0x4C4F434B;//  unlock GPIO Port F

  GPIO_PORTF_CR_R = 0x0F;// allow changes to PF0-3


  //Configure port B

  GPIO_PORTB_DIR_R |= 0x80;   // make PB-7 output (PF2
built-in LED)

  GPIO_PORTB_AFSEL_R &= ~0x80;// disable alt funct on PB-7

  GPIO_PORTB_DEN_R |= 0x80;   // enable digital I/O on PB-7

  GPIO_PORTB_PCTL_R = 0x00000000; //reset PCTL register

  GPIO_PORTB_AMSEL_R &= ~0x80;     // disable analog func-
tionality on PB-7


  //Configure port F

  GPIO_PORTF_DIR_R |= 0x0E;   // make PF1-3 output (PF2
built-in LED)

  GPIO_PORTF_AFSEL_R &= ~0x0E;// disable alt funct on PF3-1
```

```
  GPIO_PORTF_DEN_R |= 0x0E;   // enable digital I/O on PF1-3

  GPIO_PORTF_PCTL_R = 0x00000000; //reset PCTL register

  GPIO_PORTF_AMSEL_R &= ~0x0E;     // disable analog func-
tionality on PF1-3

}


void Timer1B_Init(uint16_t delay){

  uint8_t tp;

  DisableInterrupts();

  SYSCTL_RCGCTIMER_R |= 0x02;   // 0) activate TIMER1

  tp = SYSCTL_RCGCTIMER_R;

  TIMER1_CTL_R = 0x00000000;    //  Disable Timer1 during
setup

  TIMER1_CFG_R = 0x00000004;    //  Set up Timer1 for 16-bit
mode

  TIMER1_TBMR_R = 0x00000002;   //  Periodic mode, count down

  TIMER1_TBILR_R = delay;       //  Program reload value

  TIMER1_ICR_R = 0x00000100;    //  Remove TIMER1B timeout
flag

  TIMER1_IMR_R = 0x00000100;    //  Enable Timer1B interrupt

  NVIC_PRI5_R = (NVIC_PRI5_R&0xFF0FFFFF)|0x00800000; // pri-
ority 4

// interrupts enabled in the main program after all devices
initialized

// vector number 35, interrupt number 22

  NVIC_EN0_R = 1<<22;           // 9) enable IRQ 22 in NVIC

  TIMER1_CTL_R = 0x00000100;    // 10) enable TIMER1B
```

```
  EnableInterrupts();

}


void Timer1B_Handler(void){

      static uint32_t tp1 = 0x80;

      static uint32_t tp2 = 0x2;

  TIMER1_ICR_R = TIMER_ICR_TBTOCINT;// acknowledge timer1B
timeout

      GPIO_PORTF_DATA_R = tp2 & 0x02;

      if (tp2 == 0x80000) { tp2 = 0x2;}

      else {tp2 = tp2 << 1;}


      GPIO_PORTB_DATA_R = tp1 & 0x80;

      if (tp1 == 0x80) { tp1 = 0x0;}

      else {tp1 = 0x80;}

}
```

Program A.6: Creating a Square Wave Using Timer1B

Using ADC0 Sequencer 3 with Software Start to Do an Analog-to-Digital Conversion

```
// ProgA-7-ADC-BusyWait

// ADC conversion using the Busy-Wait method.

/*

 Copyright 2014 by Jonathan W. Valvano, valvano@mail.utexas.
edu

    You may use, edit, run or distribute this file
```

```
    as long as the above copyright notice remains

 THIS SOFTWARE IS PROVIDED "AS IS".  NO WARRANTIES, WHETHER
EXPRESS, IMPLIED

 OR STATUTORY, INCLUDING, BUT NOT LIMITED TO, IMPLIED WARRAN-
TIES OF

 MERCHANTABILITY AND FITNESS FOR A PARTICULAR PURPOSE APPLY
TO THIS SOFTWARE.

 VALVANO SHALL NOT, IN ANY CIRCUMSTANCES, BE LIABLE FOR SPE-
CIAL, INCIDENTAL,

 OR CONSEQUENTIAL DAMAGES, FOR ANY REASON WHATSOEVER.

 For more information about my classes, my research, and my
books, see

 http://users.ece.utexas.edu/~valvano/

 */


#include <stdio.h>

#include <stdint.h>

#include "tm4c123gh6pm.h"

#define SYSDIV2 4


void ADC_Init(void);

uint32_t ADC_In(void);

void EnableInterrupts(void);

void SysTick_Init(void);

void delay1(uint8_t );

void PLL_Init(void);
```

```
uint32_t Result;

int main(void){

  PLL_Init();// set system clock to 80 MHz

  //Initialize the ADC and GPIO Port E

  ADC_Init();

  //Continuously soibg ADC conversions

  while(1){

    Result = ADC_In();

  }

}


void ADC_Init(void){

  //Enable module ADC0

  SYSCTL_RCGCADC_R |= 0x01;

  while ((SYSCTL_RCGCADC_R & 0x01) == 0x0) {};

  //Enable GPIO Port E

  SYSCTL_RCGCGPIO_R |= 0x010; //activate port E

  while ((SYSCTL_PRGPIO_R & 0x10) == 0) {};

  //PE2 is analog channel 1 for ADC0, PE2 has alternate func-
tion 0

  GPIO_PORTE_AFSEL_R |= 0x04; //PE2

  GPIO_PORTE_PCTL_R |= 0xFFF0FFFF & GPIO_PORTE_PCTL_R;

  //PE2 is configured as an analog input

  GPIO_PORTE_AMSEL_R |= 0x04;

  //PE2 is not a digital pin
```

```
  GPIO_PORTE_DEN_R &= ~0x04;

  //PE2 is an input

  GPIO_PORTE_DIR_R &= ~0x04;

  //ADC coversion rate of 125 KHz

  ADC0_PC_R = 0x01; //125 KHz

  //Sequencer 3 has highest priority (0) and Sequencer 0 has
lowest priority (3)

  ADC0_SSPRI_R = 0x0123;

  //disable ADC0 sample sequencer 3 while doing configuration

  ADC0_ACTSS_R &= ~0x08;

  //Enable software start for an ADC conversion

  ADC0_EMUX_R &= ~0xF000; //software start

  //Analog channel input for the first sample of Sequencer 3

  ADC0_SSMUX3_R = (ADC0_SSMUX3_R & 0xFFFFFFF0) + 1; //Ain1
(PE2)  SS3 field

  //Sample is from pin PE2. This sample is the only sample of
the sequence and it will cause a raw interrupt.

  ADC0_SSCTL3_R = 0x06; //IE0, END0

  //enable ADC0 sample sequencer 3

  ADC0_ACTSS_R |= 0x08;

}


//------------ADC_In------------

// Busy-wait Analog to digital conversion

// Input: none
```

```
// Output: 12-bit result of ADC conversion
uint32_t ADC_In (void) {
  uint32_t result;
  //start conversion
  ADC0_PSSI_R = 0x08;
  //Wait for a conversion to complete
  while ((ADC0_RIS_R & 0x08) == 0) {};
  //Get the result from the FIFO
  result = ADC0_SSFIFO3_R & 0xFFF;
  //Clear the raw interrupt flag
  ADC0_ISC_R = 0x08;
  return result;
}


// configure the system to get its clock from the PLL
void PLL_Init(void){
  // 0) configure the system to use RCC2 for advanced features
  //    such as 400 MHz PLL and non-integer System Clock
Divisor
  SYSCTL_RCC2_R |= SYSCTL_RCC2_USERCC2;
  // 1) bypass PLL while initializing
  SYSCTL_RCC2_R |= SYSCTL_RCC2_BYPASS2;
  // 2) select the crystal value and oscillator source
  SYSCTL_RCC_R &= ~SYSCTL_RCC_XTAL_M;   // clear XTAL field
```

```
  SYSCTL_RCC_R += SYSCTL_RCC_XTAL_16MHZ;// configure for 16
MHz crystal

  SYSCTL_RCC2_R &= ~SYSCTL_RCC2_OSCSRC2_M;// clear oscillator
source field

  SYSCTL_RCC2_R += SYSCTL_RCC2_OSCSRC2_MO;// configure for
main oscillator source

  // 3) activate PLL by clearing PWRDN

  SYSCTL_RCC2_R &= ~SYSCTL_RCC2_PWRDN2;

  // 4) set the desired system divider and the system divider
least significant bit

  SYSCTL_RCC2_R |= SYSCTL_RCC2_DIV400;  // use 400 MHz PLL

  SYSCTL_RCC2_R = (SYSCTL_RCC2_R&~0x1FC00000) // clear system
clock divider field

                 + (SYSDIV2<<22);       // configure for 80 MHz
clock

  // 5) wait for the PLL to lock by polling PLLLRIS

  while((SYSCTL_RIS_R&SYSCTL_RIS_PLLLRIS)==0){};

  // 6) enable use of PLL by clearing BYPASS

  SYSCTL_RCC2_R &= ~SYSCTL_RCC2_BYPASS2;

}
```

Program A.7: ADC Conversion with Sequencer 3 and Software Start

Set Up ADC0 Sequencer 3 to Do Analog-to-Digital Conversions by Timer

The PLL.c routine is not listed here. It's the same as in program 6.3 of chapter 6. This program was modified from Valvano's.

```
/*

 Copyright 2014 by Jonathan W. Valvano, valvano@mail.utexas.
edu
```

```
    You may use, edit, run or distribute this file

    as long as the above copyright notice remains

 THIS SOFTWARE IS PROVIDED "AS IS".  NO WARRANTIES, WHETHER
EXPRESS, IMPLIED

 OR STATUTORY, INCLUDING, BUT NOT LIMITED TO, IMPLIED WARRAN-
TIES OF

 MERCHANTABILITY AND FITNESS FOR A PARTICULAR PURPOSE APPLY
TO THIS SOFTWARE.

 VALVANO SHALL NOT, IN ANY CIRCUMSTANCES, BE LIABLE FOR SPE-
CIAL, INCIDENTAL,

 OR CONSEQUENTIAL DAMAGES, FOR ANY REASON WHATSOEVER.

 For more information about my classes, my research, and my
books, see

 http://users.ece.utexas.edu/~valvano/

 */

#include <stdio.h>

#include <stdint.h>

#include "PLL.h"

#include "tm4c123gh6pm.h"

#include "IO.h"


void ADC_Init(void);

uint32_t ADC_In(void);

void EnableInterrupts(void);

void SysTick_Init(void);

void delay1(uint8_t );
```

```
void ADC0Seq3_Handler(void);


#define PF1       (*((volatile uint32_t *)0x40025008))

#define PF2       (*((volatile uint32_t *)0x40025010))

#define PF3       (*((volatile uint32_t *)0x40025020))


extern void Timer2_Init(unsigned long);

volatile uint8_t ADCStatus;

uint32_t Result;

int8_t logic1 = 0x02;

int main(void){

  PLL_Init();                       // set system clock to
80 MHz

  IO_Init();

  ADC_Init();

      Timer2_Init(5000000); //Set Timer2 to a frequency of
16Hz or 62.5ms

  while(1){

  }

}


void delay1(uint8_t dly) {

      int i;

      for (i = 0; i < dly; i++) {

      }
```

```
}

void ADC0Seq3_Handler(void) {

      Result = ADC0_SSFIFO3_R & 0xFFF;

  ADCStatus = 1;

  ADC0_ISC_R = 0x08;

}


void Timer2_Init(unsigned long period){

  SYSCTL_RCGCTIMER_R |= 0x04;   // 0) activate timer2

 delay1(10); // To allow time for the clock of Time2 become
stable

  TIMER2_CTL_R = 0x00000000;    // 1) disable timer2A during
setup

  TIMER2_CFG_R = 0x00000000;    // 2) configure for 32-bit
mode

  TIMER2_TAMR_R = 0x00000002;   // 3) configure for periodic
mode, default down-count settings

  TIMER2_TAILR_R = period-1;    // 4) reload value

  TIMER2_TAPR_R = 0;            // 5) bus clock resolution

  TIMER2_ICR_R = 0x00000001;    // 6) clear timer2A timeout
flag

  TIMER2_IMR_R = 0x00000001;    // 7) arm timeout interrupt

  NVIC_PRI5_R = (NVIC_PRI5_R&0x00FFFFFF)|0x80000000; // 8)
priority 4

// interrupts enabled in the main program after all devices
initialized

// vector number 39, interrupt number 23
```

```
  NVIC_EN0_R = 1<<23;            // 9) enable IRQ 23 in NVIC

  TIMER2_CTL_R = 0x00000021;     // 10) enable timer2A, TAOTE
= ADC trigger

}

void Timer2A_Handler(void){

  TIMER2_ICR_R = TIMER_ICR_TATOCINT;// acknowledge TIMER2A
timeout

}
```

Program A.8: Set up ADC0 Sequencer 3 to do Analog to Digital conversions by Timer

Using UART with Busy-Wait Approach (without Interrupts) to Echo a Character Input

In the following, we will set up UART0 to receive a character and echo it back on the serial // terminal. We are not using the interrupt to receive or transmit data. Instead, we will use the busy-wait approach to receive and transmit ASCII data.

```
void UART_Init (void) {

  SYSCTL_RCGCR1_R |= 0x01;
```

Disable UART0 to start configuring it. We don't want UART0 to start acting when the configuration is not complete.

```
UART0_CTL_R &= ~0x01;

The integer IBRD = int (16,000,000/(16*115,200)) = int(8.681)

The fraction FBRD = int (0.681*64 + 0.5) = 44

UART0_IBRD_R = 8;

UART0-FBRD_R = 44;

UART0_LCRH_R = 0x60;

UART0_CTL_R |= 0x01;

UART0_ICR_R = 0x30;

char chr1;
```

```
int main(void){

UART_Init();                // initialize UART

UART0_ICR_R = 0x10;         //Clear Receive Flag

while (1) {

//while the Receive FIFO is empty, it stays here

while ((UART0_FR_R & 0x10) != 0) {};

//if the Receive FIFO is not empty, read a character

chr1 = UART0_DR_R & 0xFF; //UART input

//Clears FIFO Receive flag

UART0_ICR_R = 0x10;

//Check to see if the Transmit FIFO is full

While ((UART0_FR_R & 0x20) != 0) {}; //FIFO Transmit full

//If not, send out the receive character

UART0_DR_R = chr1;

}

}
```

Program A.9: Using UART0 with the Busy-Wait Approach and Interrupt Disabled

Using UART with the Receive Interrupt and FIFO Disabled to Echo a Character Input

```
// UART with Int and No FiFo.

// U0Rx (VCP receive) connected to PA0

// U0Tx (VCP transmit) connected to PA1

//After power-on-reset, the default system clock frequency is
16 MHz.
```

```
#include "tm4c123gh6pm.h"

#include <stdint.h>


void EnableInterrupts(void);

void UART0_Handler(void);

void UART_Init(void);

char chr1;

int flag;

int main(void){

  UART_Init();                // initialize UART

        while (1) {

        while (flag == 0){};

              UART0_DR_R = chr1;

              flag = 0;

}

}

void UART_Init(void){

  SYSCTL_RCGC1_R |= SYSCTL_RCGC1_UART0; // activate UART0
module

  SYSCTL_RCGC2_R |= SYSCTL_RCGC2_GPIOA; // activate port A
module

  UART0_CTL_R &= ~0x01;      // disable UART module

 //For 16MHz System Clock and 115200 baud rates

  UART0_IBRD_R = 8;                  // IBRD =
int(16,000,000 / (16 * 115,200)) = int(8.681)
```

```
  UART0_FBRD_R = 44;                        // FBRD = int(0.681 *
64 + 0.5) = 44

 // 8 data bit, no parity bits, one stop bit, no FIFOs

  UART0_LCRH_R = 0x60;

  UART0_IM_R |= 0x10;              //Receive Interrupt

  UART0_CTL_R |= 0x01;             // enable UART

  GPIO_PORTA_AFSEL_R |= 0x03;    // enable alt funct (UART0)
on PA1-0

  GPIO_PORTA_DEN_R |= 0x03;      // enable digital I/O on
PA1-0

  NVIC_PRI1_R |= 0x4000; //priority = 2 (bit 15-13)

  NVIC_EN0_R |= 0x20; //IRQ 5, Interrupt Number 21

 // configure PA1-0 as UART0

  GPIO_PORTA_PCTL_R =
(GPIO_PORTA_PCTL_R&0xFFFFFF00)+0x00000011;

  GPIO_PORTA_AMSEL_R &= ~0x03;          // disable analog
functionality on PA

  UART0_ICR_R = 0x30; //Clear interrupt flags

  EnableInterrupts();

}


void UART0_Handler(void) {

 chr1 = UART0_DR_R; //UART

 flag = 1;

 UART0_ICR_R = UART_IM_RXIM | UART_IM_TXIM;

}
```

Program A.10: Using UART with the Receive Interrupt and FIFO disabled to Echo a Character Input

Using UART0 with FIFO and Interrupt Enabled

```
// Modified from one of Valvano's programs

/*

 Copyright 2013 by Jonathan W. Valvano, valvano@mail.utexas.
edu

    You may use, edit, run or distribute this file

    as long as the above copyright notice remains

 THIS SOFTWARE IS PROVIDED "AS IS".  NO WARRANTIES, WHETHER
EXPRESS, IMPLIED

 OR STATUTORY, INCLUDING, BUT NOT LIMITED TO, IMPLIED WARRAN-
TIES OF

 MERCHANTABILITY AND FITNESS FOR A PARTICULAR PURPOSE APPLY
TO THIS SOFTWARE.

 VALVANO SHALL NOT, IN ANY CIRCUMSTANCES, BE LIABLE FOR SPE-
CIAL, INCIDENTAL,

 OR CONSEQUENTIAL DAMAGES, FOR ANY REASON WHATSOEVER.

 For more information about my classes, my research, and my
books, see

 http://users.ece.utexas.edu/~valvano/

 */


// U0Rx (VCP receive) connected to PA0

// U0Tx (VCP transmit) connected to PA1


#include "UART.h"

#include "tm4c123gh6pm.h"
```

```
extern char chr1;

extern int flag;

void EnableInterrupts(void);

void UART0_Handler(void);

void RxFifo_Init(void);

char RxFifo_Get(void);

int RxFifo_Put(char);

void WaitForInterrupt(void);  // low power mode

#define FIFOSIZE   16         // size of the FIFOs (must be
power of 2)

#define FIFOSUCCESS 1         // return value on success

#define FIFOFAIL    0         // return value on failure

uint32_t volatile PutI;  //

uint32_t volatile GetI;  //


char volatile *RxPutPt; // FIFO write index

char volatile *RxGetPt; // FIFO read index

char volatile *TxPutPt; // put next

char volatile *TxGetPt; // get next

char static RxFifo[FIFOSIZE];

//------------UART_Init------------

// Initialize the UART for 115,200 baud rate (assuming 50 MHz
UART clock),

// 8 bit word length, no parity bits, one stop bit, FIFOs
enabled
```

```
// Input: none

// Output: none

void UART_Init(void){

  SYSCTL_RCGC1_R |= SYSCTL_RCGC1_UART0; // activate UART0

  SYSCTL_RCGC2_R |= SYSCTL_RCGC2_GPIOA; // activate port A

  UART0_CTL_R &= ~UART_CTL_UARTEN;      // disable UART


      //For 16MHz System Clock

  UART0_IBRD_R = 8;    // IBRD = int(16,000,000 / (16 *
115,200)) = int(8.681)

  UART0_FBRD_R = 44;   // FBRD = int(0.681 * 64 + 0.5) = 44

// 8 bit word length (no parity bits, one stop bit,
FIFO enabled)

  UART0_LCRH_R = (UART_LCRH_WLEN_8|UART_LCRH_FEN); //with fifo

  UART0_IM_R |= UART_IM_RXIM | UART_IM_TXIM;

//Set the FIFO threshold to 8 bytes

 UART0_IFLS_R = UART_IFLS_RX4_8 | UART_IFLS_TX4_8; // FIFO
1/2 full (8 bytes)

//Enable Alternate Functions on Port A pin 0 and pin 1

  GPIO_PORTA_AFSEL_R |= 0x03;           // enable alt funct
on PA1-0

//Port A pin 1 and pin 0 have digital function

  GPIO_PORTA_DEN_R |= 0x03;             // enable digital I/O
on PA1-0

//Configure Port A pin 1 and 0 to be UART0 Tx and Rx

  GPIO_PORTA_PCTL_R =
(GPIO_PORTA_PCTL_R&0xFFFFFF00)+0x00000011;
```

```
//Disable analog function of Port A pin 1 and pin 0
  GPIO_PORTA_AMSEL_R &= ~0x03;
//Set the priority of the UART0 to 2
 NVIC_PRI1_R |= 0x4000; //priority = 2 (bit 15-13)
//Enable the NVIC interrupt of UART0
  NVIC_EN0_R |= 0x20; //IRQ 5, Interrupt Number 21
//Enable UART Receive and Transmit Interrupt
 UART0_ICR_R = UART_IM_RXIM | UART_IM_TXIM;
// Enable UART 0
  UART0_CTL_R |= UART_CTL_UARTEN;
//Enable the global interrupt
      EnableInterrupts();
}

// initialize FIFO pointers
void RxFifo_Init(void){
  RxPutPt = RxGetPt = &RxFifo[0]; // Empty
}

//Put a char into a buffer
int RxFifo_Put(char data){
  char volatile *nextPutPt;
  nextPutPt = RxPutPt+1;
  if(nextPutPt == &RxFifo[FIFOSIZE]){
```

```
    nextPutPt = &RxFifo[0];  // wrap
  }
  if(nextPutPt == RxGetPt){
    return(FIFOFAIL);      // Failed, fifo full
  }
  else{
    *(RxPutPt) = data;       // Put
    RxPutPt = nextPutPt;     // Success, update
    return(FIFOSUCCESS);
  }
}

//Retrieve a received character
char RxFifo_Get(){
      char data;
  char volatile *nextGetPt;
  nextGetPt = RxGetPt+1;
  if(nextGetPt == &RxFifo[FIFOSIZE]){
    nextGetPt = &RxFifo[0];  // wrap
  }
  if(RxPutPt == RxGetPt ){
    return(FIFOFAIL); // Empty if TxPutI=TxGetI
  }
 else {
```

```
            data = *RxGetPt;
            RxGetPt = nextGetPt;       // Success, update
            return data;
      }
      }
void UART0_Handler(void) {
      int i;
      char letter;
      for (i = 0; i < 8; i++) {
    letter = UART0_DR_R;
    RxFifo_Put(letter);
      }
      flag = 1;
      UART0_ICR_R = UART_IM_RXIM | UART_IM_TXIM;
}
#include "tm4c123gh6pm.h"
#include <stdint.h>

void EnableInterrupts(void);
extern void RxFifo_Init(void);
extern char RxFifo_Get(void);

void UART_Init(void);
char chr1;
```

```
int flag;

int main(void){

        int j;

        RxFifo_Init();

  UART_Init();                  // initialize UART

        while (1) {

               while (flag == 0){};

               while (chr1 = RxFifo_Get()) {

                      UART0_DR_R = chr1;

               }

                flag = 0;

     }

        }
```

Program A.11: UART with FIFO and Interrupt Enabled

Creating a PWM Signal Using Either Count-Up/Down or Count-Down Mode

```
// Prog-A.12

//Modified from one of  Valvano's programs

// Runs on TM4C123

// Use PWM0A/PB6 to generate PWM signal output.


/*

 Copyright 2015 by Jonathan W. Valvano, valvano@mail.utexas.
edu

    You may use, edit, run or distribute this file
```

```
    as long as the above copyright notice remains

 THIS SOFTWARE IS PROVIDED "AS IS".  NO WARRANTIES, WHETHER
EXPRESS, IMPLIED

 OR STATUTORY, INCLUDING, BUT NOT LIMITED TO, IMPLIED WARRAN-
TIES OF

 MERCHANTABILITY AND FITNESS FOR A PARTICULAR PURPOSE APPLY
TO THIS SOFTWARE.

 VALVANO SHALL NOT, IN ANY CIRCUMSTANCES, BE LIABLE FOR SPE-
CIAL, INCIDENTAL,

 OR CONSEQUENTIAL DAMAGES, FOR ANY REASON WHATSOEVER.

 For more information about my classes, my research, and my
books, see

 http://users.ece.utexas.edu/~valvano/

 */

#include <stdint.h>

#include "tm4c123gh6pm.h"

void PWM0_Init(uint16_t period, uint16_t duty,
uint8_t updown);

void PWM0Generator0_Handler(void);

void  EnableInterrupts(void);

void  DisableInterrupts(void);


// change duty cycle of PB6

// duty is number of PWM clock cycles output is high
(2<=duty<=period-1)

int main(void){

      //To use the Up-Down counting mode
```

```
	//clock period = 1/16MHz = 62.5ns, PWM clock freq
= 1KHz -> it takes 1ms/62.5ns = 16000 system clocks for 1
period of the PWM clock

	//This is up-down counting so period = 16000/2 = 8000

	// -> period = 8000. 25%duty cycle = (100-25%)*8000=
6000 since PWM signal goes high on cmpA up and goes down on
cmpA down

	//PWM0_Init(8000, 6000, 1);          //Up-down count-
ing, duty cycle = 25%

	//To use the Down counting mode

	//clock period = 1/16MHz = 62.5ns, PWM clock freq
= 1KHz -> it takes 1ms/62.5ns = 16000 system clocks for 1
period of the PWM clock

	// -> period = 16000. 75%duty cycle = 75%*16000= 12000

  PWM0_Init(8000, 4000, 1);            //Up-down counting
mode, duty cycle = 50%

  //PWM0_Init(8000, 6000, 1);          //Up-down counting
mode, duty cycle = 25%

	//PWM0_Init(16000, 4000, 0);         //Down counting
mode, duty cycle = 25%

	//PWM0_Init(16000, 12000, 0);        //Down counting
mode, duty cycle = 75%

  //PWM0_Init(16000, 8000, 0);         //Down counting mode,
duty cycle = 50%

	EnableInterrupts();

  while(1) {

  }

}
```

```
// Output on PB6/M0PWM0

void PWM0_Init(uint16_t period, uint16_t duty,
uint8_t updown){

      //Activate PWM0

  SYSCTL_RCGCPWM_R |= 0x01;

      //Activate port B and port F

  SYSCTL_RCGCGPIO_R |= 0x22;

  //Wait for the clock to port F and port B to be stable

  while((SYSCTL_PRGPIO_R&0x22) == 0){};

      //Enable alt funct on PB6

  GPIO_PORTB_AFSEL_R |= 0x40;

      //Configure PB6 as M0PWM2(PWM module 0, Generator 2)

  GPIO_PORTB_PCTL_R &= ~0x0F000000;

  GPIO_PORTB_PCTL_R |= 0x04000000;

      //Disable PB6 's ananlog function

  GPIO_PORTB_AMSEL_R &= ~0x40;

      //Make PB6 a digital signal

  GPIO_PORTB_DIR_R |= 0x40;

      //Make PB6 an out signal

  GPIO_PORTB_DEN_R |= 0x40;

  //Disable alt function on PF1

  GPIO_PORTF_AFSEL_R &= ~0x02;

  //Disable alt function mapping on PF1

  GPIO_PORTF_PCTL_R &= ~0x000000F0;

      //Disable analog functionality on PF1
```

```
  GPIO_PORTF_AMSEL_R &= ~0x02;

       //Make PF1 an output signal

  GPIO_PORTF_DIR_R |= 0x02;

  //Up-down counting mode

  GPIO_PORTF_DEN_R |= 0x02;

  //Up-down counting mode

  if (updown) {

            //Set PWM Generator 0 mode to Up-down counting
mode and diable the PWM Generator 0.

       //The counter counts up to the load value from 0 and
then from the load value counts down to 0

            //and then repeat.

            PWM0_0_CTL_R = 0x2;

    //Pin PB6 is driven high when and after it matches the
value of comparator A while counting up (high on cmpA up)

            //PB6 is driven low on when and after it
matches the value of comparator A when counting down (low on
cmpA down)

            PWM0_0_GENA_R = 0xB0;

       }

       //Count-down mode

 else {

            //Set PWM Generator 0 mode to Down counting mode
and diable the PWM Generator 0.

            //The counter counts down from the load value to
0 and then wraps back to the load value

            PWM0_0_CTL_R = 0x0;
```

```
    //PB6 is driven low from the load value until the counter
matches the value of comparator A.

    //Then it's driven high until the counter reaches zero.

            PWM0_0_GENA_R = 0xC2;

      }

  //Load value for the PWM counter

  PWM0_0_LOAD_R = period - 1;

  //Value loaded to comparator A to be used to compare with
the PWM counter to generate signal cmpA

  PWM0_0_CMPA_R = duty - 1;

      PWM0_INTEN_R = 0x01;

      if (updown) {

            PWM0_0_CTL_R |= 0x00000003;     // start PWM0,
updown counting mode

    PWM0_0_INTEN_R = 0x000000002;   //INTCMPADU=1(bit 2)
Enable PWM0 interrupt on cmpA down

    //PWM0_0_INTEN_R = 0x00000000C; //INTCMPAD=1(bit 3),
INTCMPADU=1(bit 2) Enable PWM0 interrupt

      }

      else {

            PWM0_0_CTL_R |= 0x00000001;   //start PWM0, down
counting mode

    PWM0_0_INTEN_R = 0x000000009; //INTCMPAD=1(bit 3),
INTCNTZERO=1 (bit0)           Enable PWM0 interrupt

      }


  PWM0_ENABLE_R |= 0x00000001;           // enable PB6/M0PWM0
```

```
        //Bit 23-21 of register NVIC_PRI2 set priority for PWM0
Generator 0 interrupt

        NVIC_PRI2_R |= 0x1 << 21; //priority 1

        //Bit 10 to enable PWM0 Generator 0 interrupt

        NVIC_EN0_R |= 0x01 << 10;

}


//Interrupt Service Handler (ISR) of PWM0 Generator 0

void PWM0Generator0_Handler (void) {

   uint32_t pwm0_stat;

        static uint32_t red_led = 0x0;

        //Get the interrupt flag

   pwm0_stat = PWM0_0_RIS_R;

       //Reset the interrupt status

   PWM0_0_ISC_R |= pwm0_stat;

       //Flashing the Red LED at 1-Hz rate

        GPIO_PORTF_DATA_R = (red_led == 1000) << 1;

        if (red_led < 1000) {

             red_led = red_led + 1;

        }

        else {red_led = 0x0; }

 }
```

Program A.12: Creating PWM Signal Using either Count-Up/Down or Count-Down Mode

Using SysTick Timer to Create a Delay

The following is an example of using the SysTick timer to delay 500 ms. This program needs to run with file Startup.s.

Assuming we are using the 16 MHz default value of the system clock, which has a period of 62.5 ns, to delay 0.5 second, we need 8,000,000 clock ticks.

```
        AREA Ex1, CODE, READONLY, ALIGN=2


GPIO_PORTF_DATA_R   EQU 0x400253FC

GPIO_PORTF_DIR_R    EQU 0x40025400

GPIO_PORTF_AFSEL_R  EQU 0x40025420

GPIO_PORTF_PUR_R    EQU 0x40025510

GPIO_PORTF_DEN_R    EQU 0x4002551C

GPIO_PORTF_AMSEL_R  EQU 0x40025528

GPIO_PORTF_PCTL_R   EQU 0x4002552C

GPIO_PORTF_LOCK_R   EQU 0x40025520

GPIO_PORTF_CR_R     EQU 0x40025524

GPIO_LOCK_KEY       EQU 0x4C4F434B


NVIC_ST_CTRL_R      EQU 0xE000E010

NVIC_ST_RELOAD_R    EQU 0xE000E014

NVIC_ST_CURRENT_R   EQU 0xE000E018

DELAY               EQU 8000000 ; delay 0.5sec
(=8000,000*1/16MHz)


SYSCTL_RCGCGPIO_R   EQU 0x400FE608
```

```
        EXPORT Start

        ENTRY

Start

;Initialize port F

     BL Port_Init

;Initialize SysTick Timer

     BL SysTick_Init

;Turn on the Red LED

        LDR R4, = GPIO_PORTF_DATA_R

        MOV R5, #0x2

        STR R5, [R4]

LoopS

;Call SysTick_Delay with an input parameter of 8,000,000

;or 0.5 sec (=8000000*(1/16MHz))

        LDR R0,=DELAY

        BL SysTick_Delay

;After 0.5 second delay, toggle the red LED and

;repeat the delay

        LDR R4, = GPIO_PORTF_DATA_R

        LDR R5, [R4]

        AND R5, R5, #0x2

        EOR R5, R5, #0x2

        STR R5, [R4]

        B LoopS
```

```
SysTick_Init

;Disable the SysTick timer while doing configuration

    LDR R1, =NVIC_ST_CTRL_R

    MOV R0, #0

    STR R0, [R1]

;Load a max delay value into register NVIC_ST_RELOAD_R

    LDR R2, =0xFFFFFF;

    LDR R1, =NVIC_ST_RELOAD_R

    STR R2, [R1]

; Writing any value to CURRENT clears it

    LDR R1, =NVIC_ST_CURRENT_R

    MOV R0, #0

    STR R0, [R1]            ; clear counter

;Enable the SysTick Timer

    LDR R1, =NVIC_ST_CTRL_R

    MOV R0, #5

    STR R0, [R1]

    BX LR




SysTick_Delay

    SUBS R0, R0, #1

    LDR R1, = NVIC_ST_RELOAD_R
```

```
        STR R0, [R1] ; store delay

        LDR R1, = NVIC_ST_CURRENT_R

        STR R0, [R1] ; clear the Current register

Loop

        LDR R1, =  NVIC_ST_CTRL_R

        LDR R2, [R1]

        ANDS R2, R2, #0x010000 ; get the Count flag

        BEQ Loop

        BX LR


Port_Init

;Enable port F

         LDR R0, =SYSCTL_RCGCGPIO_R

         LDR R1, [R0]

        ORR R1, R1, #0x20

        STR R1, [R0]

;Wait for Port F's clock to be stable

         NOP

        NOP;


; Port F Init, port F pin 1

;Unlock Port F

         LDR R0,=GPIO_PORTF_LOCK_R ; unlock portF

         LDR R1,=0x4C4F434B
```

```
        STR R1, [R0]

        LDR R0,=GPIO_PORTF_CR_R

        MOV R1, #0x0F

        STR R1, [R0]

;Make Port F pin 1 an output

        LDR R0,=GPIO_PORTF_DIR_R

       LDR R1, [R0]

       ORR R1, R1, #0x2; output portF pin 1 (Red LED)

       STR R1, [R0]

;Disable analog functionality of PF1

        LDR R0, =GPIO_PORTF_AMSEL_R

        LDR R1, [R0]

        BIC R1, R1, #0x02

        STR R1, [R0]

;PF1 is a digital pin

        LDR R0, =GPIO_PORTF_DEN_R

        LDR R1, [R0]

        ORR R1, R1, #0x02

        STR R1, [R0]

;Turn off alternate function of PF1

        LDR R0, =GPIO_PORTF_AFSEL_R

          LDR R1, [R0]

         BIC R1, R1, #0x02

         STR R1, [R0]
```

```
;Turn off alternate function mapping of PF1

        LDR R0, =GPIO_PORTF_PCTL_R

        LDR R1, [R0]

        LDR R2, =0xFFFFFF0F

       AND R1, R1, R2;

       STR R1, [R0]

       BX LR


     ALIGN

     END
```

Program A.13: Using SysTick Timer to Create a Delay

Creating a Square Wave Using SysTick Interrupts

```
;Creating a 1-Hz square wave at PF1 using SysTick interrupts

     AREA Block1, DATA, READWRITE, ALIGN=2

cnt  DCD 0x0

 AREA Ex1, CODE, READONLY, ALIGN=2


NVIC_ST_CTRL_R      EQU 0xE000E010

NVIC_ST_RELOAD_R    EQU 0xE000E014

NVIC_ST_CURRENT_R   EQU 0xE000E018

NVIC_SYS_PRI3_R     EQU 0xE000ED20  ; Sys. Handlers 12 to 15
Priority


GPIO_PORTF_LOCK_R   EQU 0x40025520

GPIO_PORTF_CR_R     EQU 0x40025524
```

```
GPIO_PORTF_AMSEL_R EQU 0x40025528

GPIO_PORTF_PCTL_R  EQU 0x4002552C

GPIO_LOCK_KEY      EQU 0x4C4F434B

GPIO_PORTF_DATA_R  EQU 0x400253FC

GPIO_PORTF_DIR_R   EQU 0x40025400

GPIO_PORTF_AFSEL_R EQU 0x40025420

GPIO_PORTF_PUR_R   EQU 0x40025510

GPIO_PORTF_DEN_R   EQU 0x4002551C

DELAY             EQU 8000000 ; delay 0.5sec
(=8000,000*1/16MHz)


SYSCTL_RCGCGPIO_R  EQU 0x400FE608


       EXPORT Start

       EXPORT SysTick_Handler

       ENTRY

Start

;Initialize PF1

     BL Port_Init

;Initialize SysTick Timer

;Reload value = DELAY = 8000000 (=0.5 second delay)

       LDR R0,=DELAY

     BL SysTick_Init

LoopS

       B LoopS
```

```
;SysTick ISR

SysTick_Handler

;Toggle PF1 (flashing red LED at 1 Hz)

        LDR R4, = GPIO_PORTF_DATA_R

        LDR R5, [R4]

        AND R5, R5, #0x2

        EOR R5, R5, #0x2

        STR R5, [R4]

;Keep counting the number of SysTick interrupts

        LDR R0, =cnt

        LDR R1, [R0]

        ADD R1, R1, #1

        STR R1, [R0]

        BX LR



SysTick_Init

; Disable the global interrupt

     MOV R3, #1

     MSR    PRIMASK, R3

     MOV R1, #1

     MSR    PRIMASK, R1

     LDR R1, =NVIC_ST_CTRL_R

     MOV R2, #0
```

```
        STR R2, [R1]

;Load the delay value into register NVIC_ST_RELOAD_R

        MOV R2, R0

        LDR R1, =NVIC_ST_RELOAD_R

        STR R2, [R1]

; Writing any value to CURRENT clears it

        LDR R1, =NVIC_ST_CURRENT_R

        STR R2, [R1]            ; clear counter

        ; set NVIC system interrupt 15 to priority 2

       LDR R1, =NVIC_SYS_PRI3_R

       LDR R2, [R1]

       AND R2, R2, #0x0FFFFFFF          ; R2 = R2&0x00FFFFFF
(clear interrupt 15 priority)

       ORR R2, R2, #0x40000000          ; R2 = R2|0x40000000
(interrupt 15's priority is in bits 31-29)

       STR R2, [R1]                    ; set SysTick to priority 2


        LDR R1, =NVIC_ST_CTRL_R

        MOV R0, #7

        STR R0, [R1]

; Enable the global interrupt

        MOV R3, #0

        MSR    PRIMASK, R3

        BX LR
```

```
Port_Init

;Enable port F

      LDR R0, =SYSCTL_RCGCGPIO_R

      LDR R1, [R0]

     ORR R1, R1, #0x20

     STR R1, [R0]

;Wait for Port F's clock to be stable

      NOP

      NOP;

;Unlock Port F

      LDR R0,=GPIO_PORTF_LOCK_R ; unlock portF

      LDR R1,=0x4C4F434B

      STR R1, [R0]

      LDR R0,=GPIO_PORTF_CR_R

      MOV R1, #0x0F

      STR R1, [R0]

;Make Port F pin 1 an output

      LDR R0,=GPIO_PORTF_DIR_R

     LDR R1, [R0]

     ORR R1, R1, #0x2; output portF pin 1 (Red LED)

     STR R1, [R0]

;Disable analog functionality of PF1

      LDR R0, =GPIO_PORTF_AMSEL_R

      LDR R1, [R0]
```

```
      BIC R1, R1, #0x02
      STR R1, [R0]
;PF1 is a digital pin
      LDR R0, =GPIO_PORTF_DEN_R
      LDR R1, [R0]
      ORR R1, R1, #0x02
      STR R1, [R0]
;Turn off alternate function of PF1
      LDR R0, =GPIO_PORTF_AFSEL_R
        LDR R1, [R0]
       BIC R1, R1, #0x02
       STR R1, [R0]
;Turn off alternate function mapping of PF1
       LDR R0, =GPIO_PORTF_PCTL_R
       LDR R1, [R0]
       LDR R2, =0xFFFFFF0F
      AND R1, R1, R2;
      STR R1, [R0]
      BX LR

    ALIGN
    END
```

Program A.14: Using SysTick Timer to Create a Square Wave

C-Based Program to Create a Square Wave Using SysTick Timer

```
#include <stdint.h>

#include "tm4c123gh6pm.h"


void DisableInterrupts(void);

void EnableInterrupts(void);

void SysTick_Init(uint32_t );

void GPIO_init(void);

void SysTick_Handler(void);

uint32_t reg_val;

//System clock's default frequency is 16 MHz

//Use SysTick to create a 1-Hz periodic waveform output on
PF2

//delay = 1/2 of 1-Hz period = 0.5 second = (0.5)/
(1/16000000) = 8000000

int main(void){

  GPIO_init();

  SysTick_Init(8000000);

  while(1){

  }

}

void SysTick_Init(uint32_t delay){

  //Disable the global interrupt while configuring the SysTick
Timer

  DisableInterrupts();
```

```
  //Disable the SysTick Timer

  NVIC_ST_CTRL_R = 0;

  //Load reload value into the Reload register

  NVIC_ST_RELOAD_R = delay - 1;

  //Clear the Current Value register so the SysTick timer can
start counting from 0

  NVIC_ST_CURRENT_R = 0;

  //Enable the SysTick Timer, SysTick interrupt and select
the System Clock as SysTick clock source

  NVIC_ST_CTRL_R = 0x7;

  //Set the SysTick priority to 2 (bit 31-29 of
register NVIC_SYS_PRI3)

  NVIC_SYS_PRI3_R |= 0x2 << 29; //priority 2

  //Enable the global interrupt

  EnableInterrupts();


}

void GPIO_init(void) {

  int delay1;

  SYSCTL_RCGCGPIO_R |= 0x20;  // activate port F and port B

  delay1 = SYSCTL_RCGCGPIO_R;

  //Configure port F pin 2 (blue LED)

  //Make PF2 output (PF2 built-in LED)

  GPIO_PORTF_DIR_R |= 0x04;

  //Disable alt funct on PF2
```

```
    GPIO_PORTF_AFSEL_R &= ~0x04;

    //Enable digital functionality on PF2

    GPIO_PORTF_DEN_R |= 0x04;

    //Reset PCTL mapping register on PF2

    GPIO_PORTF_PCTL_R &= ~0x00000F00;

    //Disable analog functionality on PF2

    GPIO_PORTF_AMSEL_R &= ~0x04;

  }

  void SysTick_Handler(void) {

    static uint8_t tp = 0x04;

    //reset the Count Flag status bit

    reg_val = NVIC_ST_CTRL_R;

    //Flashing PF2 at 1 Hz rate

    GPIO_PORTF_DATA_R = tp & 0x04;

    if (tp == 0x04) {tp = 0x0;}

    else {tp = 0x04;}

  }
```

Program A.15: C-based Program Using SysTick Timer to Create a Square Wave

CPSIA information can be obtained
at www.ICGtesting.com
Printed in the USA
FSHW022056131221
86895FS

9 781516 585830